Brushless DC Motors

Electronics Commutation and Controls

Thomas J. Sokira
and Wolfgang Jaffe

Alnico is a trademark of Magnetics and Electronics Inc.

FIRST EDITION
FIRST PRINTING

Library of Congress Cataloging in Publication Data

Sokira, Thomas J.
Brushless dc motors : electronic commutation and controls / by Thomas J. Sokira and Wolfgang Jaffe.
p. cm.
Includes index.
ISBN 0-8306-9267-3 ISBN 0-8306-3267-0 (pbk.)
1. Electric motors, Direct current. 2. Electric motors, Brushless. I. Jaffe, Wolfgang. I. Title.
TK2681.S65 1989
621.46—dc20 89-34728
CIP

TAB BOOKS Inc. offers software for sale. For information and a catalog, please contact TAB Software Department, Blue Ridge Summit, PA 17294-0850.

Questions regarding the content of this book should be addressed to:

Reader Inquiry Branch
TAB BOOKS Inc.
Blue Ridge Summit, PA 17294-0214

Acquisitions Editor: Roland S. Phelps
Technical Editor: B. J. Peterson

Contents

Acknowledgments

The authors are indebted to the companies that supplied material for this book (individually acknowledged where applicable). We are also indebted to Bernadine Streifel who so diligently created the extensive artwork for this book. We would like to express our special appreciation to our wives who spent so much time and effort in typing, copying, compiling, and performing the many other chores necessary in readying a manuscript.

Preface

After decades of stagnation, electric motor technology finds itself in a state of transition. New materials, an explosion in electronics, and ever more stringent and varied motor requirements are forcing change. All of a sudden the engineer faces choices between old and new drive systems, and the wrong decision could prove detrimental to a product or service. The authors found that there is a crying need for a book that covers, in a comprehensive way, the present state of the art of electric motor technology and controls. Emphasis is needed on brushless dc motors as typical of new drive systems. We feel that this book fills a vacuum at a time when courses on electric motors have all but disappeared from the engineering curriculum.

Introduction

This book is intended to provide the practicing engineer with much needed theoretical and practical information required to choose among the myriad of options of drive systems available. It also provides engineers and technicians with the information needed to test and evaluate a motor or drive system. In addition, it should prove invaluable to students who, although not specializing on motor design, need a general theoretical and practical background of modern motor technology. This book tries to answer the many questions asked daily of manufacturers of motors and controls by customers who suddenly find that an obsolete drive system could prove very detrimental to their product.

The information available also should prove beneficial to component suppliers of motors and controls who are trying to keep up with rapidly occurring changes. Much of the material is also suitable for in-house training by companies.

The chapters are organized along each author's disciplines. Chapters 1, 2, 3, and 5 cover the whole range of electric motors. These chapters include discussion of principles common to all motors. A great variety of ac, dc, stepper and *BLDC* (brushless direct current) motors are covered, their modes of operation, and their characteristics. Theory is provided where needed in concise and easy-to-understand form, and mathematical equations are used only where needed to show results. Attention is paid to such important factors as inherent noise, vibration, and electromagnetic interference associated with each type of motor. The BLDC motor is discussed at great length in a step-by-step fashion so that the engineer or technician will understand the meaning and consequences of the different options available.

Chapters 4, 6, and 7 describe electronic drive concepts such as two- and three-phase standard drives and variations. Also covered are speed and position control systems. Various commutation methods are discussed, including types of sensors and their impact on cost and performance.

Chapter 8 covers test procedures and instrumentation and deals with the inadequacies of many of the most commonly used meters.

Applications are touched upon throughout the book, and there is a special section on applications for BLDC motor systems.

1

Conventional DC Motors

1.1 INTRODUCTION

The main purpose of this book is to cover the brushless dc motor—its theory, design concepts, performance possibilities, and limitations. As is pointed out in chapter 5, although this motor has much in common with present-day conventional motors, certain operational and performance aspects differ radically from traditional concepts. Therefore, it is important to review conventional motors, in particular the dc motor with which the brushless dc motor is most often compared.

Because of electronic component limitations, the vast majority of brushless dc motors built at present are below a 3 hp rating and mostly in the fractional horsepower range, and this is the area covered in this book.

Electric motor action is based on the interaction of magnetic forces repulsing or attracting each other. Continuous relative change of the magnetic forces is accomplished with electromagnets capable either of being turned on or off or of changing polarity due to reversal of current. In most ac motors, the latter is accomplished with an ac current at a frequency determined by the supply. In the case of the dc motor, the polarity is changed by reversing the current mechanically in the rotating member (called the armature) by a switch consisting of commutator and brushes. In brushless direct-current motors and stepper motors, the currents in the winding are switched electronically.

The various possibilities of producing torque with an array of electromagnets, each one interacting in time and space with the rest, is the reason so many different types of motors are presently available.

Direct-current motors were developed first because the early commercial power generated was direct current. With the coming of ac power and ac motors, the dc motor went into decline. The arrival of the automobile and the use of batteries again gave a boost to dc motors. The ever lower cost of rectification and the development of new magnet materials and of relatively low-cost rechargeable batteries increased the use of fractional horsepower motors in the home since the end of World War II. The development of *SCRs* (silicon-controlled rectifiers) in the 1950s and 1960s permitted easy speed control and started to blur the distinction between the universal motor and dc series motor.

With the development of power transistors and control circuitry, the dc motor has become dominant in servo motor applications, in the motion and control fields, in robotics, machine tools, etc.

Originally, all dc motors were shunt field, series field, or a combination of the two (called *compound field*) depending on the performance requirements. Today, however, fractional-horsepower motors are mostly of the permanent-magnet or series-field variety.

Certain features of the dc motor have, to some extent, hindered widespread use. First is the maintenance requirement of brushes, which must be regularly replaced because of mechanical wear. Second, brushes can emit electrical interference due to arcing and often will produce acoustic noise as well. Proper filtering can reduce *EMI* (electromagnetic interference), but never totally eliminate it. Another problem is that in certain hazardous atmospheres any sparking, however minute, is unacceptable.

1.2. STRUCTURES

Physically the dc motor consists of a rotating part called the *armature,* which generally consists of a shaft and core made up of slotted-steel laminations, a copper winding inserted in the slots, with connections to a commutator. (See Fig. 1-1).

The stationary part is called the *field* and contains an iron core with pole shoes and windings around the pole shoes. There might be one pair of poles (two-pole) or several pairs of poles. There might be a housing around the core. Alternately, if it is a permanent-magnet motor, there might be arc magnets attached to a steel pipe (Fig. 1-2).

Then there are end caps, which hold bearings. One of the end caps contains the brush rigging—consisting of brushes, springs, brush tubes, leads, etc. The brushes line up with the commutator. It is the brushes that carry the current to and from the field or power supply to the commutator and to the armature. Larger dc motors also

Fig. 1-1. Armature and wound field. (Courtesy of ELECTRIC INDICATOR Co. Inc., Norwalk, CT)

have interpoles as part of the field structure, but interpoles are not present in fractional-horsepower motors.

Depending on the environment, motors can be totally enclosed (with or without fan), open, drip proof, etc. Motors also are rated according to temperature rise; this rating might well determine the size of a motor.

Certain performance characteristics—such as acoustical noise, EMI, bearing life, and brush life—are either partly or totally dependent on the physical construction of the motor, as much on the basic design as the quality of manufacturing.

It takes common sense to evaluate your own or someone else's design. If the end brackets are flimsy, you can expect acoustical noise, shorter bearing and brush life, and probably higher EMI. If the brush rigging is sloppy, brush life is at stake and EMI

Fig. 1-2. Permanent magnet field stator. Two arc magnets glued to the inside of a steel pipe. (Courtesy of ELECTRIC INDICATOR Co. Inc., Norwalk, CT)

might be higher. Where efficiency is a factor, initial spring pressure on the brushes might be low and might cause problems later on.

Where safety standards such as *U.L.* (Underwriters Laboratory) approval are optional, it is advisable to meet the minimum standards. Both the designer and user should be aware of this.

1.3. BASIC RELATIONSHIPS

The basic theory behind the operation of a dc motor is a relatively simple one. A current in a conductor forms a magnetic field around that conductor (Fig. 1-3). If this current-carrying conductor is located in a magnetic field at right angles to the field, a force will be exerted on this conductor as indicated in Fig. 1-4. While the flux lines above the conductor are in the same direction or polarity, they will repel each other. In contrast, the flux lines below the conductor, which are in opposite direction or opposite polarity, are attracting each other. Therefore, there is a net downward force on the conductor. If either the number of lines in the field are doubled or the current in the conductor is doubled, the force will also be doubled.

The actual motor action is illustrated in Fig. 1-5. A coil in a magnetic field consists of coil-sides M and N creating a torque $F \cdot r$. If the coil is allowed to rotate, at some point the current must reverse for the torque to maintain the same direction. This happens at a point where commutator segment "a" loses contact with the positive brush and contacts the negative brush. At the same time, segment "b" leaves the negative brush and contacts the positive brush. In general, an armature is made up of many coils and commutator bars. For further details see chapter 2; for testing and evaluating dc motors see chapter 8.

If a conductor is moved in a magnetic field as in Fig. 1-6, it does what is called *cutting flux* and generates a voltage in the conductor. The more flux, or the faster the movement of the conductor—that is, the cutting of flux—the higher the generated voltage. This generated voltage in a motor is frequently called back EMF (electromotive force or E_b) or counter EMF.

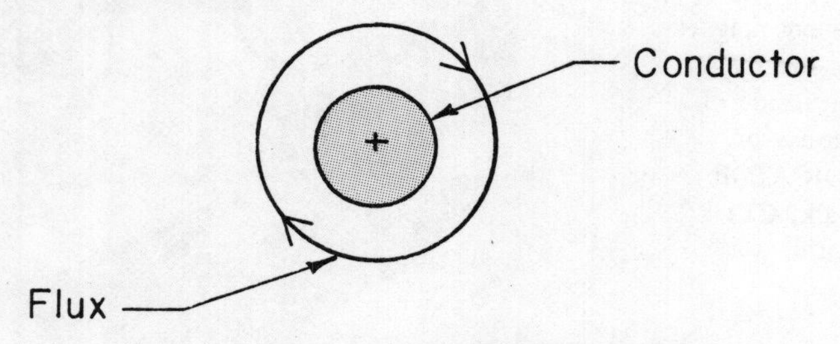

Fig. 1-3. Field formed by current carrying conductor.

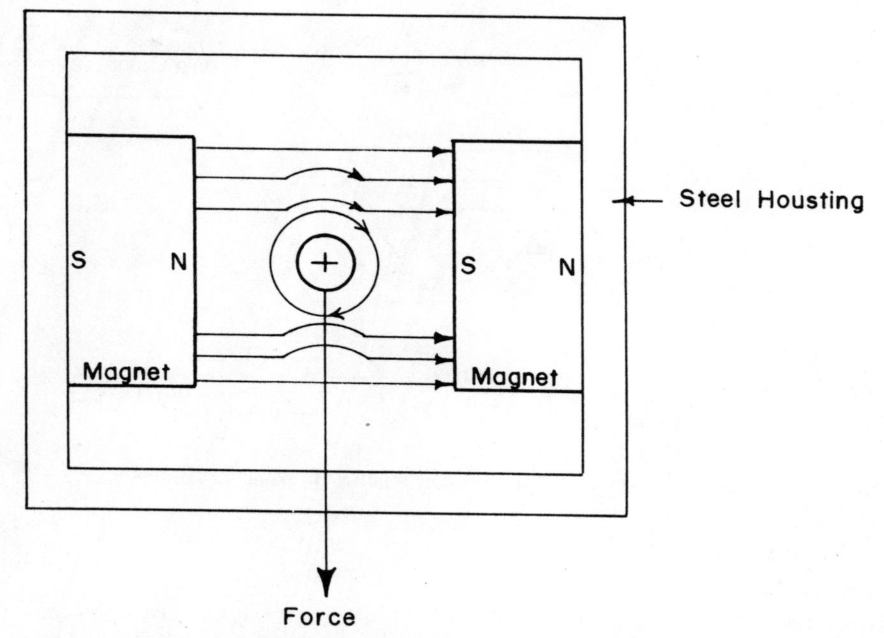

Fig. 1-4. Interaction of field flux and flux formed by a current-carrying conductor.

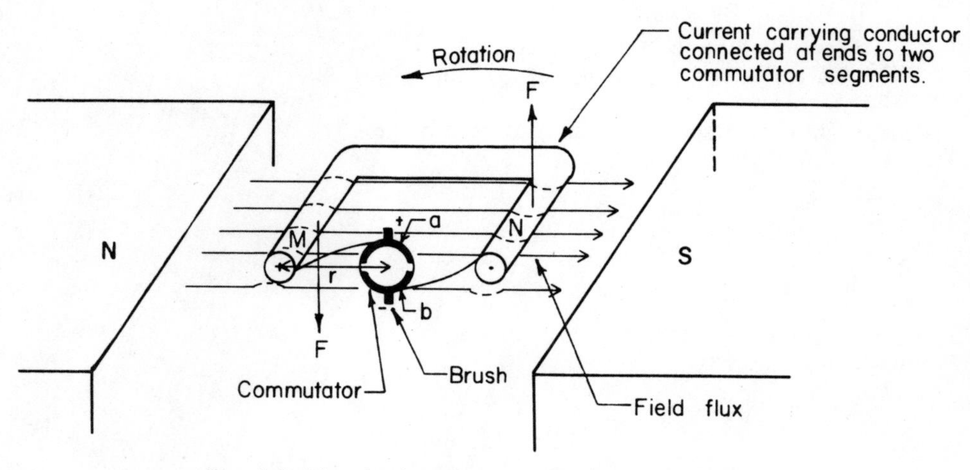

Fig. 1-5. Motor action of coil rotating in magnetic field.

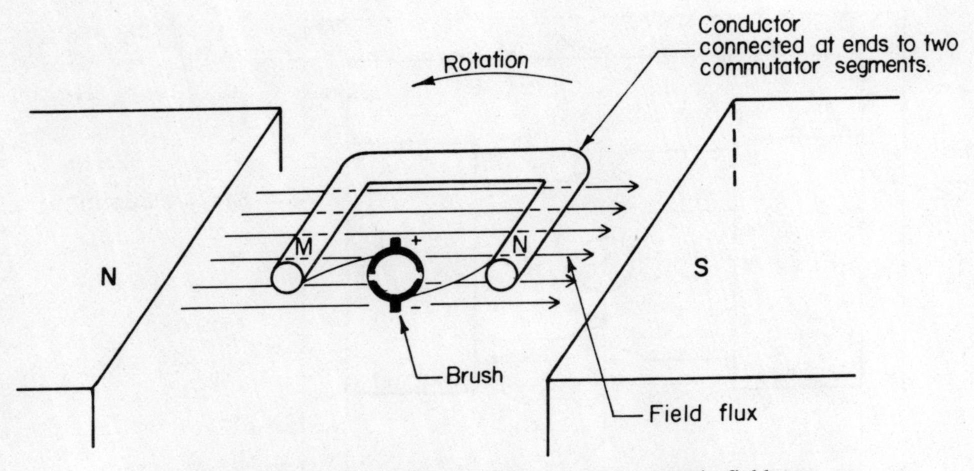

Fig. 1-6. Generator action of coil rotating in magnetic field.

From the preceeding paragraphs it follows that in a two-pole construction:

$$T \approx Z_a \Phi I_a \quad (1\text{-}1)$$

$$E_b \approx Z_a \Phi S \quad (1\text{-}2)$$

where T = torque
Z_a = the number of armature conductors
Φ = flux, *Wb* (webers)
I_a = armature current, A (amperes)
S = speed, RPM (revolutions per minute)

Relationship (1-1) and (1-2) can also be rewritten:

$$Z_a \Phi \approx \frac{T}{I_a} \quad (1\text{-}3)$$

$$Z_a \Phi \approx \frac{E_b}{S} \quad (1\text{-}4)$$

From which follows:

$$\frac{T}{I_a} \approx \frac{E_b}{S} \quad (1\text{-}5)$$

where the field flux remains constant.

The expression T/I_a is called the torque constant K_T in newton-meters per ampere (N · m/A). The expression E_b/S is called the voltage constant K_E in volts per radians per second^{-1} or volts per thousand revolutions per minute (V/rad s^{-1} or V/kRPM).

These constants are true not only for two-pole but any number of pole pair constructions. As discussed in this book, these are very important design constants, particularly for the permanent-magnet motor in the design of servo motors and electronic controls.

Finally, gross power output ($P_{G\text{-}out}$) of a dc motor is

$$P_{G\text{-}out} = E_b \times I_a \tag{1-6}$$

To arrive at the net output of the motor, deduct internal losses, such as friction, windage, and magnetic losses from the gross output.

1.4. DC SHUNT MOTORS

If the field winding is connected in parallel with the armature, the motor is called a *shunt motor* (Fig. 1-7). The path of the flux produced by a current in the field winding is illustrated in Fig. 1-8. How much flux will depend on the number of turns and the current in the field as well as the length of the air gap (l_g), provided the flux densities in the steel are low, saturation due to armature reaction is negligible, and brushes are on neutral. An equivalent circuit representing this motor is shown in Fig. 1-9, from which you can obtain the following relationships:

$$E_L = I_a R_a + E_b \tag{1-7}$$

where E_L = line voltage
I_a = armature current
R_a = armature resistance
E_b = back EMF

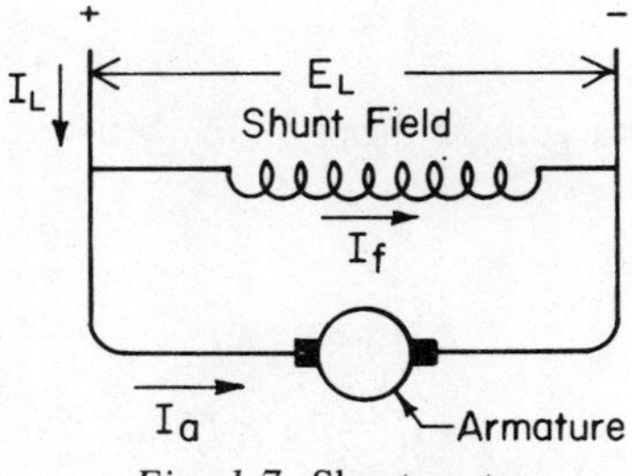

Fig. 1-7. Shunt motor.

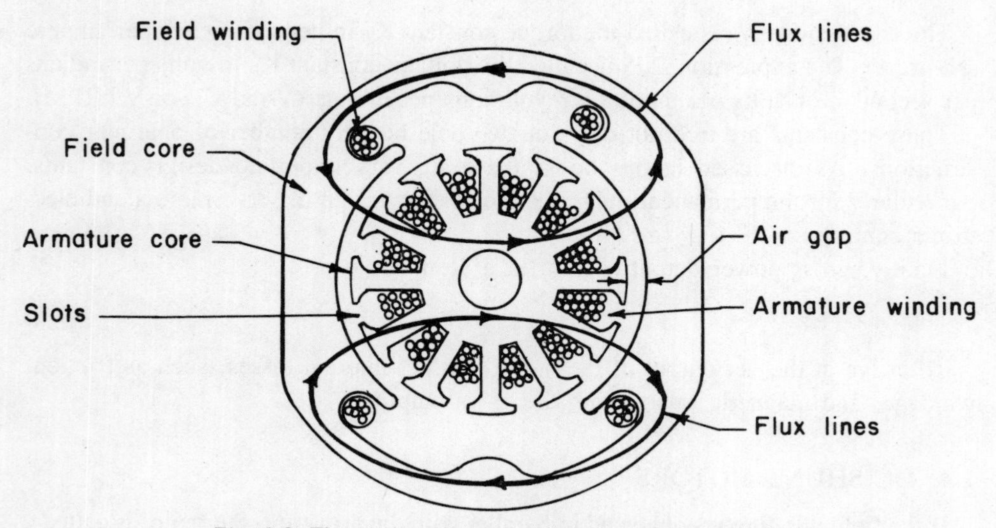

Fig. 1-8. Flux path produced by current in field winding.

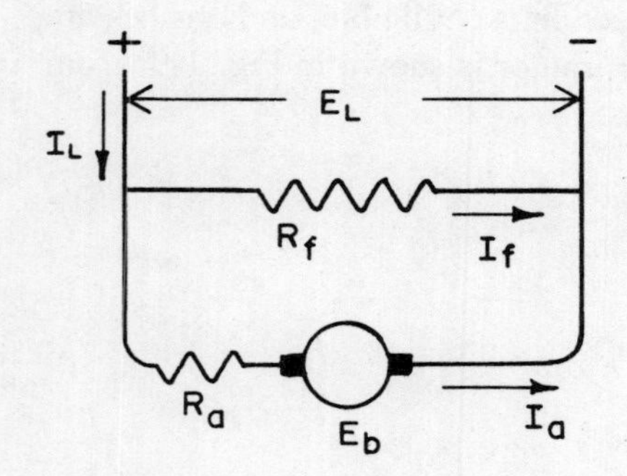

Fig. 1-9. Equivalent circuit of shunt motor.

The above equation neglects voltage drops in the brushes, which must be considered if they are large.

Other relationships follow:

$$E_L = I_f R_f \tag{1-8}$$

$$I_L = I_a + I_f \tag{1-9}$$

$$E_b = \frac{Z_a S \Phi P}{60a} \tag{1-10}$$

where I_f = field current
R_f = field resistance
I_L = line current
Φ = flux per pole
P = number of poles
a = number of parallel paths in armature
S = speed

Equation 1-10 for E_b is similar to relationship (1-2) and:

$$E_b = K_E \times S \quad (1\text{-}11)$$

In the *SI* (System International) system:

$$K_E = K_T \text{ in V/rad s}^{-1}\text{, N} \cdot \text{m/A}$$

and (1-12)

$$\text{V/rad s}^{-1} = 104.72 \text{ V/kRPM}$$

Higher field currents increase the flux produced, causing higher flux densities in the field as well as in armature core. At higher flux densities, the relative permeability of steel decreases very rapidly. The result is that the field current ceases to be proportional to the flux in the air gap, and therefore a further increase in the field current is not proportional to an increase in torque.

The concept of permeability in a magnetic medium is similar to the concept of conductivity for electrical components. *Permeability* of a material or medium can be thought of as the ability of handling flux and is referenced to a vacuum or air. (They both have the same permeability.) In more technical terms, in dc applications, permeability is a general term used to express relationships between flux density B and magnetic field strength H. These relationships are either absolute permeability μ, which is the ratio of change in B to change in H, or relative permeability, which is the ratio of μ to the magnetic constant Γ_m.

$$\mu = \Gamma_m \times \mu_r \quad (1\text{-}13)$$

where μ = absolute permeability
Γ_m = permeability in vacuum, also referred to as magnetic constant
μ_r = relative permeability

In vacuum or air:

$$B = 4\pi 10^{-7} H \quad (1\text{-}14)$$

where B = flux density in Wb/m^2
H = magnetic field strength in AT(tesla)/m

In steel, μ_r is variable. As can be seen from Fig. 1-10. The relative permeability varies with the flux density from a high value to that approaching air at very high flux densities. When flux densities in steel approach these high values, it is often said that steel is saturated.

Typical torque-speed curves of a shunt motor are shown in Fig. 1-11. Curve (a) indicates a motor where the effect of armature reaction is negligible. Curve (b) shows the effect of armature reaction, which causes a net loss of flux due to saturation at the pole tips. *Armature reaction* is a magnetic field created in quadrature with the main field due to the current in the armature. See chapter 2 for a more complete explanation.

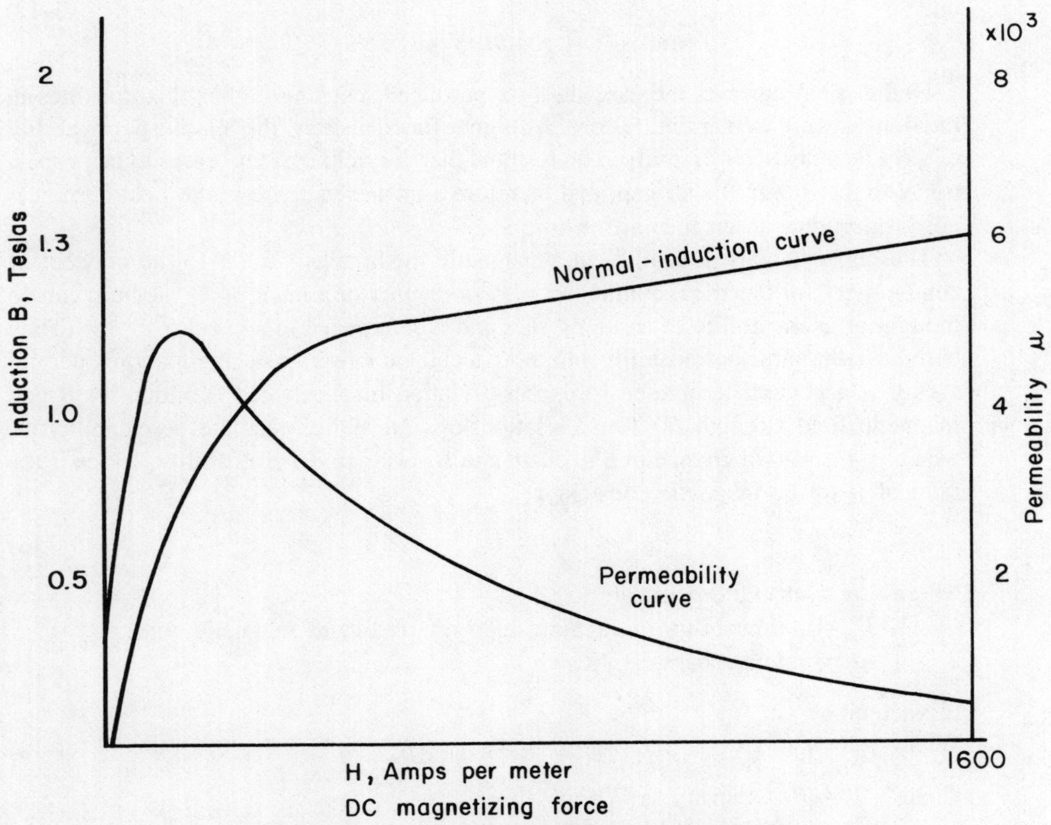

Fig. 1-10. Typical magnetization curve for electrical sheet steel.

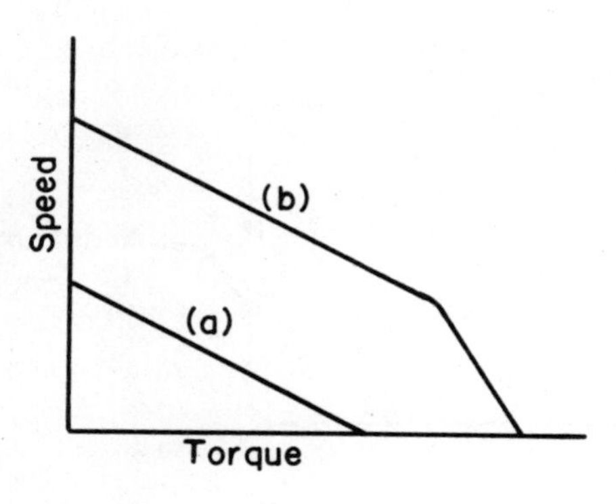

Fig. 1-11. Torque-speed curve for a shunt motor: (a) a motor where armature reaction is negligible. (b) a motor where there is a net field flux loss due to armature reaction.

Power losses associated with the shunt motor:

- Field: $I_f^2R_f$
- Armature: $I_a^2R_{a'}$ core (iron) losses, short-circuit currents
- Other: Friction, windage, brush contact losses

Of these losses, the I^2R and brush contact losses are supplied by the external power supply, and the rest of the losses are supplied internally by the motor and act like a load. If the resistance of the brushes is a factor, armature terminal resistance R_t can be substituted for R_a. Gross motor output equals net output plus internal losses.

The field winding is usually made up of many turns of small wire, therefore it has a very high resistance and inductance. The armature is made up of coils of fewer turns of larger wire, which results in a lower resistance and inductance than the corresponding field.

Applying ac current to a typical motor would result in the currents I_f and I_a being considerably out of phase, generating more heat than anything else.

1.5. SERIES MOTORS

When the field winding of the motor is connected in series with the armature, the motor is called a series motor as shown in Figs. 1-12 and 1-13. In Fig. 1-12, the whole field winding is connected between one side of the line and a brush terminal of the armature. In Fig. 1-13 the field is split into halves: one half is connected to one side of the line and armature, and one half to the other side of the line and armature. In most performance characteristics the two motors are identical, but the split-field winding in Fig. 1-13 is generally preferable from the point of view of electromagnetic interference. The field connection in Fig. 1-12 might be preferable in some solid-state

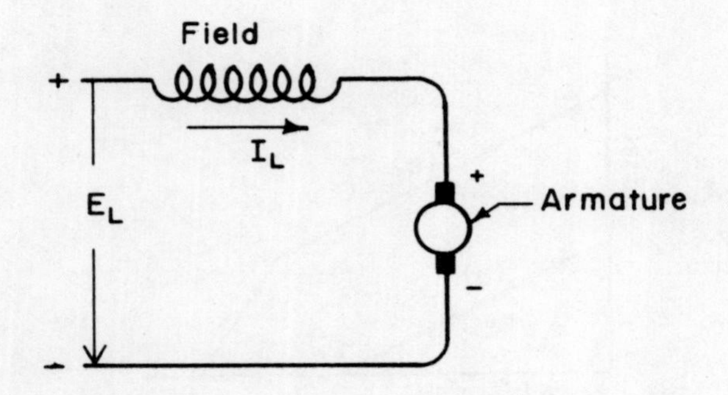

Fig. 1-12. Series motor with field coils connected in series with armature. One brush is connected to line, the other brush to field.

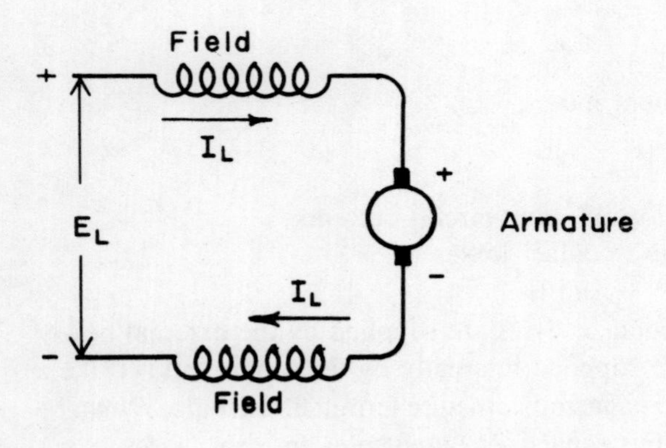

Fig. 1-13. Series motor with half the field connected to one brush, the other half to the other brush.

control applications. The following equations can be derived from the equivalent circuit (Fig. 1-14), neglecting brush drop.

$$E_L = I_L(R_f + R_a) + E_b \tag{1-15}$$

from chapter 1:

$$T \approx Z_a \Phi I_a$$

but as can be seen from Fig. 1-12:

$$\Phi \approx I_L$$

therefore:

$$T \approx Z_a I_L^2 \tag{1-16}$$

rewriting equation 1-15:

$$\frac{E_L - E_b}{R_f + R_a} = I_L \tag{1-17}$$

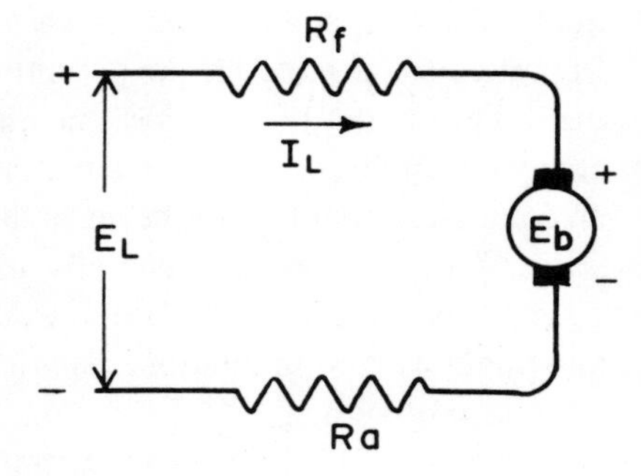

Fig. 1-14. Equivalent circuit for series dc motor.

combining equation 1-15 with 1-16 and combining all constants into k:

$$T = k(E_L - E_b)^2 \tag{1-18}$$

The above equation neglects saturation due to high currents.

No-load speed theoretically could approach infinity with I_L and Φ approaching 0; however, internal losses limit the no-load speed. With smaller motors, there is no danger of the motor speed running away.

For a typical torque-speed curve of a series motor, see Fig. 1-15. Saturation would change the curve somewhat. With heavy saturation, the flux would approach a constant with an increase of current, and the torque would become a linear function of current. However, the flux never quite approaches a constant, even though locked rotor currents can be as much as five to seven times running currents.

One obvious disadvantage of this motor is that a slight change in the load or small change in the supply voltage can cause a large change in the speed of the motor. The

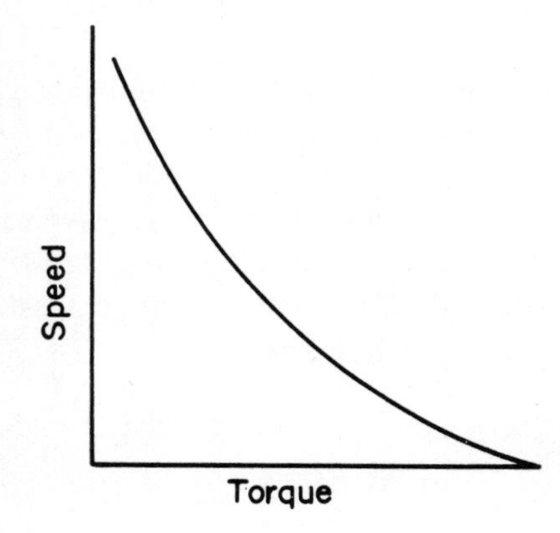

Fig. 1-15. Torque-speed curve for series motor.

motor also has important advantages. One advantage is that starting torques are high. In particular, starting torque per ampere is considerably higher than in a corresponding shunt motor. If you pulse the current, the current in the field and armature will always be in phase. The series motor might have an advantage in manufacturing over an equivalent shunt motor because the series field requires fewer turns and uses larger wires. Larger wires are generally more suitable for winding machines.

The voltage drop in the field reduces the voltage across the armature (Fig. 1-14) and might help commutation. The field inductance in series with the armature helps in EMI suppression.

If ac power is supplied to the motor it becomes the ac series motor also commonly called the universal motor, which is covered separately in chapter 3.

1.6. COMPOUND MOTORS

If a motor has both series and shunt fields, then it is called a compound motor (see Fig. 1-16). These fields can be connected so that they aid each other; this connection

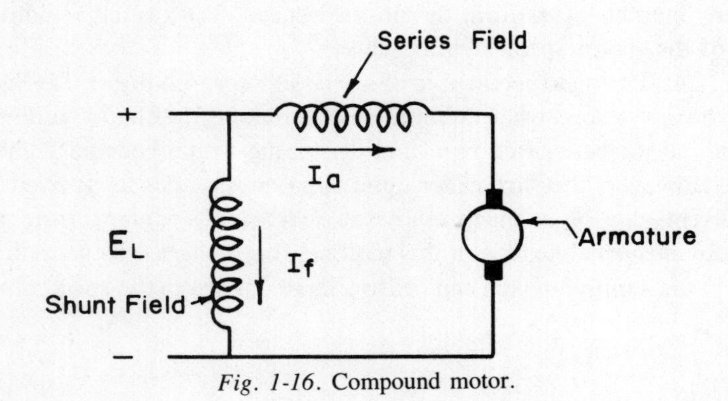

Fig. 1-16. Compound motor.

is called *cummulative compound*. If the series field is connected to oppose the shunt field, it is called *differential compound*. A typical torque-speed curve is shown in Fig. 1-17, which is a compromise between series and shunt characteristics.

The compound motor is a typical example of how motor characteristics can be tailored to a specific application without recourse to electronic controls. Despite its flexibility, this motor is not extensively used in smaller sizes except in applications such as special pumps.

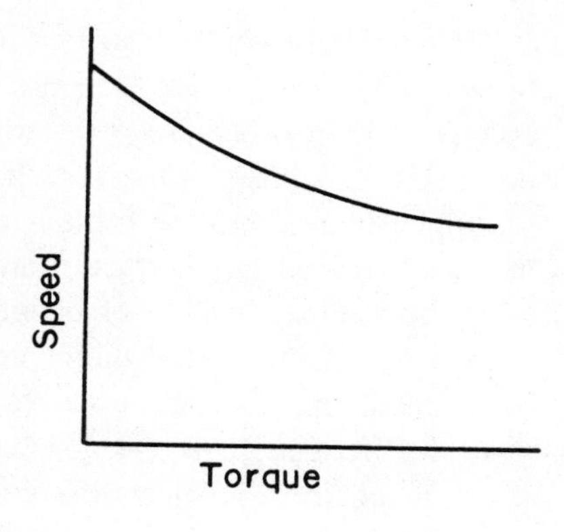

Fig. 1-17. Torque-speed curve for compound motor.

1.7. PERMANENT-MAGNET MOTORS

1.7.1. Introduction

The development of new magnet materials has made the *PM* (permanent magnet) motor a most exciting one. If the shunt field in the shunt motor discussed in section 1-4 is replaced by high coercive-strength permanent magnets, the resulting torque-speed curve is linear (Fig. 1-18). With a constant field, the armature current will also be a linear function of the gross torque.

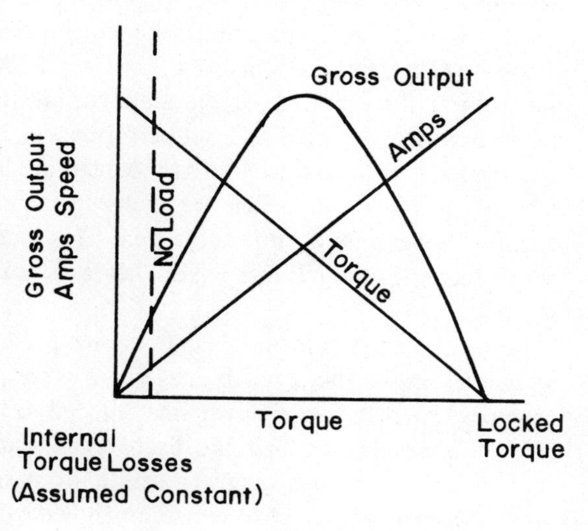

Fig. 1-18. Typical torque-speed and current-torque curves for permanent-magnet motor.

This motor is well represented in battery-operated toys, automobiles, pumps, and blowers. They are used in heavy-duty applications like hoists and winches. Other common applications are golf carts, garden tractors, floor scrubbers, etc. They are dominant as servo motors in such applications as machine tools and robotics.

Emphasis on motor performance varies with applications. In larger, battery-operated uses such as garden tractors and golf carts, efficiency is of primary importance to keep the size and weight of batteries down.

In a toy motor, price might count more than efficiency. In servo motors, the mechanical and electrical time constant as well as size might be important; in aerospace applications, size, weight, and efficiency count. Often a very smooth-running motor is required. To meet different requirements, there are a variety of motor configurations and there are different magnetic materials suitable for different applications.

1.7.2. Magnetic Materials

Among the magnetic materials most often used are ceramic magnets, rare-earth magnets, and Alnicos. (See Table 1-1.)

The ceramic magnets are the lowest cost magnets. They have the lowest energy product of those listed in the table. The coercive strength is high so that the motor is protected from permanent demagnetization if properly designed. Air-gap flux density of between 0.3T and 0.4T or less is relatively low. One of the biggest drawbacks is the reversible loss of flux with temperature rise. With a 75°C temperature rise, there is a flux loss of 15 percent, and there is a corresponding loss in K_T and K_E.

As an example of the difference between cold and hot performance of a motor, assume a temperature rise in the armature of 75°C. This means a rise in the armature resistance of almost 30 percent. If the temperature rise of the magnet at the same time was only 60°C, this amounts to a flux loss of 12 percent. For a given torque output, the motor will require 12 percent more current so that the total I^2R loss has increased 63 percent between cold and hot performance. Just looking at these numbers makes you realize that unless a motor is mounted and used properly, it is easy for thermal runaway to occur while you are trying to maintain a given output. An increase in magnet temperature decreases the flux. This increase requires an increase in current, which increases the I^2R loss which increases temperature, which decreases flux, and so on.

Rare-earth magnet materials improve the performance of these motors considerably by increasing the flux available, as you can see in Table 1-1. The SmCo magnets are expensive, and the price never was reduced to levels originally hoped for. Also the possible shortage of cobalt has discouraged many users. The recent development of neodymium-iron-boron magnets (made from readily available materials) with 10 times the energy product of ceramic magnets will alter the use of magnets consider-

Table 1-1. Properties of Permanent Magnets.

Magnet Material		Typical max. energy product,[1] KJm^{-3}	Density, $Kg/m^3 \times 10^{-3}$	Typical air-gap flux density conv. motor, Teslas	Typical reversible flux change with temperature, % per °C	Resistance demagnetization	Possible nonreversible flux loss with temperature	Relative physical features	Remarks to relative cost
Ceramic	ceramic I	8.4	4.7	0.17–0.2	−0.2	good	at very low temperature	no oxidation	low cost
	ceramic 8	28–31[2]	4.8	0.3–0.38	−0.2	good	at very low temperature	no oxidation	low cost
Rare earth	$Sm\ Co_5$	140–160[2]	8.3	0.7–0.8	−0.045	excellent	none	oxidizes[3]	very high cost
	$Sm_2\ Co_{17}$	200–220[2]	8.4	0.8–0.9	minimal	excellent	none	oxidizes[3]	very high cost
Rare earth	Nd-Fe-B	200–300[2]	7.4	0.9–1.1	−0.13	excellent	at higher temperatures	improved tensil strength	projected lower cost
Alnico	Alnico 5 cast	40–50[2]	7.3	0.6–1.0	negligible	poor	generally negligible	higher tensil strength	medium cost
	Alnico 8 cast	32–36[2]	7.3	0.6–0.7	negligible	fair	generally negligible	oxidizes[3]	higher cost than alnico 5

1. J/m^3 (SI) = BH (CGS) $\times 7.96 \times 10^{-3}$
2. Anisotropic.
3. Magnets must be protected against oxidation.

ably. With higher-energy magnets, motors can be smaller, more efficient, or both for a given output.

Alnicos are still used extensively because they provide good flux density, and they are temperature stable. However, because of their weak coercive strength, air gaps have to be small, the motor has to be magnetically stabilized, and the motor often can not be taken apart without a keeper or remagnetization.

1.7.3. Analysis

The equivalent circuit of the permanent magnet motor is given in Fig. 1-19. This circuit neglects brush drop. Depending on the characteristics of the brushes, deduct a constant voltage of 0.1 V to 5 V from E_L or add a value of R to R_a.

$$E_a = R_a I_L + E_b. \tag{1-19}$$

Multiplying by I_L:

$$E_a I_L = R_a I_L^2 + E_b I_L. \tag{1-20}$$

If the resistance of the brush is a factor, substitute the terminal resistance R_t for R_a. Gross output of the motor is maximum when $E_b I_L = R_a I_L^2$ where I_L is half the locked rotor current (see Fig. 1-18).

Depending on the internal torque losses as percent of gross torque output, peak efficiency of the motor generally occurs at an operating current anywhere from 1/4 to 1/9 times locked current. The smaller the ratio at which peak efficiency occurs, the higher the peak efficiency of the motor.

High locked currents might not always be desirable and might have to be limited. Magnets might have to be stabilized at a lower operating point to avoid demagnetization. Large currents can be detrimental to batteries, and if electronic controls are used, the current might exceed the ratings of the components.

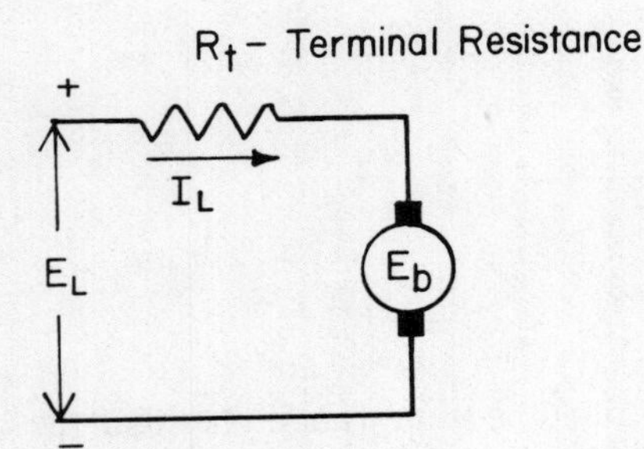

Fig. 1-19. Equivalent circuit for permanent-magnet motor.

1.7.4. Permanent-Magnet Motor Constants

K_T and K_E have been defined in equations 1-3 and 1-4. These constants are extremely important in servo motor applications. Many additional constants are used, with the more important ones listed below. The mechanical time constant of the motor is the time required for the armature to reach 63.2 percent of its final speed after the application of the dc voltage:

$$\tau_m = \frac{R_t J}{K_E K_T} \quad \text{seconds} \tag{1-21}$$

where J = Rotor moment of inertia in kilograms meter^2
R_t = Motor terminal resistance

The electrical time constant is simply the ratio of the motor inductance to resistance:

$$\tau_e = \frac{L}{R_t} \quad \text{seconds} \tag{1-22}$$

where L = Armature inductance in henries (H)

As the torque-speed relationship is linear (Fig. 1-18), the slope constant is:

$$R_m = \frac{R_t}{K_T K_E} \tag{1-23}$$

where R_m is the speed regulation constant.

Acceleration of armature:

$$a = \frac{J}{T} \tag{1-24}$$

where a = acceleration in radians/second^2
T = gross torque generated in N · m

1.7.5. Motor Types

There are different types of permanent magnet motors to accommodate different requirements. Frequently the motor length must be short. The most suitable motor for this might be the *pancake motor* (Fig. 1-20) where the rotor is in disc form with the conductors arranged radially. Magnetically the armature itself is nothing but an air gap, which also classifies the motor as a moving-coil motor. Even though the length of the core is short, the large armature diameter required and the added inertia of the outer connections cause the armature inertia to be somewhat higher than the inertia of a shell armature motor. The electrical time constant is short.

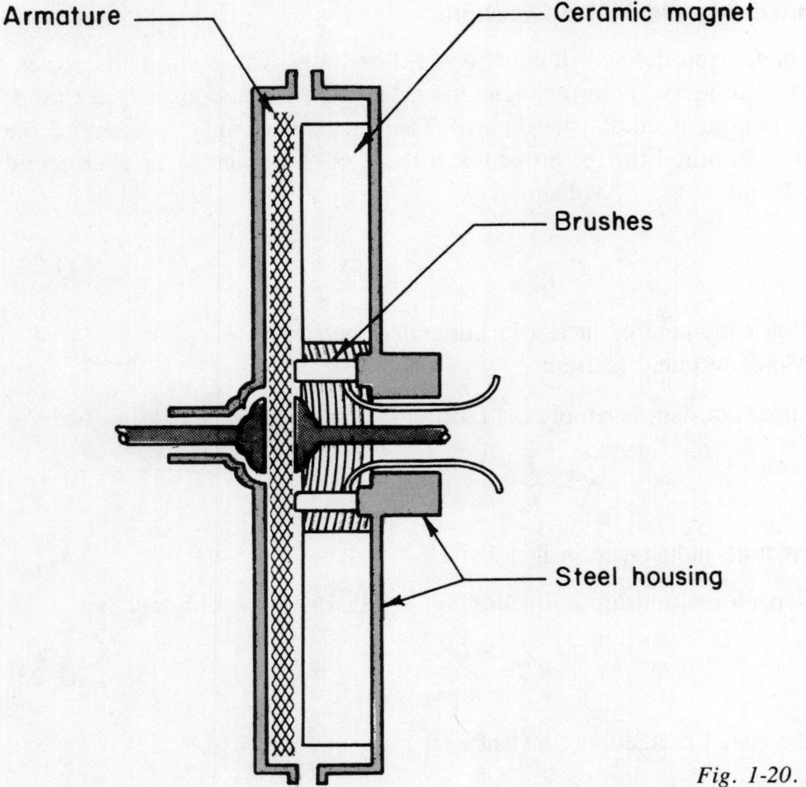

Fig. 1-20. Pancake motor.

The *shell-type armature motor* (see Fig. 1-21) is another moving-coil motor designed to have very low inertia and low inductance. The armature is made up of a winding that forms a hollow cylindrical rotor in which the wires are bonded together. This construction results in a very low electrical time constant. The construction of this motor is less rigid than conventional motors and is likely to have more mechanical resonance points.

Another alternative is a winding wound on the periphery of the iron core of the armature instead of in slots. This construction reduces the inductance, again resulting in lower electrical time constants and a smoother-running motor.

Other applications require *inside-out motors* where the armature is on the outside, and the stationary member with the magnet forms the inside of the motor. This motor is basically a high-inertia motor.

1.7.6. Rectified Power Supplies

If a permanent-magnet motor is connected to a full-wave rectifier bridge (Fig. 1-22), which is connected to an ac line, the resulting current will be a pulsating current (Fig. 1-23). The result is that the *RMS* (root mean square) value of the current (I_{RMS}) is larger than the average value of the current or dc current (I_{dc}). The ratio of these values is often called the *form factor* (see Fig. 1-24). The torque is only proportional to the dc while the winding I^2R_a losses are a function of I_{RMS}, which could also be thought of as the heating value of the current. This means that the motor would operate more efficiently with a pure dc current. Under these conditions, a motor with a high inductance might be desirable because the inductance acts as a filter. The filtering improves the form factor. Half-wave rectification increases motor losses even more.

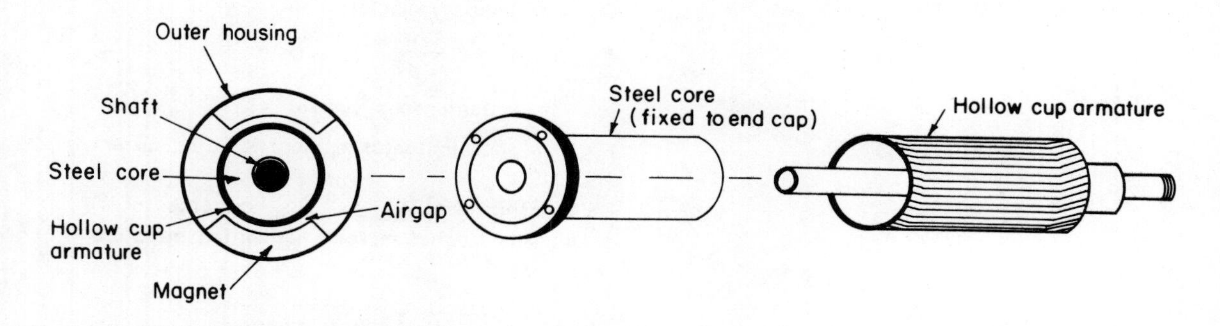

Fig. 1-21. Shell-armature motor.

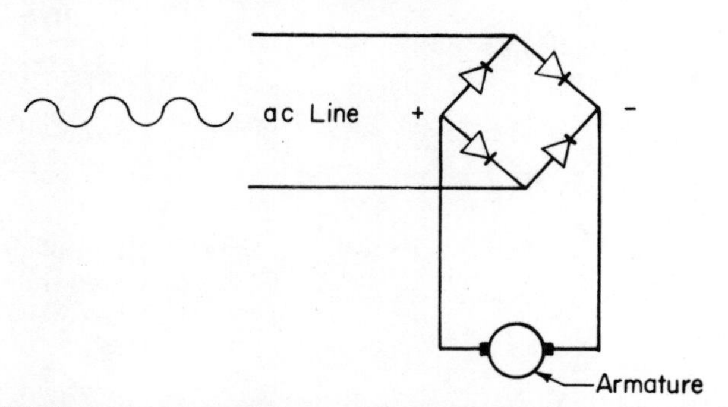

Fig. 1-22. Permanent-magnet motor connected to full-wave rectifier bridge.

Fig. 1-23. Pulsating current resulting from a rectifier bridge operating a permanent-magnet motor.

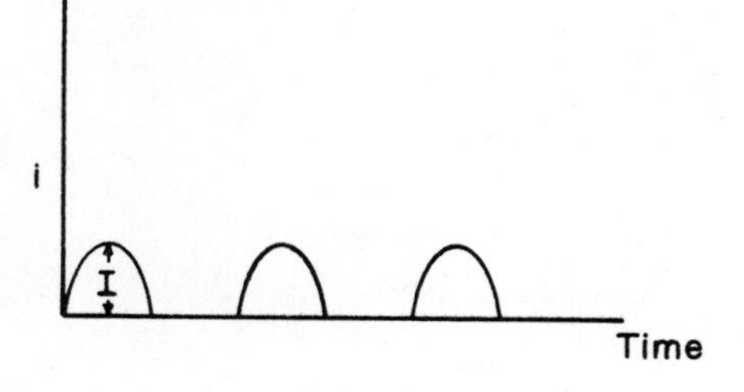

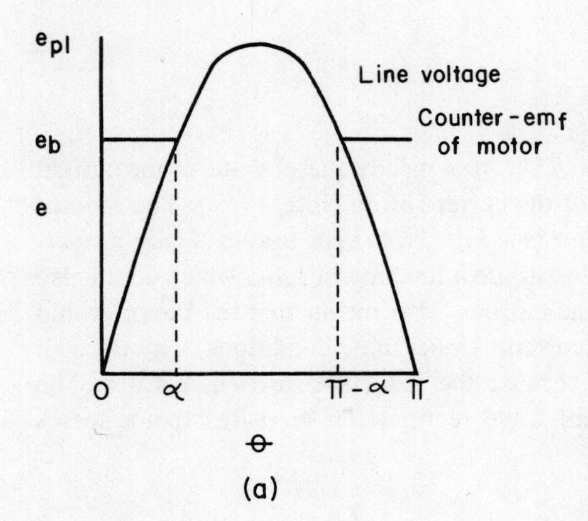

(a)

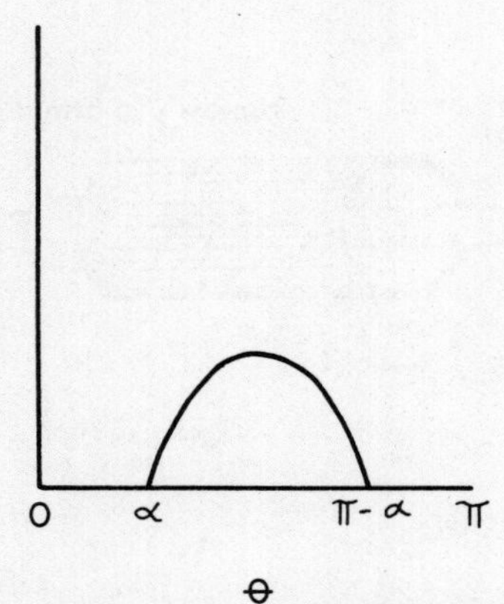

Current during conduction period α to (π − α)

(b)

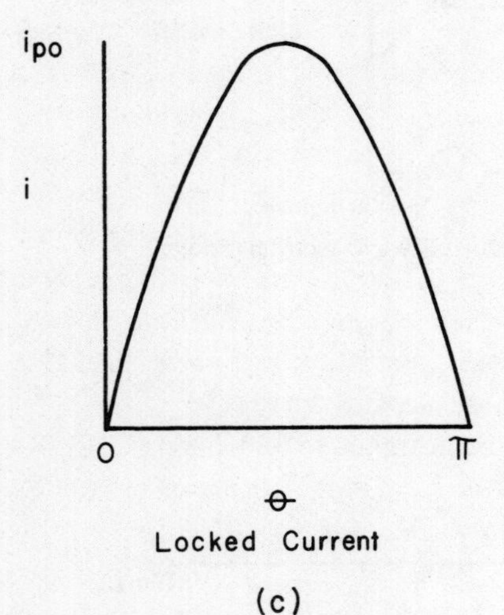

Locked Current

(c)

e = instantaneous voltage

e_{pl} = peak instantaneous line voltage

e_b = counter-emf at a given motor speed

θ = angular displacement

$\alpha = \sin^{-1} \dfrac{e_b}{e_{pl}}$

i = instantaneous current

i_{po} = peak instantaneous locked rotor current

Relationship of I_{RMS} to I_{DC} currents for permanent magnet motors neglecting armature reactance.

$$I_{RMSO} = 0.707 \; I_{PO}$$

$$I_{RMS} = I_{RMSO} \cdot C_i$$

$$C_i = \sqrt{\frac{1}{\pi}\left[\pi - 2\alpha - 3\sin 2\alpha + (2\pi - 4\alpha)\sin^2\alpha\right]}$$

$$I_{avgO} = \frac{2}{\pi} \; I_{PO}$$

$$I_{avg} = I_{avgO} \cdot C_t$$

$$C_t = \frac{2\cos\alpha - (\pi - 2\alpha)\sin\alpha}{2}$$

Note: All symbols with subscript O refer to locked rotor condition i.e. $\alpha = 0$

Fig. 1-24. Voltage and current relationships in a permanent-magnet dc motor operated from an unfiltered full-wave rectified, sinusoidal ac power supply.

2

Armature Windings and Commutation

2.1. ARMATURE REACTION

In chapter 1, the performance characteristics of dc motors are described as being determined largely by the *MMF* (magnetomotive force) generated by the field and the resulting air-gap flux. However, currents flowing in the armature coils set up their own fields and can cause some modification in those characteristics. Figure 1-3 shows a field formed by a current carrying conductor. Figure 2-1 shows the field created by current-carrying conductors in the armature. The armature field is in quadrature with the main field. The net result is that the armature field opposes the main field at point A substracting from the main flux and adds to the main field at point A′. The same occurs at B and B′ and can be repeated at any number of points. This is called *armature reaction*. The net effect on the field flux depends on the magnetic circuit of the motor. If the armature MMF is relatively small and the flux added on one pole side equals the flux reduction on the other pole side, no net flux has been lost even though the flux field axis (and therefore the magnetic neutral) has been shifted. However, if the pole tips of the wound field poles were saturated, then more flux would be lost than added, and there would be a net loss of flux.

In permanent-magnet motors, the magnet must be designed to withstand the opposing armature MMF. The distortion of the field does have an effect on commutation and this effect is discussed in section 2.3.5.

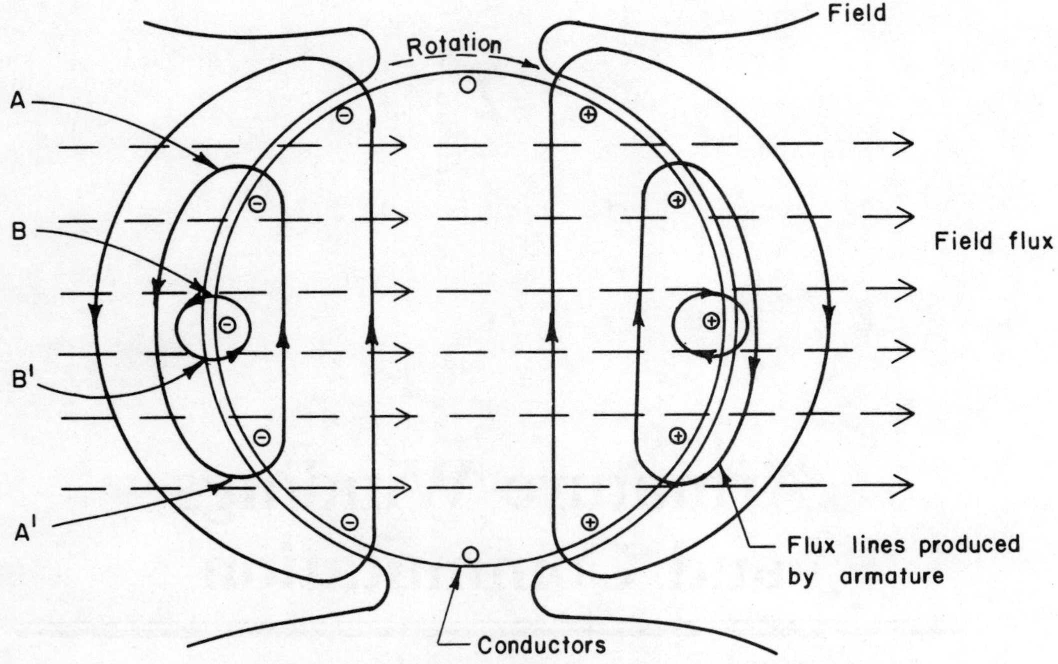

Fig. 2-1. Armature reaction effect due to current in the armature.

2.2. ARMATURE WINDINGS

2.2.1. Function of Armature Windings

An armature winding consists of a number of coils, all of them connected to each other and each one connected to two commutator bars. The start of each coil is connected to one bar and the finish to another bar. The coils are distributed around the armature, commonly by inserting them in slots in the armature core (Fig. 1-8). The commutator consists of bars that are insulated from each other. The number of bars are either the same as or a multiple of the number of slots. Motor action of a single coil rotating in a magnetic field is described in chapter 1 (Fig. 1-5). There are a number of different winding patterns such as lap and wave windings, but the basic functions are always the same. Figure 2-2 represents a typical two-pole, eight-slot armature. The winding consists of one coil per slot. There are eight coils. The start of each coil is marked with a dot. The armature rotates in the direction opposite to the coil numbering sequence. When the armature is in position (a), coils eight and four are short circuited. Coils one, two, and three are in parallel with coils 5, 6, and 7. The

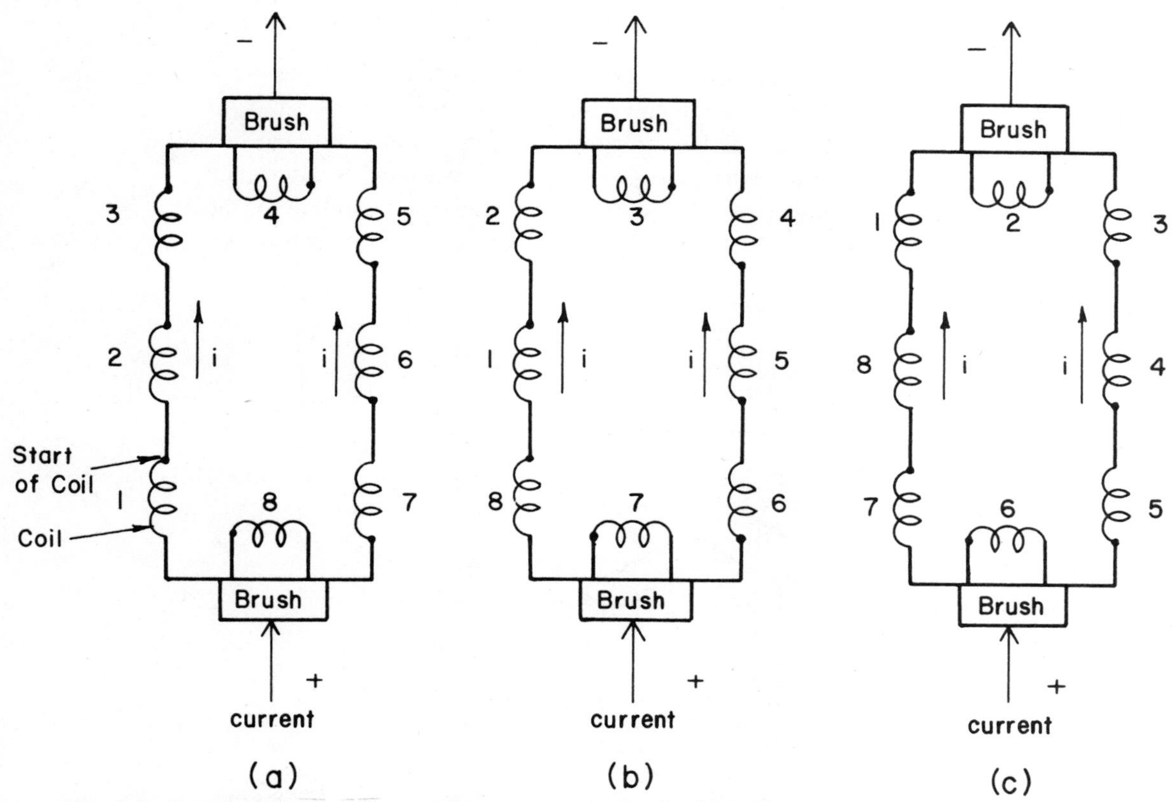

Fig. 2-2. Currents in a two-pole, eight-slot armature: (a) current direction in coil three is from finish to start. (b) coil three under commutation. (c) current direction in coil three is from start to finish.

direction of current in coil three is from finish to start, in coil 7, the direction of current is from start to finish. When the armature has moved to position (b), coils 3 and 7 are short circuited by the brushes, coils 8, 1, and 2 are in parallel with coils 4, 5, and 6. When the armature is in position (c), coil 2 and 6 are short circuited by the brushes; coils 1, 8, and 7 are in parallel with coils 3, 4, and 5. The direction of current in coil 3 is now from start to finish, and the direction of current in coil 7 is now from finish to start. To sum up, while the armature rotated from position (a) to position (c), the currents in coil 3 and 7 were reversed, and the reversing occurred during the period the coils were short circuited by the brushes.

2.2.2. Lap Winding

By far, the most popular winding configuration for smaller dc motors is the simplex lap winding. Figure 2-3 illustrates the coil connection for a full-pitch, simplex-lap winding for a two-pole, six-slot, six-bar armature. Full pitch means that each side of the coil is located in a slot 180 electrical degrees apart. In a two-pole armature, the number of electrical degrees equals mechanical degrees. A full-pitch winding for the six-slot armature in Fig. 2-3 means that the coil with coil-side in slot 1, must have the

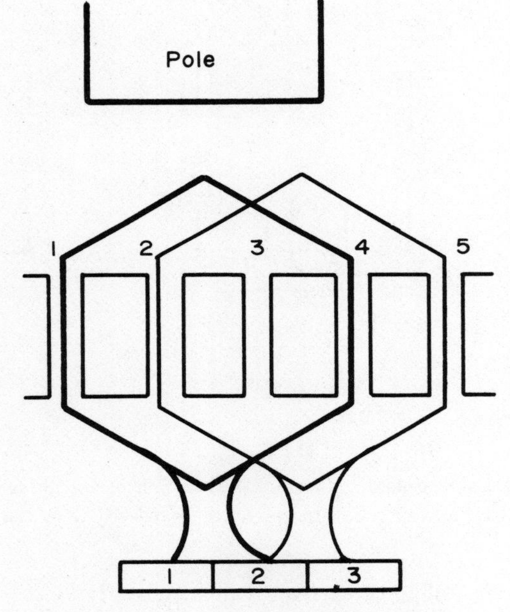

Fig. 2-3. Coil connection for full-pitch, simplex-lap winding for one coil per slot, two-pole, six-slot, six-commutator bar armature.

other coil-side in slot 4 for a coil-throw of three. This amounts to half of six slots or 180 electrical degrees. If the coil-throw had only been two, it would be called a fractional coil pitch, and it would amount to 120 electrical degrees. It is generally easier to wind a fractional coil pitch while at the same time the winding overhang is reduced to make a shorter armature. However, the coil pitch should exceed the pole-shoe arc or magnet arc of the motor.

It is often desirable to have more than one coil per slot. Figure 2-4 illustrates the coil connections for a full-pitch, simplex-lap winding of two coils per slot for a two-pole, six-slot, twelve-bar commutator armature. As there are now 12 coils, there must be 12 commutator bars; that is, the number of coils always equals the number of commutator bars.

The reason for having more coils and therefore more commutator bars than slots is to reduce the voltage between commutator bars. This can be important to increase

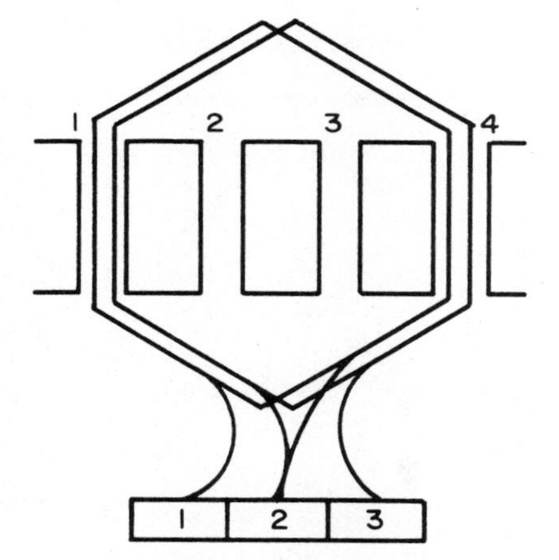

Fig. 2-4. Coil connection for full-pitch, simplex-lap winding for two coils per slot, two-pole, six-slot, twelve-commutator bar armature.

brush life and reduce EMI. With a simplex-lap winding, there are always as many parallel paths in the armature as there are numbers of poles. There are also as many brushes as there are poles. A two-pole motor would have two parallel paths and two brushes as shown in Fig. 2-1. A four-pole motor would have four parallel paths and four brushes. Only the simplex-lap winding has been described here. Other lap windings, such as duplex and triplex, are not applicable for motor sizes that are considered in this book.

2.2.3. Wave Winding

A typical simplex-wave winding for a nine-slot, nine-bar commutator, four-pole armature is shown in Fig. 2-5. It differs from the lap winding in that the coil connections to the commutator are close to, but not quite, a pole pitch apart. (A pole pitch is 180 electrical degrees.) There are only two parallel paths no matter how many poles. Conceivably, you could always get away with only two brushes if these can handle the currents. Dummy coils might be required as in the case of an armature with twice as many commutator bars as slots. The wave winding is more difficult to wind and does not lend itself readily for automatic winding. Wave winding is generally only used in large dc motors. Combinations of lap and wave windings are possible.

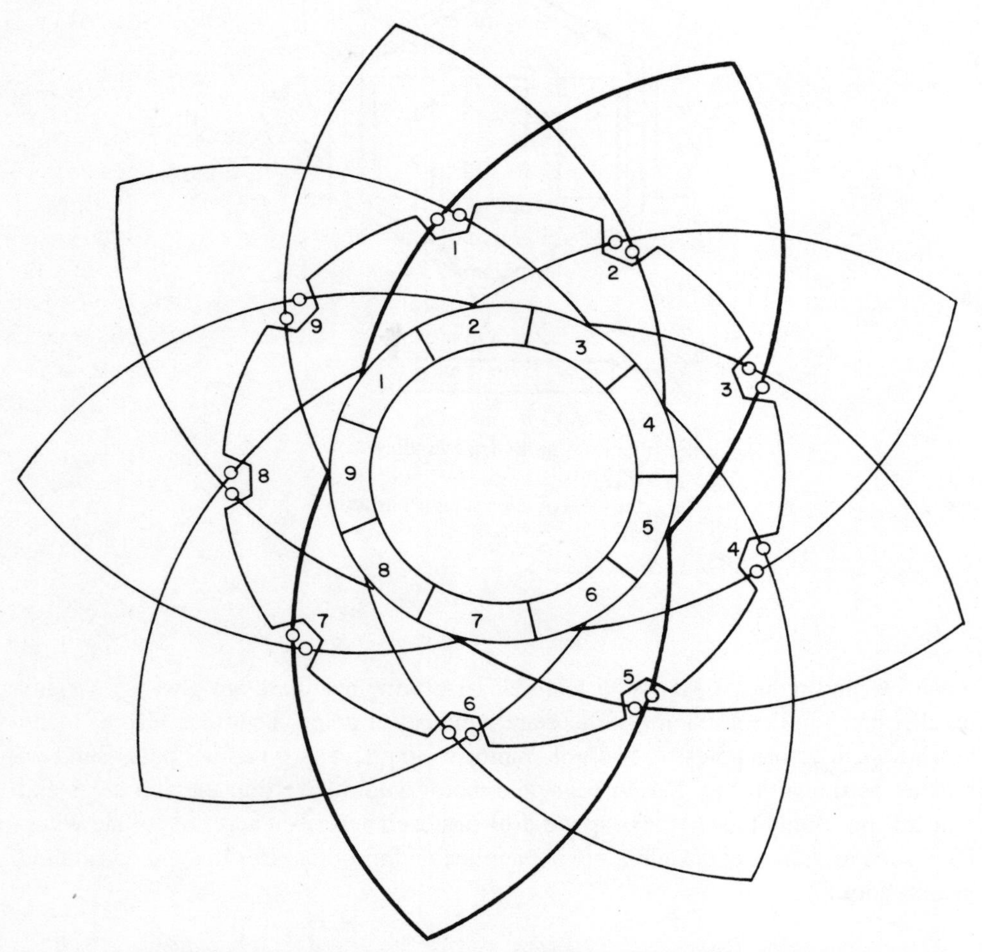

Fig. 2-5. Simplex-wave winding for a nine-slot, four-pole, nine-commutator bar armature.

2.3. COMMUTATION

2.3.1. General Considerations

The physical process of reversing the current in a coil in the armature is called *commutation*. How well this is accomplished in any one dc motor determines its overall performance and durability.

The components that make commutation possible are:

- The commutator
- Brushes, springs, brush tubes, and other hardware that is necessary to carry the current to the commutator
- The coils that make up the armature winding

2.3.2. Commutator

For smaller motors, either molded mica or molded air-gap commutators are used as illustrated in Fig. 2-6. Both commutators are made of hard copper bars, separated by either mica or an air gap. The copper alloy usually has a silver content of 10 to 25 ounces per ton. The molding material is usually a mineral and glass or only mineral-filled phenolic. Eccentricity is very important. It helps to determine how closely the brush can follow the commutator surface. Typically, commutator eccentricity would be kept within 0.025 millimeters with a bar to bar deviation of between 0.0025 millimeters to 0.005 millimeters. However, these tolerances will vary with the size of the commutator as well as with the speed of the motor. Also, tight tolerances will permit longer brush life and will cut down brush noise.

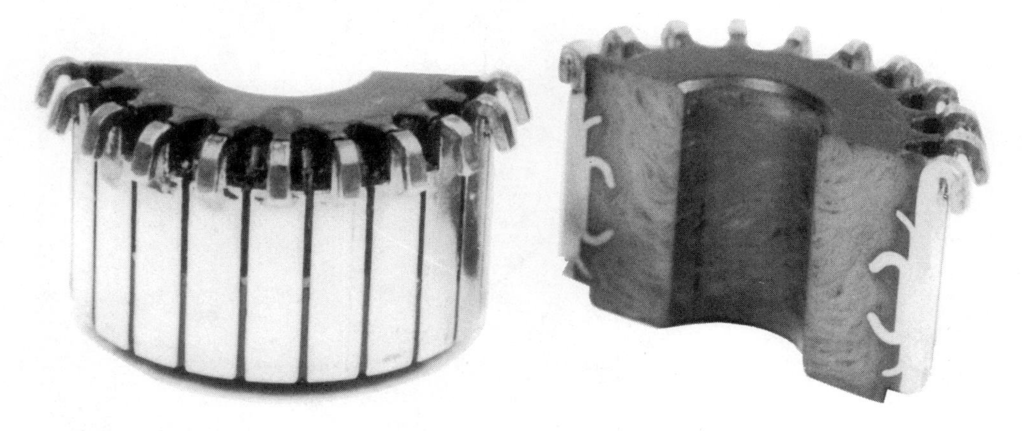

Fig. 2-6. Molded airgap commutators. (Courtesy of MORGANITE, Inc., Dunn, NC)

2.3.3. Brush Assembly

The brush assembly consists of a brush with or without a shunt, a spring, and a brush holder. There can also be a cap at the end of the shunt. Typical brushes are shown in Fig. 2-7.

Direct-current motors vary in horsepower output, speed, voltage input, brush life, noise etc. Physical and electrical demands on the brush vary and therefore there is a very large variety of brushes, with each brush designed to meet specific requirements. Table 2-1 lists some types of brushes and how they typically compare to each other. The choice of the right brush is essential to a motor operating successfully. But no brush will perform satisfactorily unless the spring exerts the correct force on the brush. The correct spring force varies with the grade of the brush, the speed of the motor, the commutator, etc. Compression-type and torsion-type springs are in general use.

Brush holders for smaller motors are usually of the box type and are either of copper or molded plastic. Except for small motors, brushes usually have a shunt that might consist of stranded copper wire and that carries the current from the brush to the armature terminal. It is of utmost importance that the brush and spring movement not be impeded by the brush holder to such an extent that the brush hangs up inside the tube and looses contact with the commutator. Therefore, the amount of clearance between brush and brush holder is important. Typical clearances vary from 0.06 to 0.30 millimeter and somewhat more for metal-graphite brushes to account for tem-

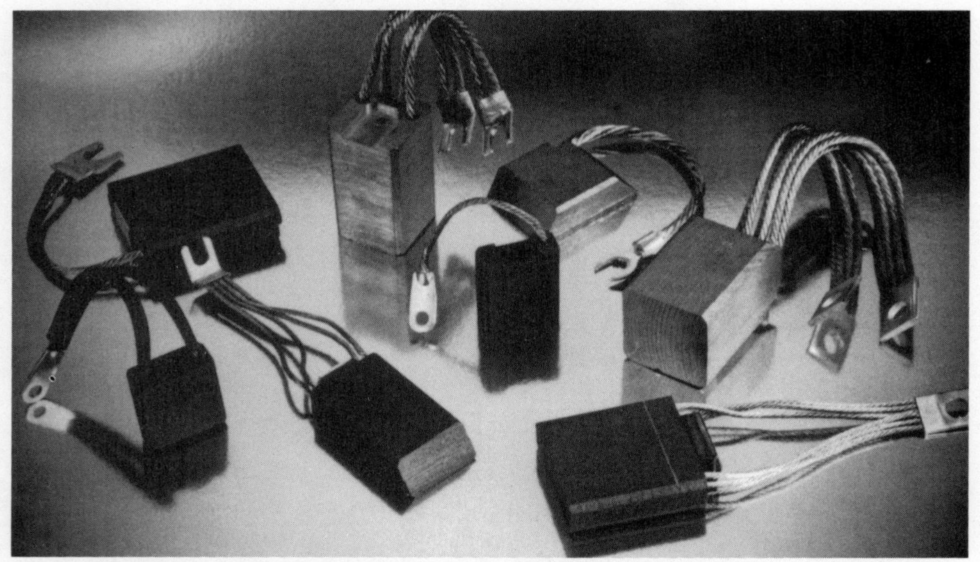

Fig. 2-7. Selection of industrial brushes. (Courtesy of MORGANITE, Inc., Dunn, NC)

Table 2-1. Relative Characteristics of Different Types of Brushes.

Type	Friction	Contact drop	Current capacity	Specific resistance	Surface speeds	Comments
Carbon graphite	medium to high	high	low	medium to high	low	abrasive, good for flush commutators
Electrographitic	low	medium	high	medium	high	low abrasive
Graphite	medium to low	medium	medium	low to high	medium to high	quiet operation for undercut commutators
Metal graphite	very low	very low	high	very low	low	low voltage motors

perature expansion. The clearances also vary somewhat with the size and configuration of the brushes. If the clearance is excessive, the brush might tip, gradually increasing the contact area with the commutator. Clearance becomes even more critical for reversible motors.

It is the brush assembly, commutator run-out and surface finish that always seem to be prime targets for cost cutters. It is important to realize that making the whole system sloppier might not noticeably change the initial performance of the motor. But after a short time in operation, the motor could start running noisier and the brush wear become excessive. The wear could cause early motor failure.

2.3.4. Effect of Electrical Constants

Electrical design considerations also play a major role in commutation. Larger motors have an extra pair of poles (called *interpoles*) between the main poles to aid in commutation. However, the smaller-size motors covered here do not have them and therefore they will not be discussed.

The armature winding is pivotal in the process of commutation. Figure 2-8 and Figure 2-9 illustrate the process. Figure 2-8 (a) shows coil 2–3 just coming under commutation, the current i still in its original direction. Figure 2-8 (b) illustrates commutation in that coil reaching the end with current i already reversed. When the brush leaves commutator bar 3 while the current i differs from $I_a/2$, arcing will occur. Figure 2-9 shows a linear commutation if the current reversal follows path o–b. If it follows path o–a it is called *under-commutation,* which means that not all the current has reversed within the commutation path. If reversal follows path o–c it is called *over-commutation,* which indicates that the current reversal exceeded the line current by an amount of bc. The path the current follows is largely dependent on the coil winding constants such as self inductance, mutual inductance, coil resistance, brush

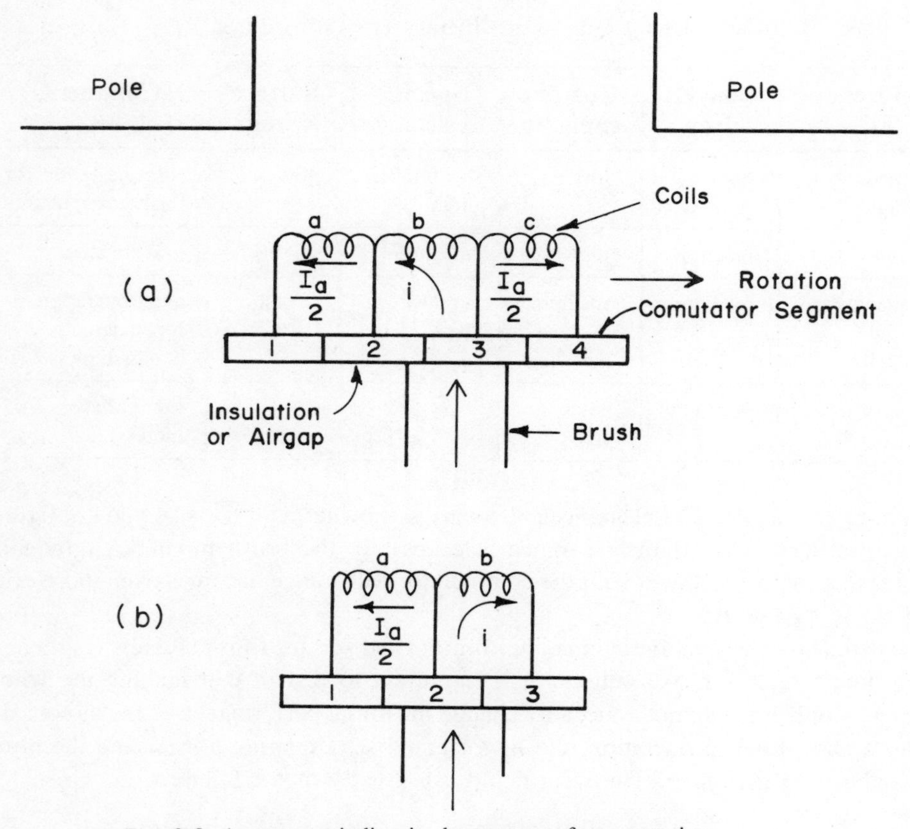

Fig. 2-8. Armature winding in the process of commutation.

shift, brush resistance, and contact drop. The impedance will have a tendency to limit the current while the electrical time constant at any one time will determine the speed of reversal. The voltage between bars also has a marked effect on commutation. The higher the voltage, the more arcing might occur. To reduce the voltage between commutator bars there are often two or even three bars per armature slot.

2.3.5. Brush Shifting

Section 2.1 notes that there is a distortion in the field due to armature reaction. This means that there is a shift of the magnetic neutral away from the physical neutral. This is against the direction of rotation in the case of a motor. Therefore, for improved commutation, brushes should be rotated against rotation. The shift of the field is a function of armature current, which is a function of load; you can only shift to a

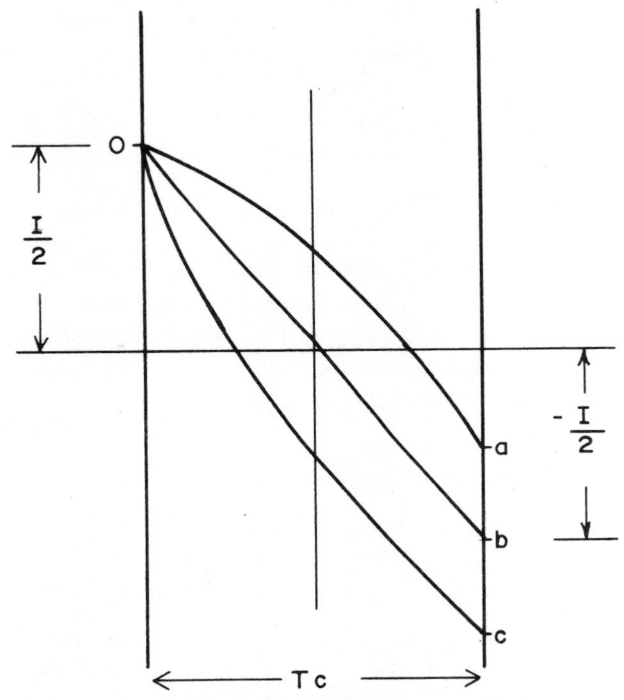

Fig. 2-9. Alternate commutation paths. Curve o–a is under-commutation, o–b is linear-commutation, and o–c is over-commutation. I is load current in the machine. The gap between segments is neglected.

brush position most favorable for a certain load. For reversible motors, brushes must remain on mechanical neutral. In case of a full-pitch coil winding, brush shifting results in reducing the main field flux effectively. For a two-pole motor, this demagnetization is expressed in equation 2-1:

$$\frac{\alpha}{360} \times \frac{Z_a I_a}{a} \tag{2-1}$$

where α is the brush shift from neutral in degrees.

If the winding is a short-pitched winding to an extent that the pitch is smaller than 180 degrees minus α, no demagnetization will occur.

As a matter of interest, brush shifting has not only been used to improve commutation, but also for speed control. By varying brush position, the effective field changes and this changes the speed of the motor.

2.3.6. Cogging

When an armature turns slowly, rotation might not be uniform because of the tendency of the armature to favor certain angular positions over others. This phenomenon is generally referred to as *cogging*. The main causes for this preference of position are the discrete variations of reluctance in the magnetic circuit of the motor and the winding configuration. Figure 2-10 shows the cross-section of a permanent

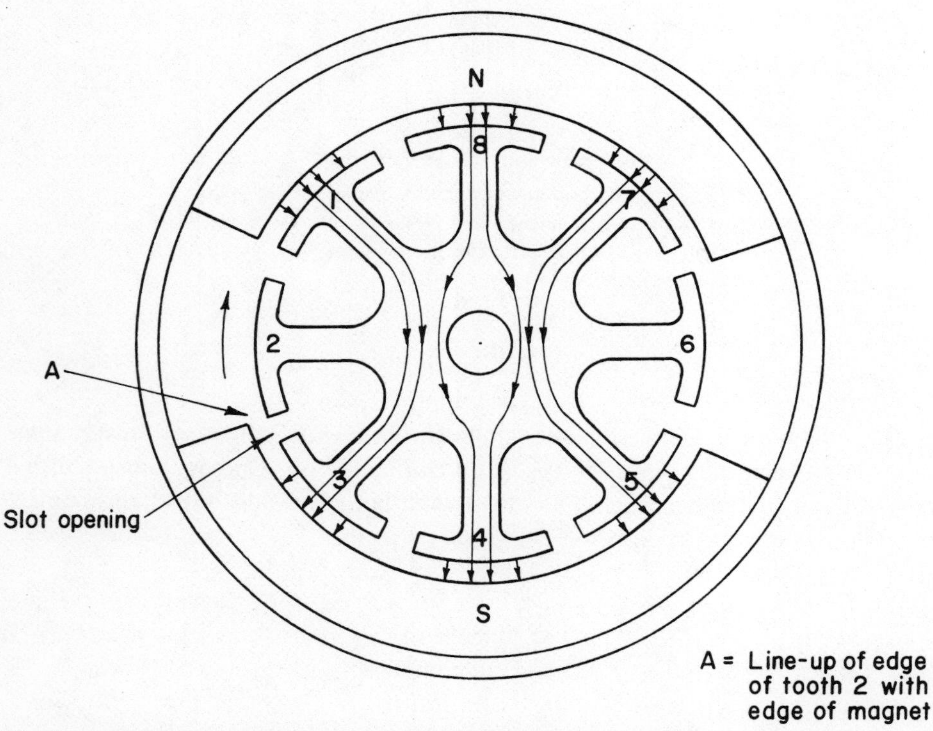

Fig. 2-10. Cross section of two-pole, eight-slot, PM DC motor, clockwise rotation with flux locking in teeth, causing cogging.

magnet dc motor. Rotation is clockwise. Point A shows the line up of tooth 2 with the edge of the magnet. There is a slot opening between tooth 2 and 3, which magnetically is an air gap. Therefore, the magnet flux will have a tendency to not let go or hold on to tooth 2 and it will take extra effort to move it away from the magnet into the neutral zone. To minimize this effect, armature slots are frequently skewed as shown in Fig. 2-11 (B). However, skewing might decrease the K_E and increase

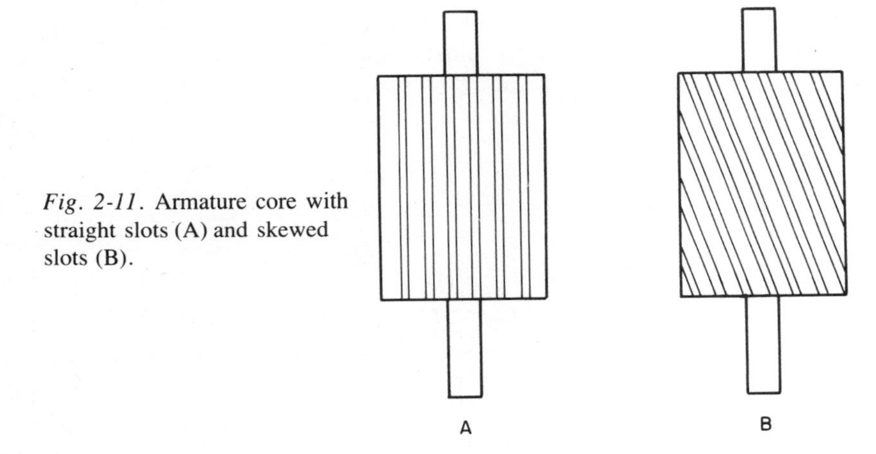

Fig. 2-11. Armature core with straight slots (A) and skewed slots (B).

armature resistence. The extent of the magnetic cogging can actually be felt by turning the shaft of a motor by hand without applying power to the motor.

Another cause for an uneven distribution of torque is the winding itself. The terminal resistance of the armature varies with the angular position of the armature. At locked and at slow speed, the varying resistance causes the current and the torque to vary. This effect is particularly noticable with permanent-magnet and shunt-wound dc motors.

The number of torque-producing coils can vary. In an armature of uneven coils and commutator bars, sometimes two or three coils might be under commutation. In general, the fewer the number of slots and commutator bars, the more likely that the locked torque will vary considerably with position of the armature.

3

AC Motors and Stepper Motors

3.1. INTRODUCTION

The current that enters homes and factories is most likely to be alternating current, called ac for short. The corresponding voltage is ac voltage. The majority of motors in use today are ac motors. There are a great variety of ac motors but they can be categorized into three groups: induction, synchronous and ac commutator motors.

An alternating current referred to in this book is one that reverses regularly, being alternatively positive and negative at regular intervals as shown in Figure 3-1. One complete period of positive and negative values is called a cycle and every cycle is divided into 360 electrical degrees. The same applies to an ac voltage. Figure 3-2 shows three currents going into a resistance network. Although the magnitude of the currents are the same and the intervals between change in polarity are identical, the point in time at which each current reaches its peak differs as shown in Fig. 3-3. In terms of electrical degrees, the peak of current i_2 occurs 120 electrical degrees after the peak of current i_1, and current i_3 peaks 120 degrees after current i_2. This is what is called a three-phase system. Assuming a frequency of 60 Hz (hertz) or cycles/second, a complete cycle lasts 16.67 milliseconds. With i_2 lagging i_1 by 120 degrees, or a third of a cycle, i_2 lags i_1 by 5.56 milliseconds. Current i_3 lags i_2 by the same time element. It is this time differential that forms the basis for most ac motors.

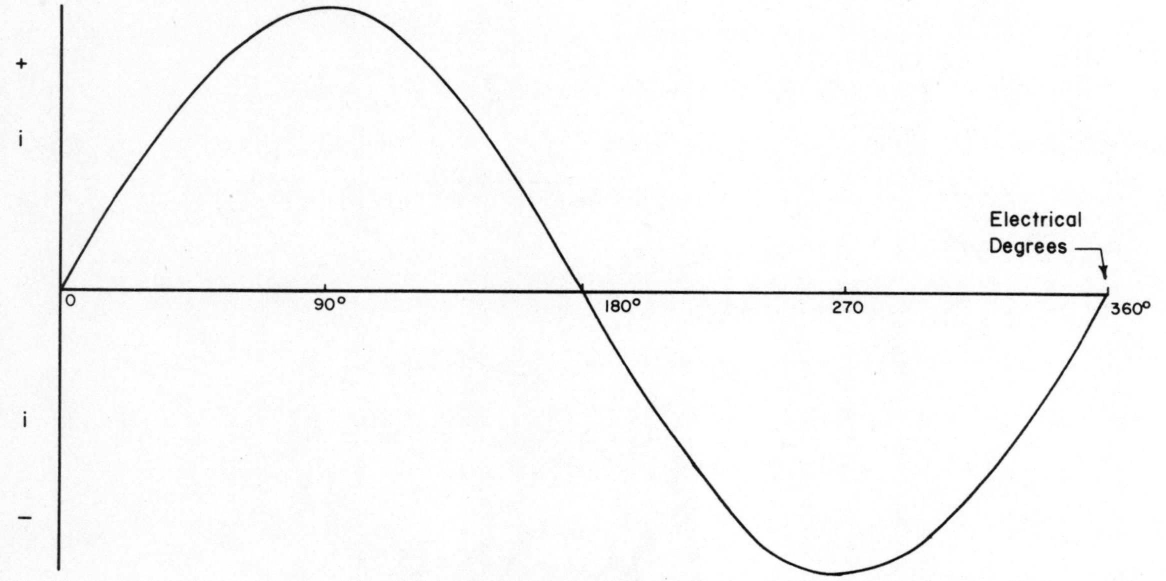

Fig. 3-1. ac current curve.

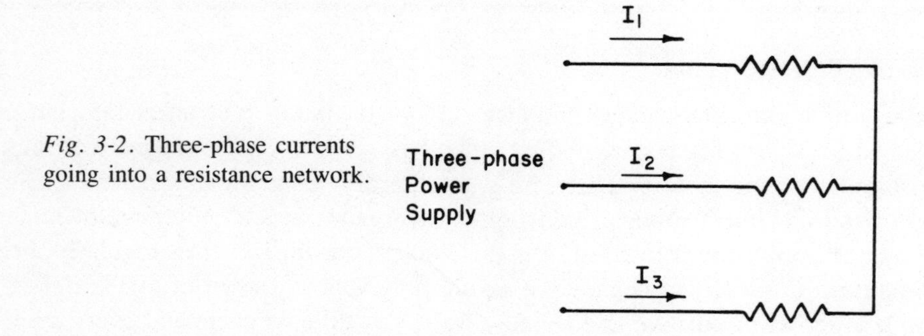

Fig. 3-2. Three-phase currents going into a resistance network.

Suppose the three resistors in Fig. 3-2 were substituted by three electromagnets as shown in Fig. 3-4. The electromagnets are physically located in a circle 120 degrees apart and each consists of a coil wound on a cold-rolled steel rod. Three-phase, 1 Hz power is supplied to this circuit. The instantaneous sequence of the current in the three phases are as shown in Fig. 3-5. Initially, at time 0, i_1 in coil 1 is at its peak positive value, creating a north pole facing the circle, while currents in i_2 and i_3 in coils 2 and 3 are negative, creating a south pole. This is shown in Fig. 3-4 position 1. The instantaneous current relationships keep changing with time, and 0.33 seconds

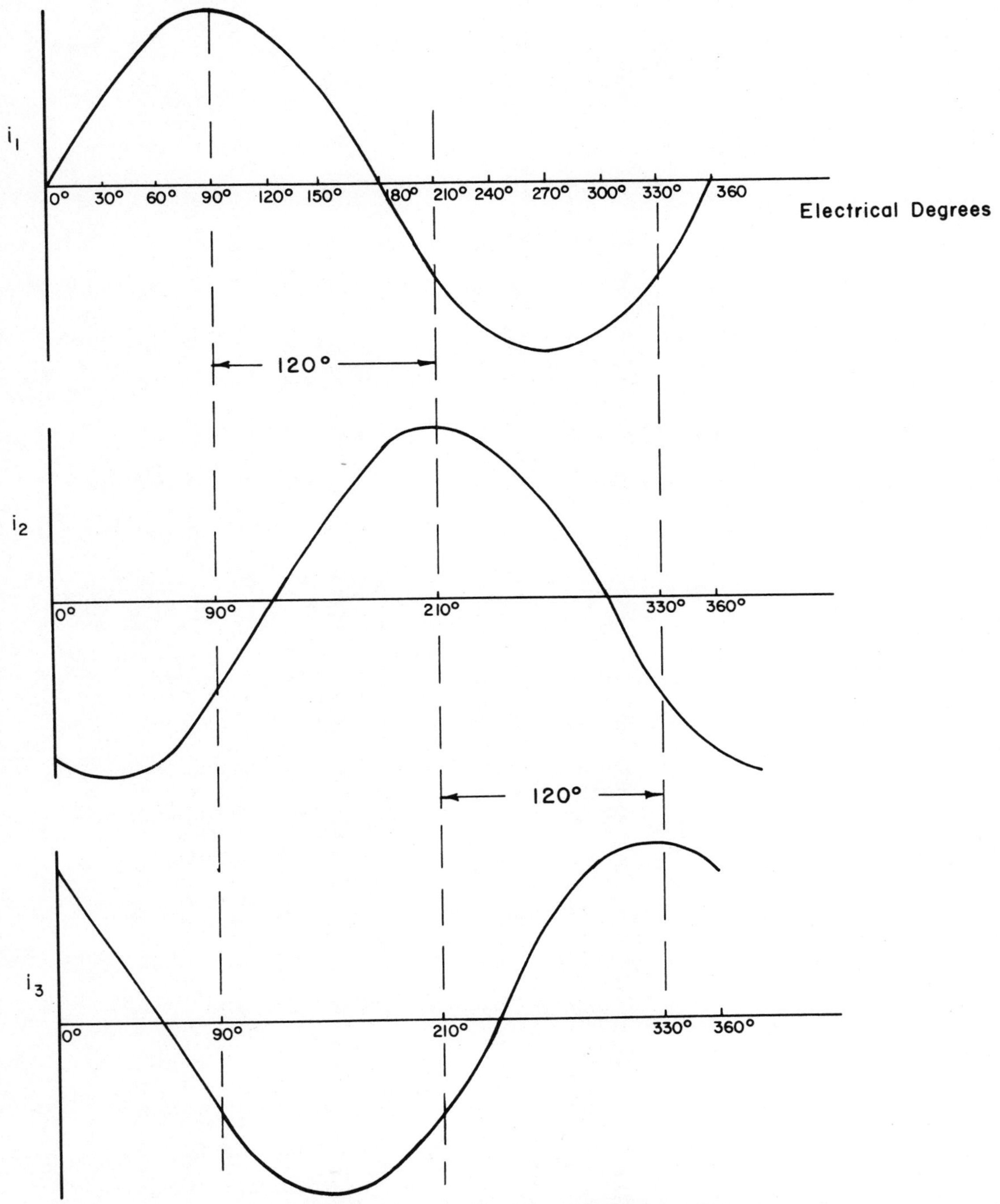

Fig. 3-3. Instantaneous phase relationships of three-phase currents.

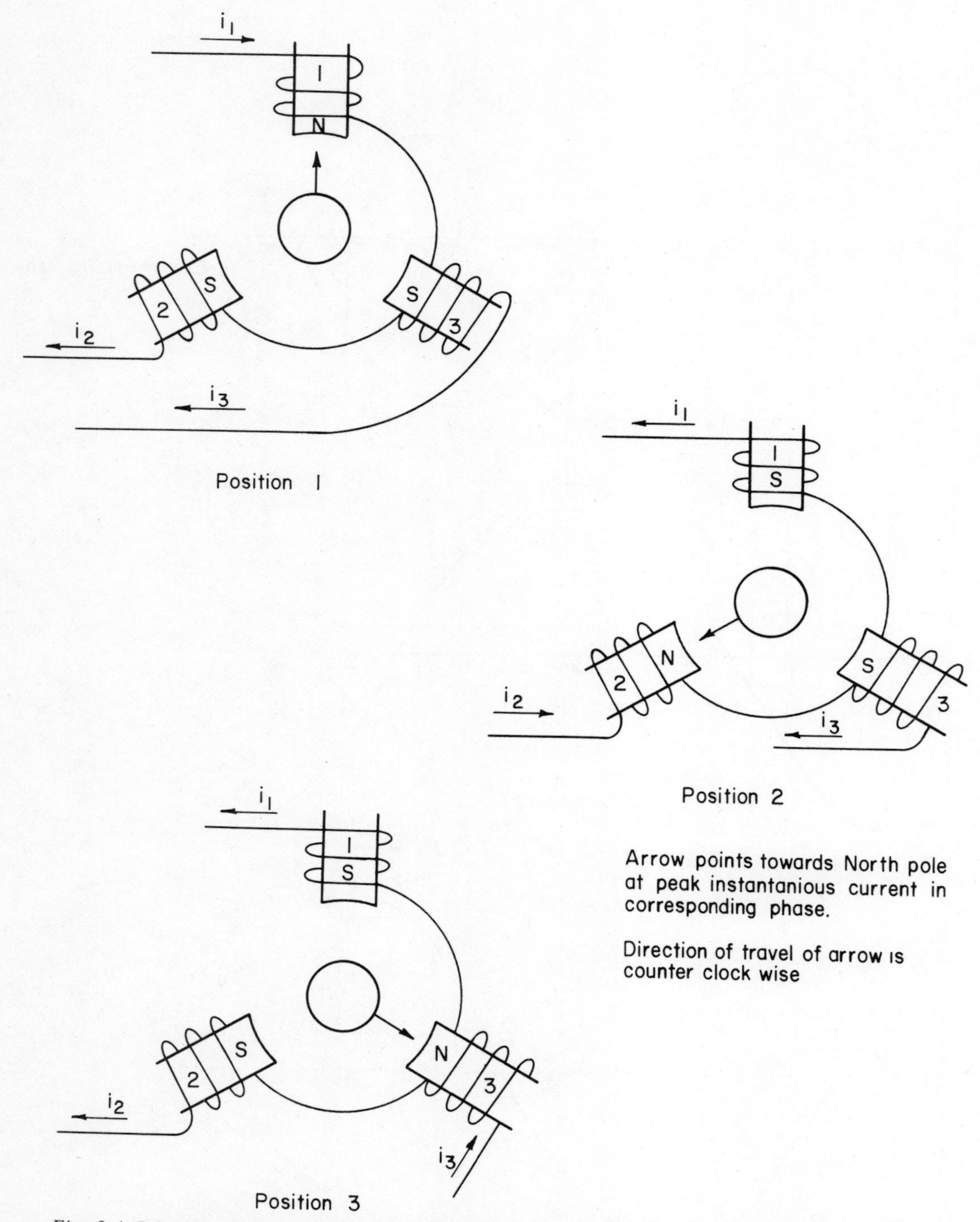

Fig. 3-4. Principle of a rotating electromagnetic field: electromagnets establishing a rotating field.

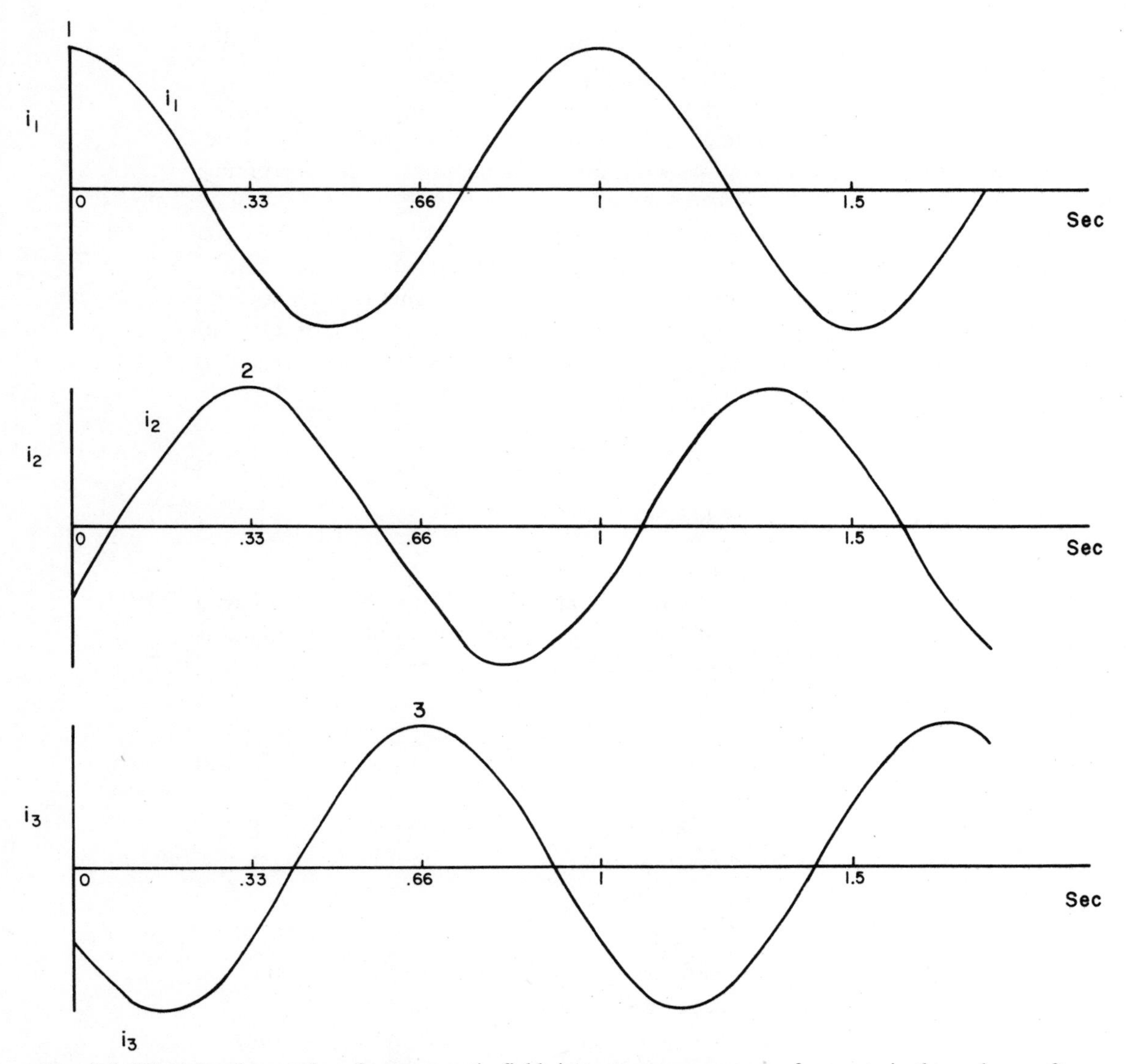

Fig. 3-5. Principle of a rotating electromagnetic field: instantaneous sequence of currents in three phases after applying three-phase, 1 Hz power.

later i_2 has reached its peak positive magnitude in coil 2, while i_1 and i_3 are negative. The resulting polarities are shown in Fig. 3-4 position 2. In the same way, 0.33 seconds later, electromagnet 3 will be a north pole as the current is positive in coil 3 and negative in coils 1 and 2. After another 0.33 seconds, position 1 will have been restored, and the process can be repeated. The north pole will have rotated at one revolution per second. In a very rudimentary way, this description illustrates how a magnetic field can be made to rotate by strictly electrical means.

The foregoing description could have been explained much the same way by considering the differences in the phase angle between each phase current in a three-phase system, but if you are not familiar with vectors and phasors, the concept of time differential might be easier for you to follow.

A motor winding is made up of current carrying conductors. In section 1.3, you learned that a current in a conductor creates a field around the conductor (Fig. 1-3). If the current reverses, it follows that this field also reverses. This continuous field reversal due to an ever-reversing current induces an electromotive force in that conductor and this property is called *self-inductance*. The self-induced voltage in a coil or winding can be expressed as:

$$e_s = L_s \frac{\mathrm{di}}{\mathrm{dt}} \tag{3-1}$$

where e_s = self-induced voltage, in volts
L_s = inductance, in henries

If there are two coils in close proximity to each other, or if they are wound around a common magnetic core, a change in the current in one coil, which of course is accompanied by a change in its magnetic field, will induce an EMF in the other coil. This can be expressed:

$$e_1 = -M \frac{\mathrm{di}_2}{\mathrm{dt}} \qquad e_2 = -M \frac{\mathrm{di}_1}{\mathrm{dt}} \tag{3-2}$$

where M = mutual inductance, in henries: M is considered a constant in these two equations
e_1, i_1 = volts and amps in coil one
e_2, e_2 = volts and amps in coil two

Transformers operate on the principle of mutual inductance. The magnetic field created by the primary winding induces a voltage in the secondary winding.

In ac motors, the self-inductances of coils play a major role in motor performance. Mutual inductance due to various coils in close proximity with each other also plays a large role in design.

So far we have dealt with instantaneous values of current. In practice, alternating currents are expressed in *root-means-squared* values, which is the square root of the mean of the square of the current over one complete cycle. Alternating-current voltages are similarly defined. Following relationships apply to ac circuits:

$$X = 2\pi fL \tag{3-3}$$

where X = reactance, in ohms
f = line frequency
L = inductance, in henries

in phasor terms:

$$Z = R + jX \tag{3-4}$$

where Z = impedance, in ohms;

or in scalor quantity, in ohms:

$$Z = \sqrt{R^2 + X^2} \tag{3-5}$$

The relationship between current and voltage is:

$$E = IZ \tag{3-6}$$

If the impedance consists of a resistance only, then the voltage and the current are in phase. In phase means that the voltage and current peaks occur at the same time.

Power in single-phase currents is expressed:

$$P = E_{RMS} \times I_{RMS} \cos \theta^* \tag{3-7}$$

where $\cos \theta$ is the power factor.

In sinusoidal relationships, θ (theta) is the angle by which the current leads or lags the voltage. This is illustrated in Fig. 3-6 (a and b) where the inductance in the circuit causes the current to lag by an angle θ.

For three-phase circuits:

$$\text{Power} = \sqrt{3}\, E_L\, I_L \cos \theta \tag{3-8}$$

where E_L and I_L are line values.

Figure 3-7 shows three-phase relationships.

Table 3-1 lists additional relationships such as horsepower, watts input, and power factor for single and polyphase motors.

---

* All voltages and currents in capital letters in this chapter will be RMS values, unless otherwise indicated. Small letters e and i will continue to represent instantaneous values.

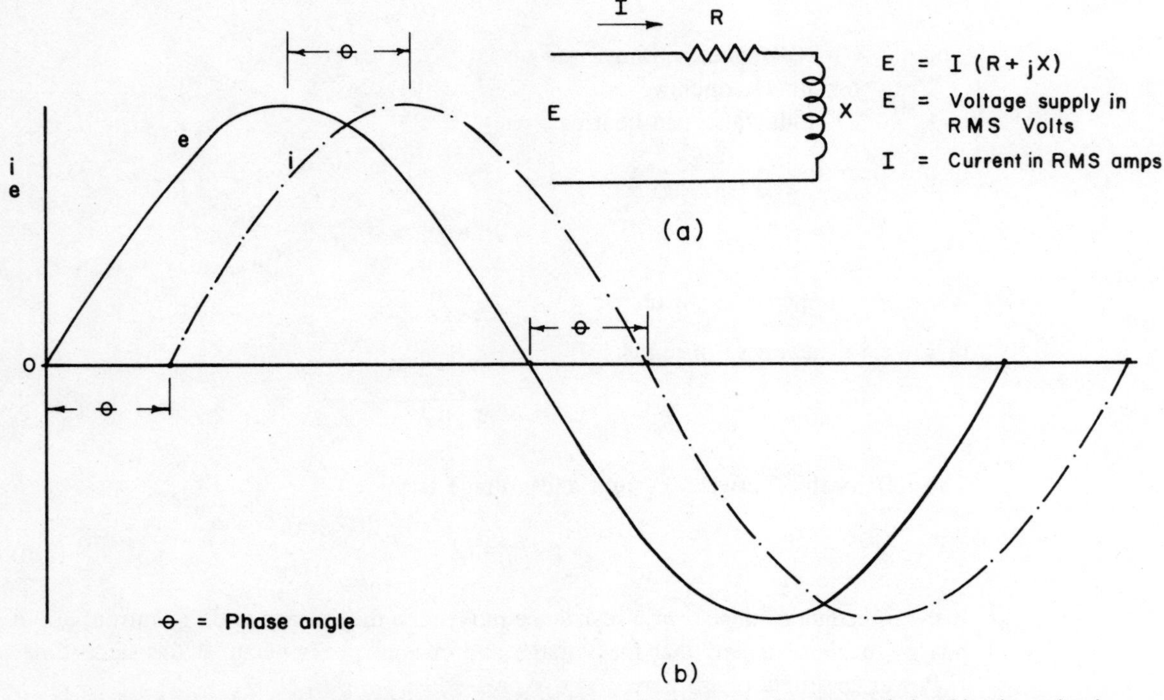

Fig. 3-6. Resistance and inductance: (a) circuit diagram. (b) voltage and current relationships in a circuit.

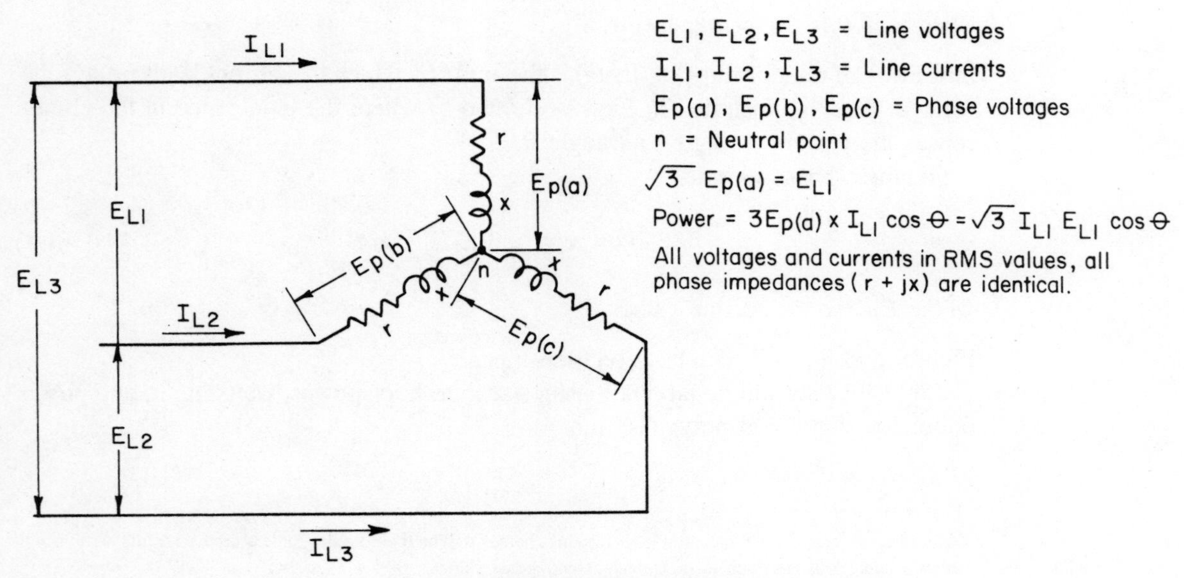

Fig. 3-7. Power in a three-phase system.

Table 3-1. Power and Power Factor.

$$\text{Horsepower(hp)} = \frac{\text{Full-Load Torque (oz} \cdot \text{ft)} \times \text{rpm (revolution/minute)}}{8400}$$
$$\text{Watts Input} = \frac{\text{hp} \times 746}{\text{efficiency}}$$
For single-phase motor: $\text{power factor(pf)} = \frac{\text{Watts Input}}{E_L \times I_L}$ For three-phase motor: $\text{power factor} = \frac{\text{Watts Input}}{\sqrt{3}\, E_L I_L}$ E_L = line voltage I_L = line current

3.2. THE INDUCTION MOTORS

3.2.1. Introduction

The induction motor is by far the most popular and widely used of all ac motors. Its simple construction generally assures trouble-free operation. It is considered a constant-speed motor even though present-day inverters permit variable speed by changing the frequency supplied to the motor.

There are several ways to classify induction motors. There are single-phase or polyphase induction motors depending on the power supplied to the motor, such as single-phase, three-phase, or two-phase. In industry, three-phase power is readily available. Most motors in the home and office operate on a single-phase supply. Power from an inverter is usually polyphase.

Although polyphase motors are self-starting, the single-phase motor needs special starting arrangements and they can be classified as split-phase-start, repulsion-start, or capacitor-start motors. Often a second phase is formed with the permanent addition of a capacitor to an auxiliary winding, and this motor is called a permanent-split capacitor motor. A second phase also can be created with a specially designed short-circuited coil called a *shading coil,* and this is a shaded-pole motor.

Induction motors also can be classified according to their rotor construction. The types of rotor construction are: the squirrel-cage rotor, which is the most common one; the wound rotor with slip rings and brushes; and the repulsion-type rotor. The repulsion-type rotor is also a wound rotor connected to a commutator and brushes, similar to a dc armature.

Motors can also be classified as to their enclosure and temperature rise.

Multispeed versions of induction motors are available such as 2/4 pole, 4/8 pole, or even 4/6/8 pole versions. Knowing the number of poles, you can determine a theoretical synchronous speed of an induction motor.

$$\text{Synchronous RPM} = \frac{120 \times \text{line frequency}}{\text{number of poles}} \tag{3-9}$$

The actual speed will be lower due to slip. For instance, a four-pole induction motor at full load might turn at 1720 RPM if connected to a 60 Hz supply. The reason for the slip is explained in the following section.

3.2.2. Mode of Operation

The basic principle of operation of an induction motor is illustrated in Fig. 3-8. Coil L, which consists of one closed turn, is free to rotate. Magnet M is driven at a certain speed. While the magnet is turning counterclockwise, flux is cut by the conductors (there are two conductors per turn), causing a current to flow in that coil (refer to Flemming's right-hand rule in Fig. 3-9 for the direction of the generated voltage). A force is produced by the interaction of the rotating field from the magnet and the field generated by the current in the conductors. The force is in the same direction as the rotation of the magnet. This means that the coil will follow the magnet (relative to the magnet, the coil moves in the opposite direction). However, the coil can never turn at the same speed as the magnet. If it did, no flux would be cut. If no flux is cut, there will be no current and no force on the conductors. The difference in the speed of the coil and the magnet is called *slip*.

Figure 3-8 shows the magnet positions with respect to coilside G. In (a), coilside G lines up with the N-pole of the magnet. As indicated, the force on the coil will be in a counterclockwise direction. Sometime later, in position (b), coilside G is between the N-pole and S-pole of the magnet, and the magnet flux will be 0. Therefore, the force will be 0. The position in (c) shows the S-pole of the magnet lining up with coilside G; the current in the coil will be reversed and the resulting force will again be in a counterclockwise direction. The relative change of position of coilside G with respect to the magnet is due to slip. If a hollow cylinder made up of many conductors evenly distributed over the surface of the air gap and all short circuited at both ends is substituted for the one coil, the sum of the individual forces will add up to a steady, average counterclockwise force.

The above rotating permanent magnet can be replaced by a rotating electromagnetic field, as briefly described in section 3-1. A rotating field created by a three-phase wound stator is illustrated in Figs. 3-10 and 3-11.

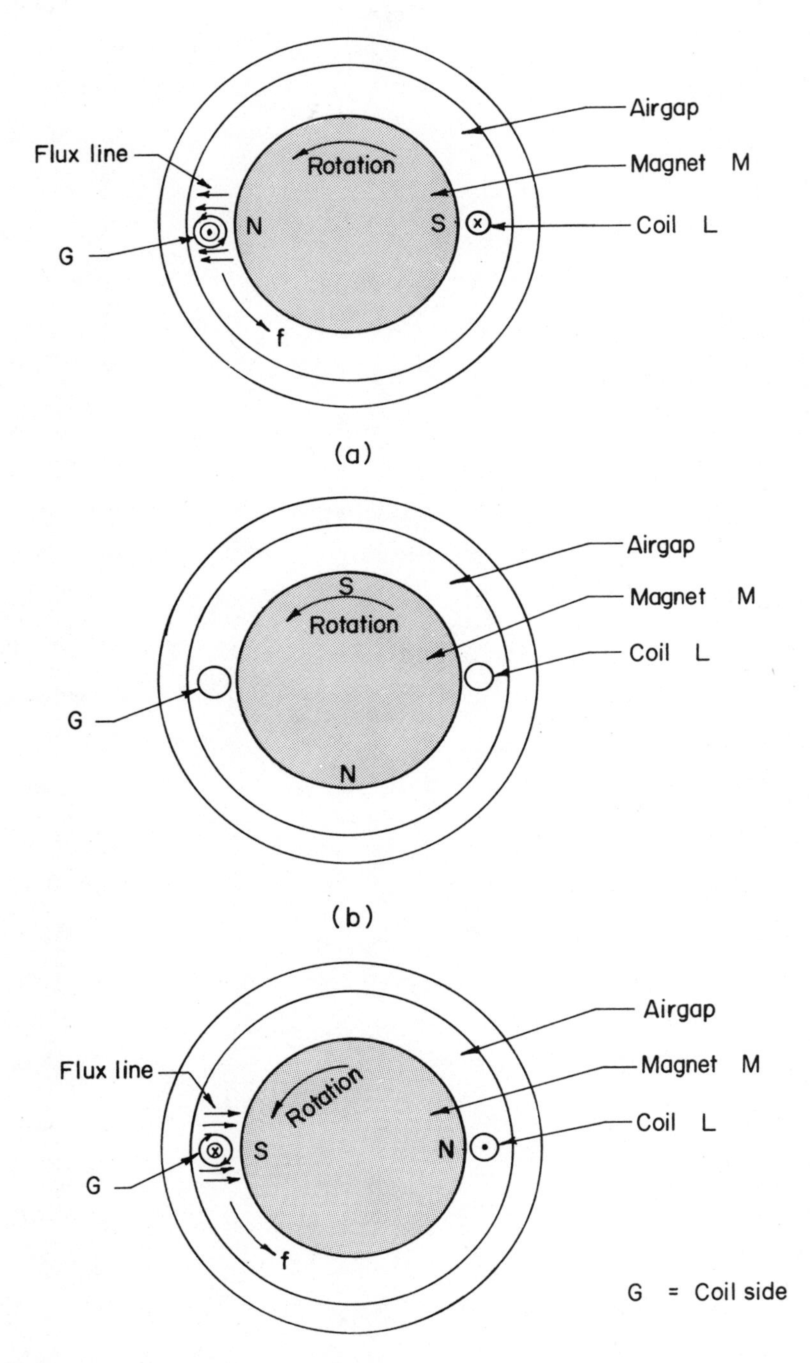

Fig. 3-8. Basic principle of induction motor operation.

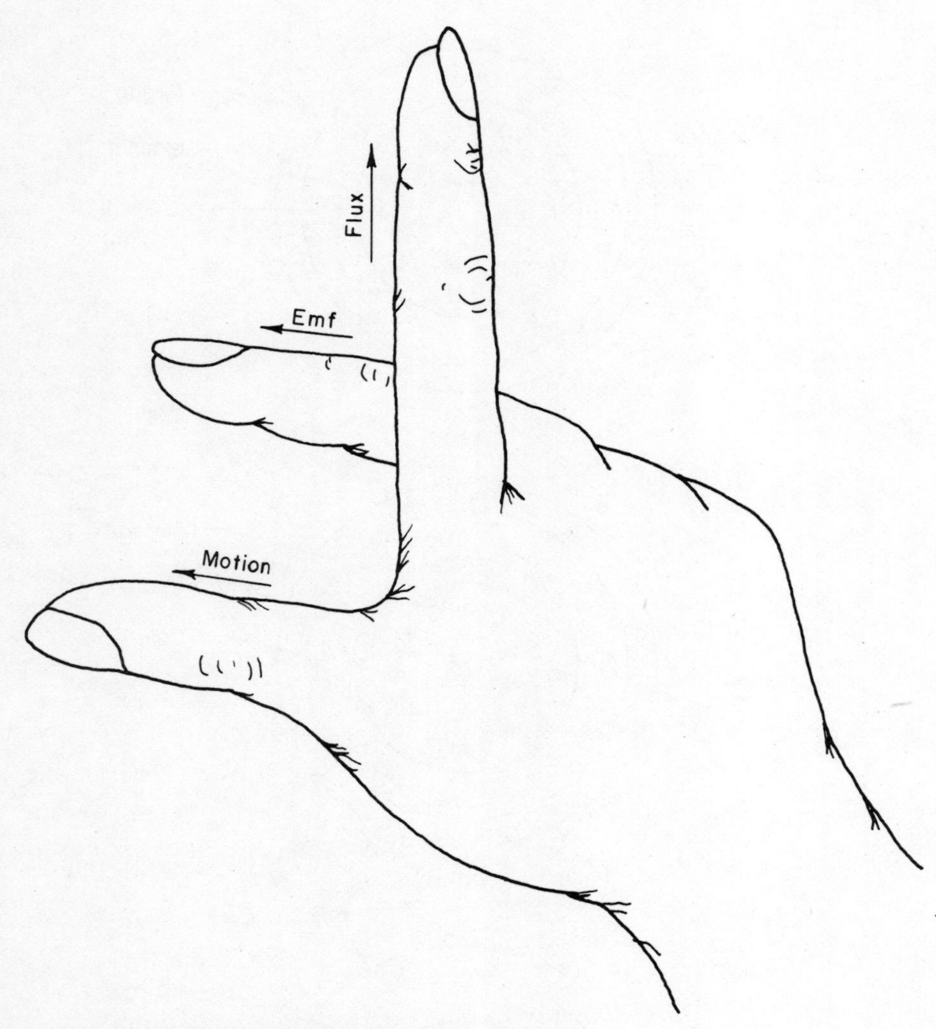

Fig. 3-9. Flemming's right-hand rule.

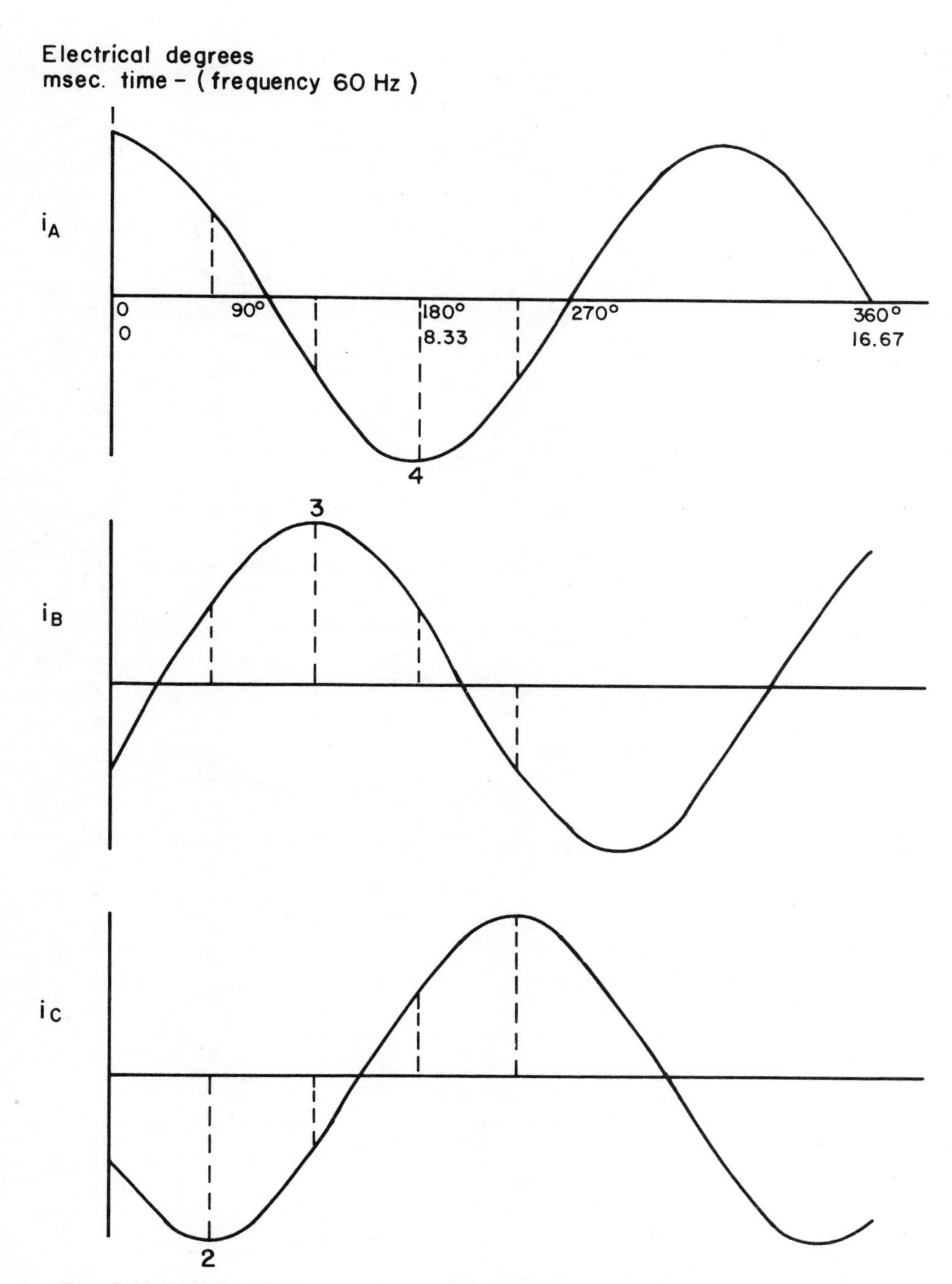

Fig. 3-10. Rotating field set up by stator: instantaneous currents going into the stator.

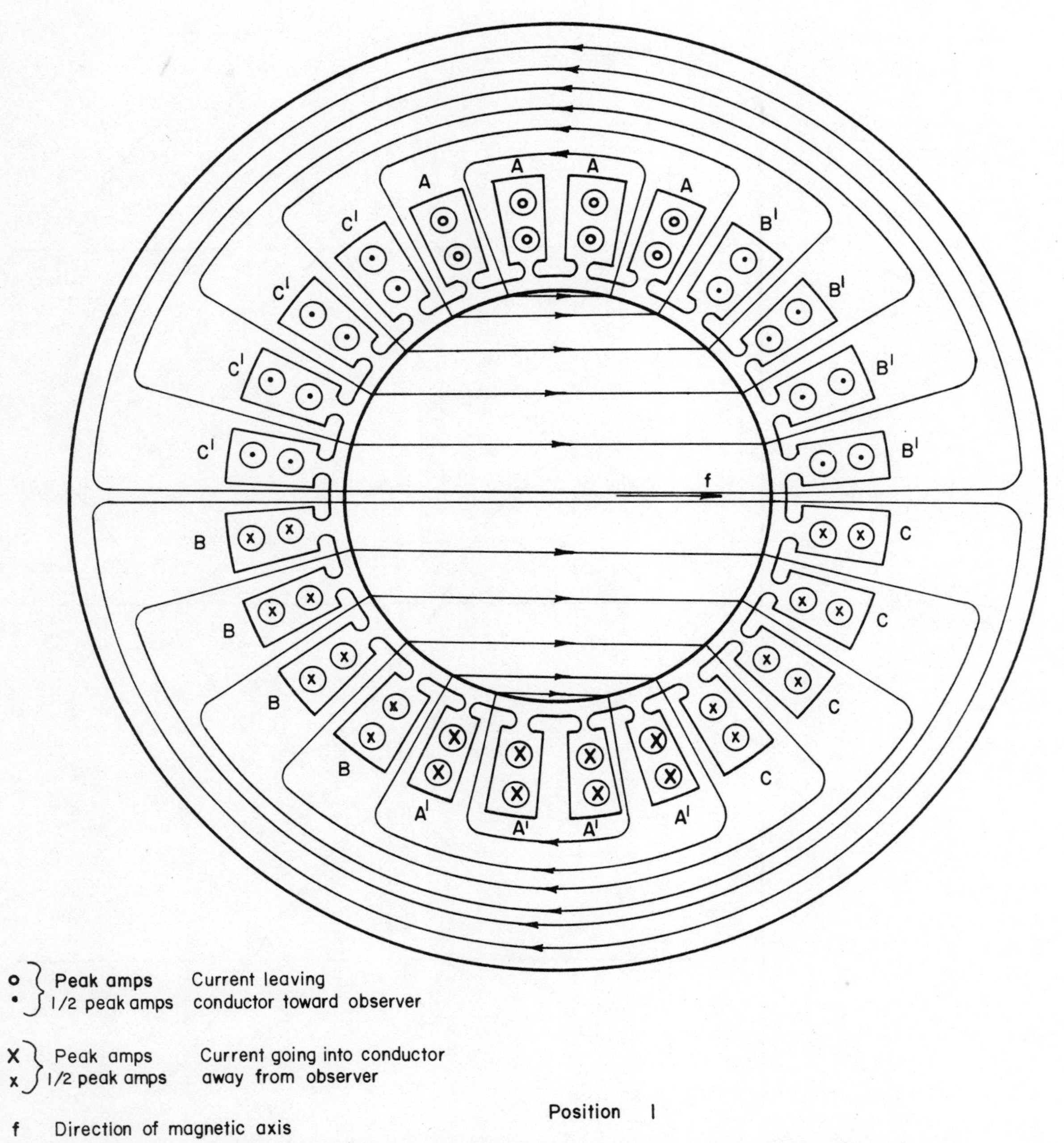

Fig. 3-11. Rotating field set up by stator: direction of the field at four different points.

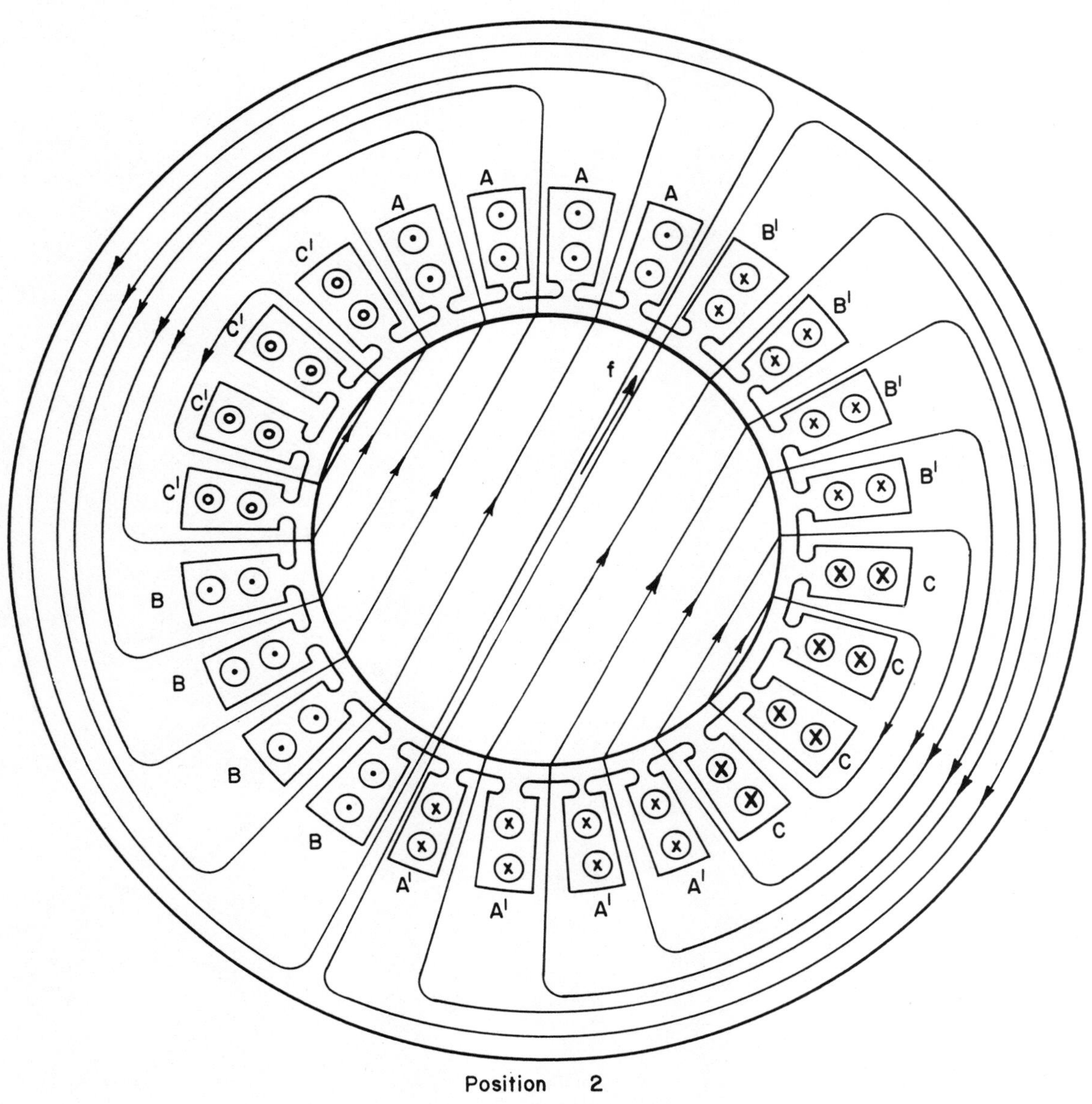

Fig. 3-11. (Continued.)

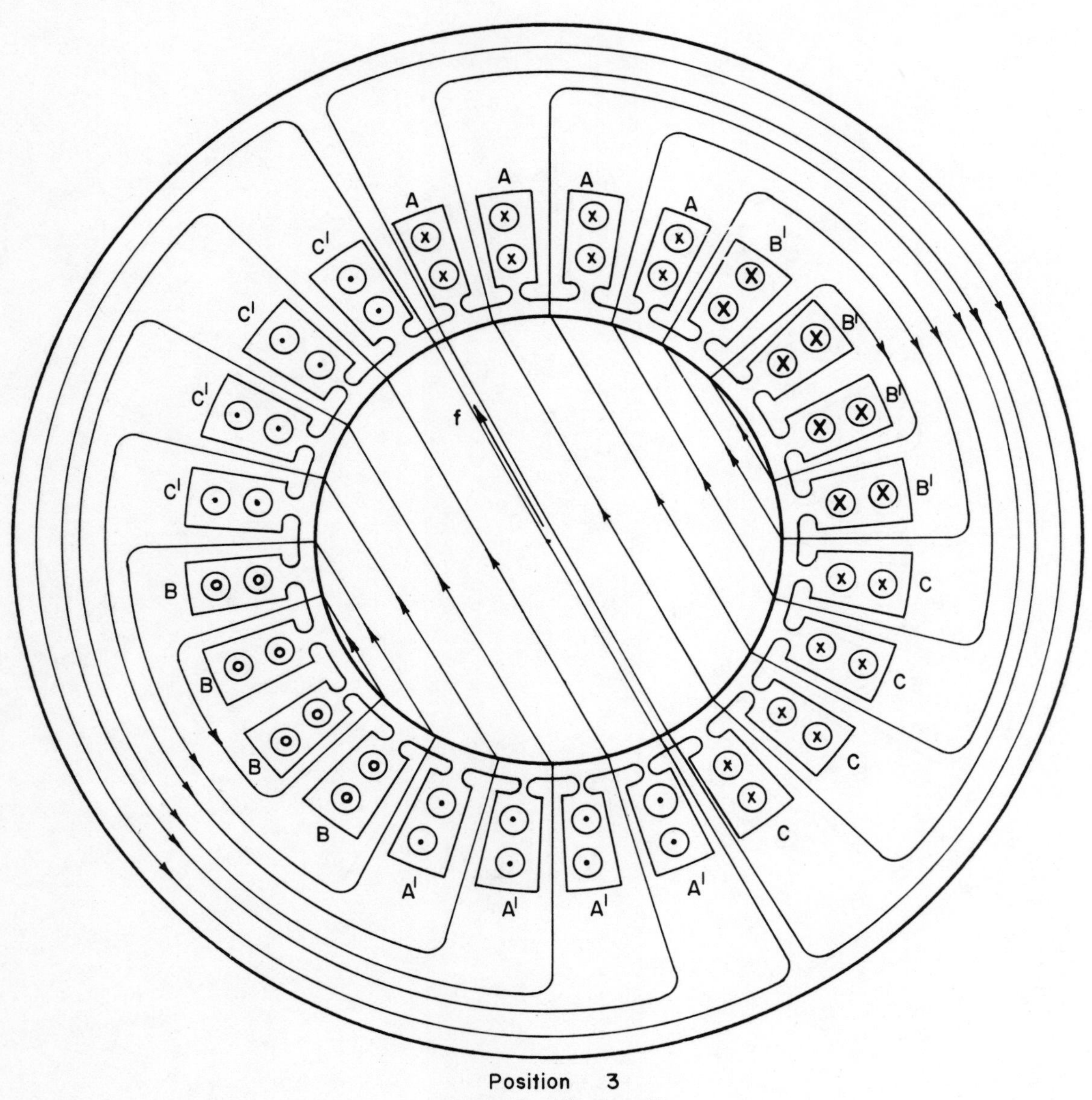

Position 3

Fig. 3-11. (Continued.)

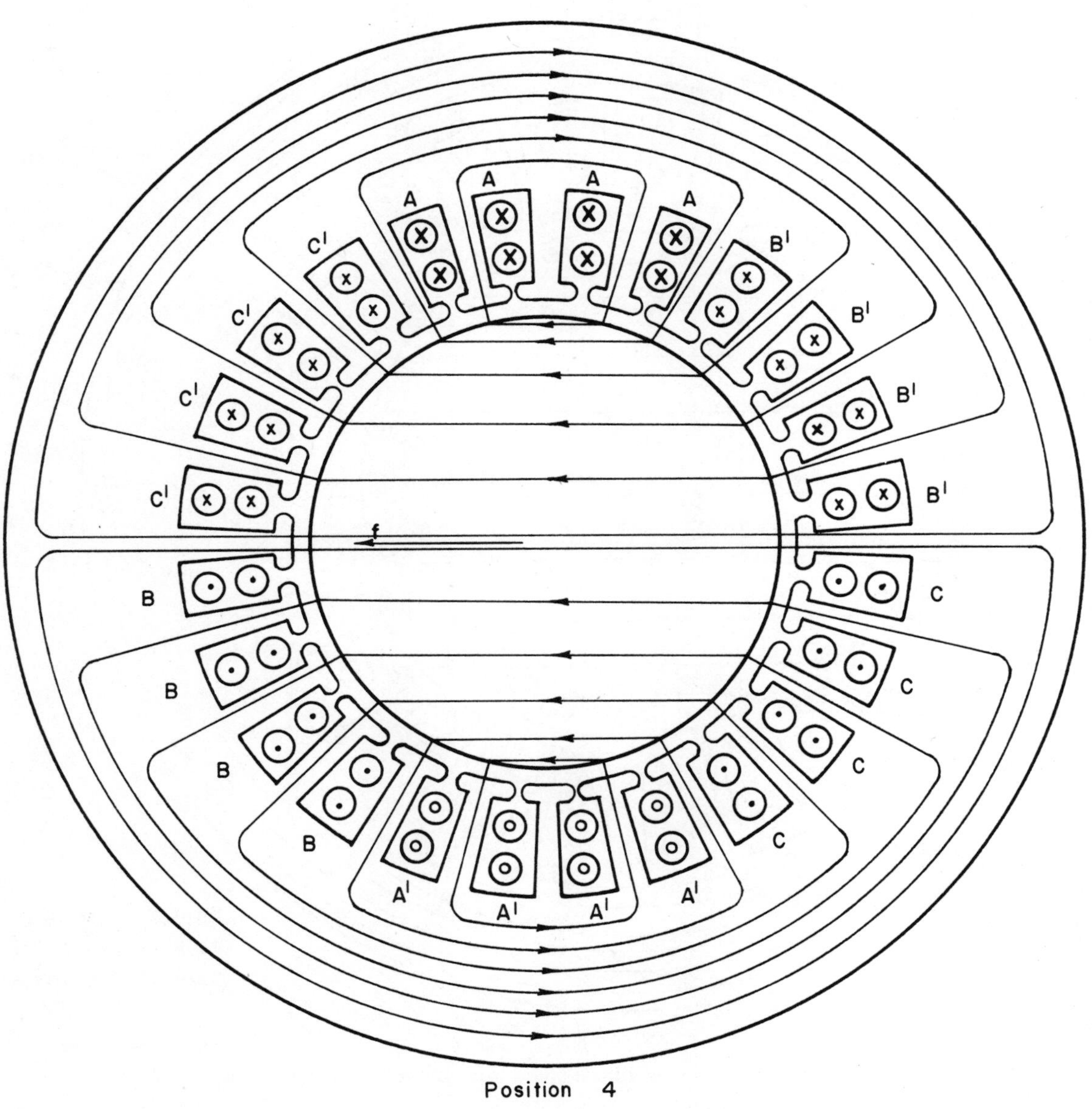

Position 4

Fig. 3-11. (Continued.)

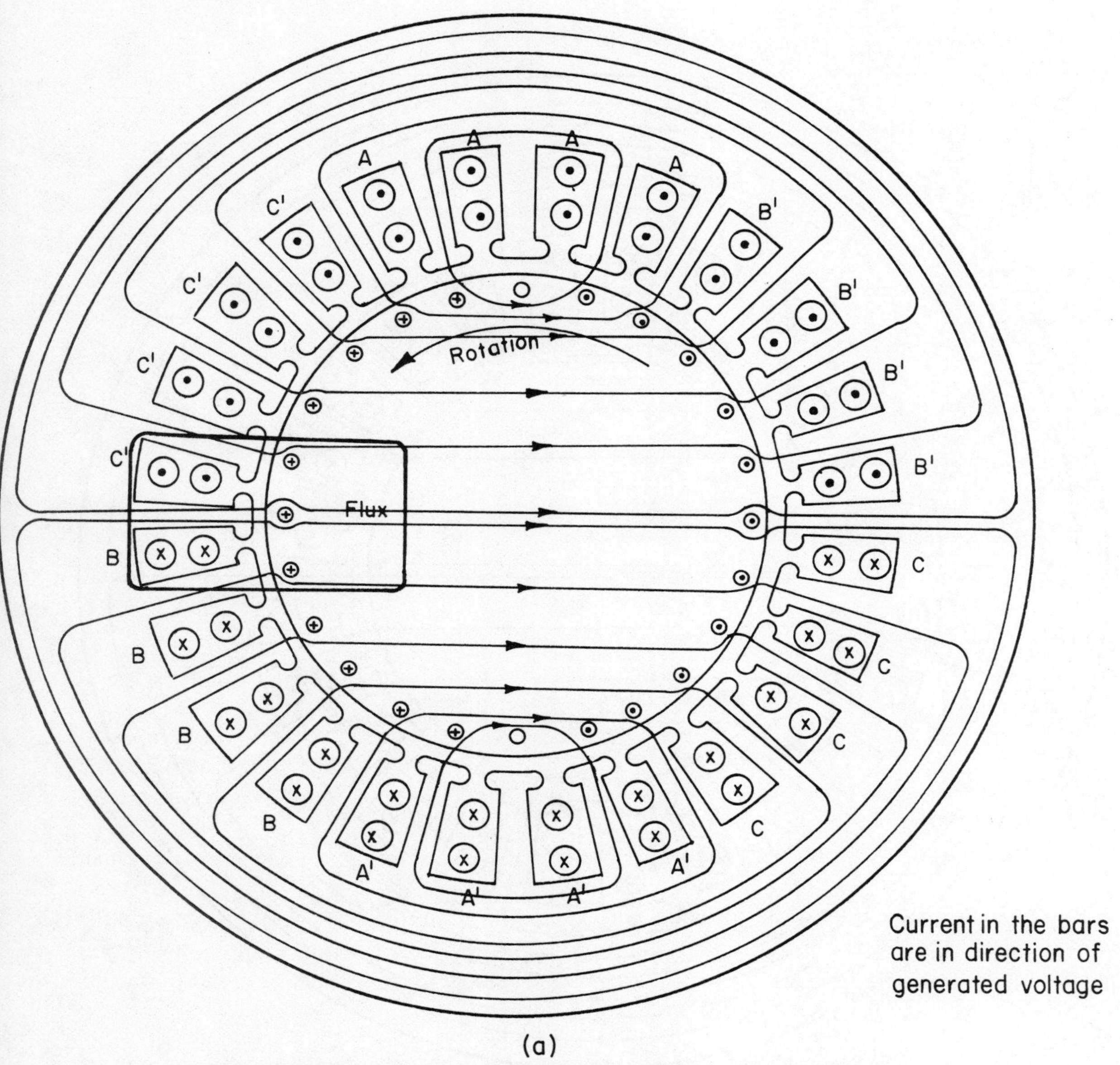

Fig. 3-12. Mode of operation of a three-phase, squirrel-cage induction motor.

Figure 3-10 illustrates instantaneous currents going into the stator and Figure 3-11 shows four resulting field positions at successive times when one of the phase currents reaches its peak.

If a squirrel-cage rotor, consisting of a laminated steel structure and conductors that are short circuited at each end is introduced into the stator, the condition becomes similar to the one described in Fig. 3-8 with a rotating magnet. Figure 3-12 shows the

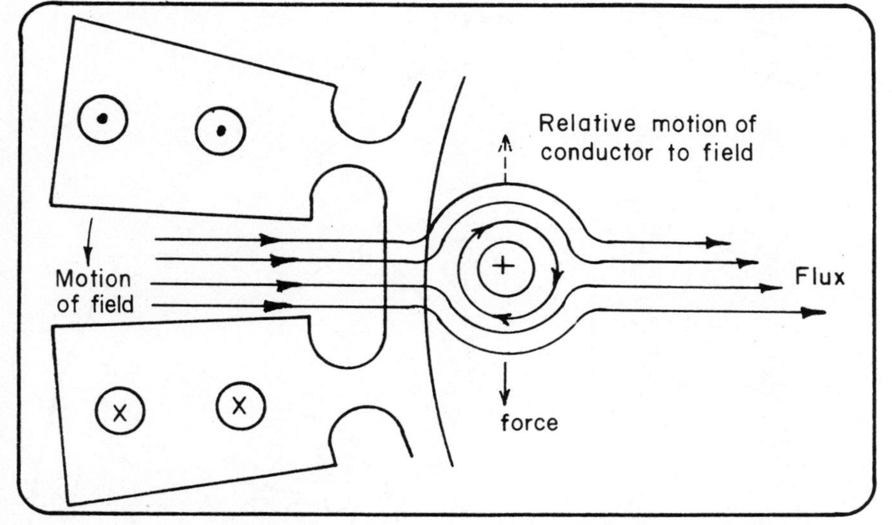

Effect of fields due to currents in neighboring rotor bars have been neglected.

(b)

Fig. 3-12. (Continued.)

resulting rotation of the rotor with the field traveling in counterclockwise rotation as is shown in Fig. 3-11.

The mode of operation of a motor described in connection with Fig. 3-12 is that of a polyphase, squirrel-cage induction motor. If the squirrel-cage rotor is replaced by a wound, three-phase rotor with slip rings on the end, it would be called the rotor-wound induction motor.

Returning to the motor described in Fig. 3-10, assume the motor is running and all of a sudden phase C is opened. The rotating field generated by the stator has become a stationary alternating field, and the direction of the generated voltages, while the rotor is in motion, are shown in Fig. 3-13. The currents in the rotor bars set up their own field perpendicular (also called in *quadrature*) to the stationary field as shown in Fig. 3-14. The currents also will lag the generated voltages by close to 90 degrees.

As seen from the stator, the rotor field will fluctuate at the same frequency as the stator field does. The field fluctions equal line frequency. With all the above in mind, you might speculate that the rotor sets up a field that is out of phase in space and time to the stator field the same way as if there had been a second phase and winding in the stator. This assumption implies that a rotating field is restored, permitting the motor to keep on running. Once the motor is stopped, there is no rotational generated voltage in the rotor bars, no rotating field, and therefore no torque. At the locked state, all the currents induced in the rotor bars are due to transformer action, which does not produce any torque.

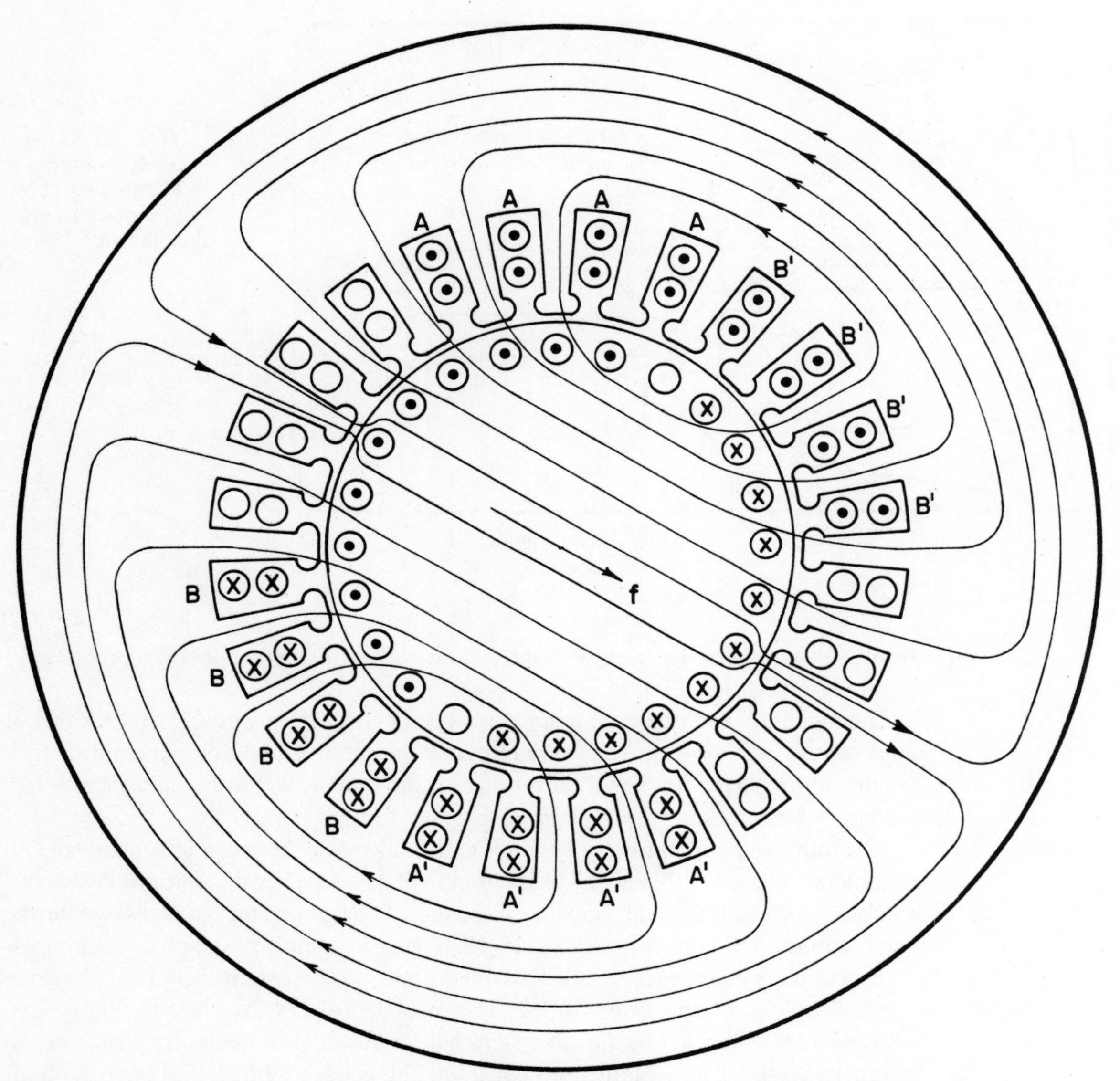

Fig. 3-13. Three-phase motor with one phase open. Rotor is in motion.

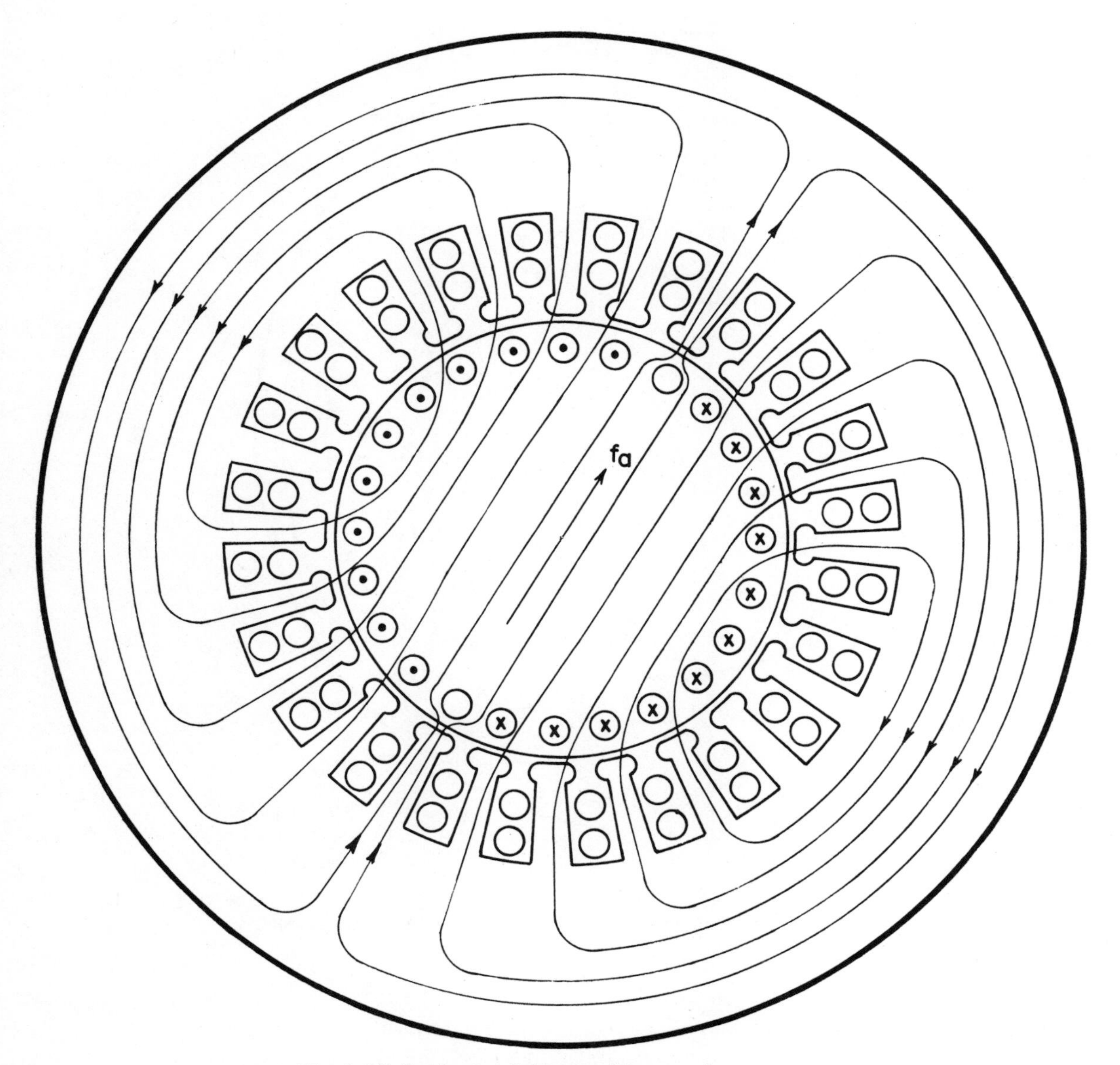

Fig. 3-14. Quadrature field caused by rotor bar currents.

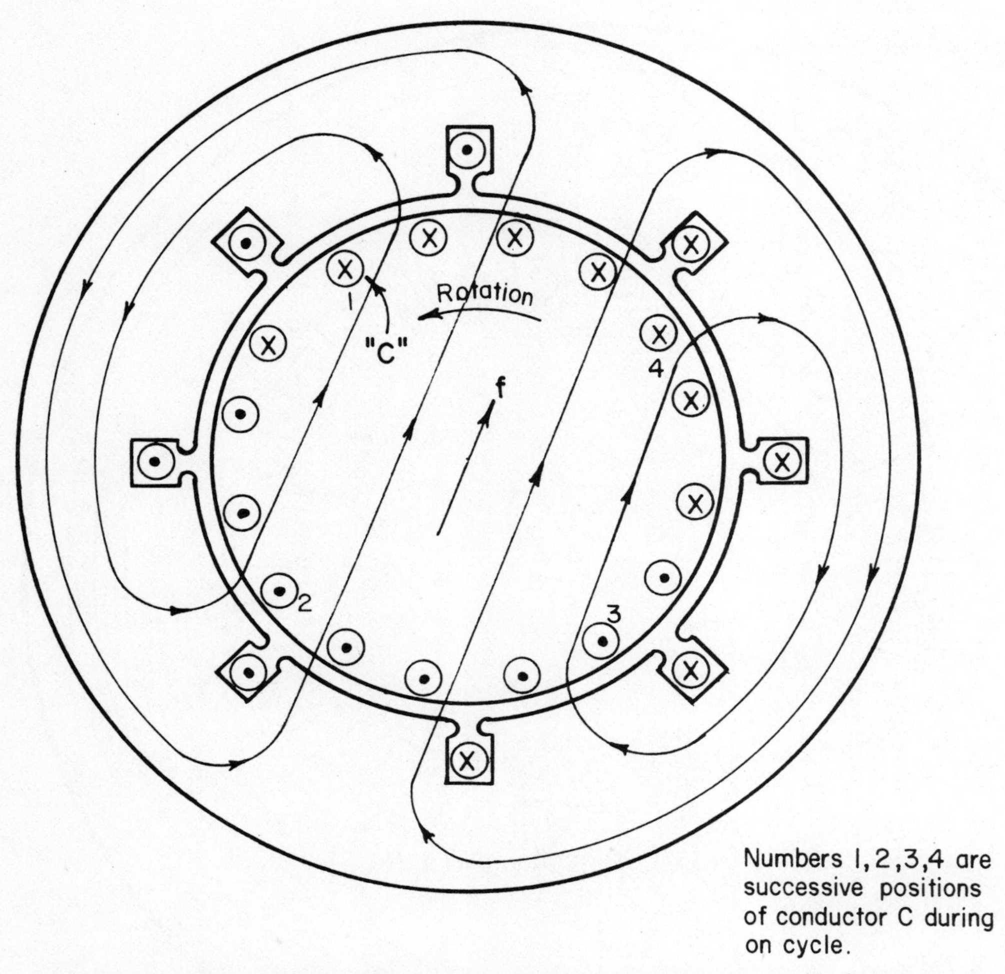

Fig. 3-15. (a) Single-phase field distributions and resulting motor currents with the rotor turning counter-clockwise.

Figure 3-15(a) shows a single-phase field distribution and resulting voltages generated in the rotor while the rotor is turning counterclockwise. Figure 3-15 (b) shows the direction of the voltage generated in conductor C at the four positions indicated in (a) while the field flux is pulsating at a rate equal to line frequency. For simplicity, assume the rotor to run at almost synchronous speed. In position 1 and 2, the direction of the generated voltages are as indicated in (a); but in 3 and 4, they are the reverse of the voltages indicated in (a) because the field current has reversed during the interval. The result is that the generated voltage in the rotor conductor has reversed twice as often as the field flux. Because there is slip, the frequency would have been reduced.

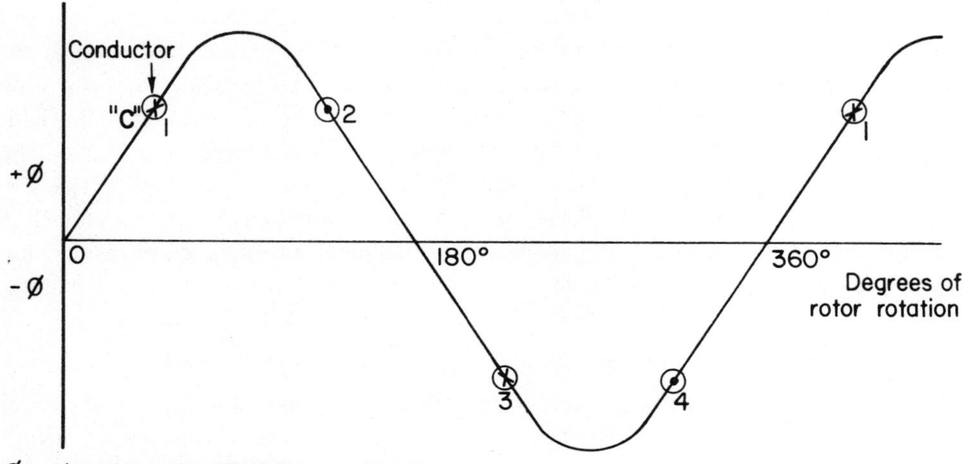

Ø = Instantaneous field flux produced by the current in the stator winding.

During one hertz conductor "C" shows four reversals of current.

Rotor assumed to rotate at synchronous speed.

Fig. 3-15. (b) Current direction in conductor C at the four positions indicated in (a).

The actual frequency would have been:

$$f_c = f(2 - s) \tag{3-10}$$

where f_c = frequency of current in rotor conductor
f = pulsating frequency of the field which is line frequency
s = percent slip

This relationship indicates that there is power generated in the rotor at a rate almost double the line frequency that acts like a load, resulting in a higher slip than the corresponding polyphase motor. Much of this power translates into negative torque. This means that single-phase motors are less efficient, and noisier, and run less smoothly. The higher frequency power makes itself felt in the form of noise and vibration.

The currents in the rotor bars will be out of phase with the generated voltages due to the reactance of the rotor.

To sum up, in single-phase operation the main field is continuously alternating, and the rate of change of flux will induce voltages in the rotor bars in addition to the voltages generated due to cutting flux. What it all adds up to while the rotor is in motion, its winding creates a field out of phase in space and time with the main field.

That there is a rotor current of almost twice the line frequency setting up a magnetic field at that frequency complicates matters. There are two widely used theories to explain the operation of single-phase induction motors. They are the revolving-field theory and the cross-field theory. Mathematically they both give good results, but theoretically they are poles apart. They are primarily of interest to the motor designer.

3.2.3. Polyphase Stator Windings

The stator winding of a single-speed, polyphase induction motor consists of one set of coils per phase. A three-phase motor will have three sets of coils as shown in Fig. 3-16 for a four-pole, three-phase winding. There are two ways to connect these phases together as shown in Fig. 3-16. When the phases are connected as in (a), it is

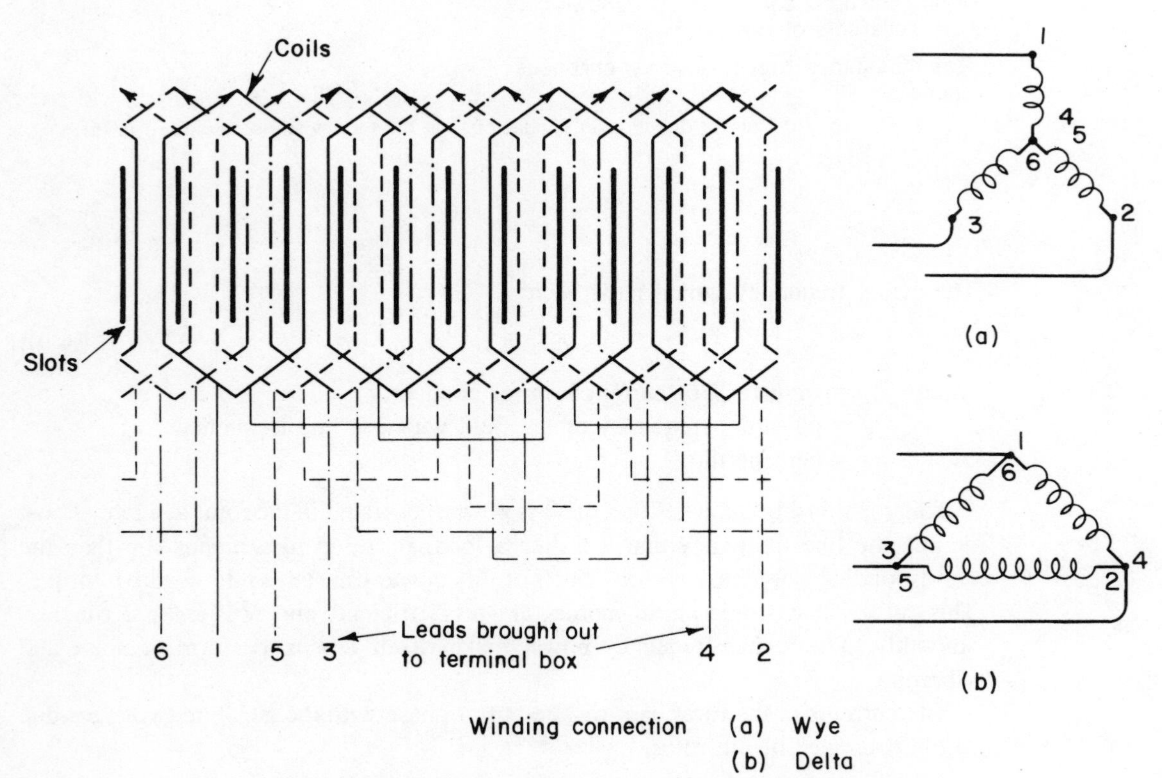

Fig. 3-16. Single-speed, three-phase, four-pole induction motor.

called a wye (Y) connection, and when connected as in (b), it is called a delta (Δ) connection. Occasionally six leads are brought out to the terminal box, which allows the motor to run at two different voltages. When connected in wye, the motor might operate at 120 V, 60 Hz. If the windings are connected in delta, the winding is good for a 208 V, 60 Hz supply. For larger motors, the delta/wye connection can also be used to limit locked rotor currents. The motor starts wye connected and runs delta connected.

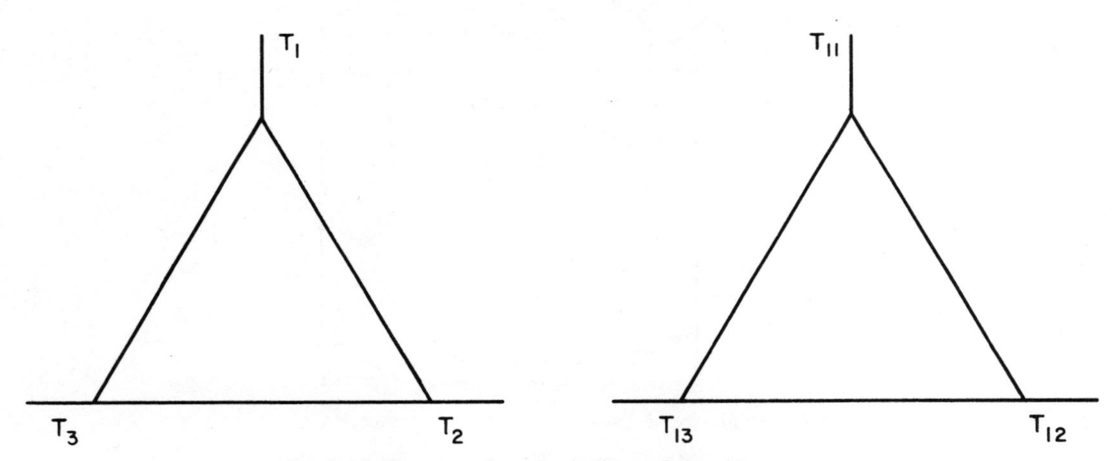

Fig. 3-17. Two-speed, two-windings, three-phase motor.

Several windings can be accommodated in one stator for multispeed motors. Figure 3-17 shows a two-speed motor with two separate windings. If it were a two- and four-pole motor, synchronous speed would be 3600 RPM and 1800 RPM, respectively, for a 60 Hz supply. There are any number of combinations of tapped windings and multiple windings, parallel windings, etc. to accommodate different voltages and speeds. For example, in a two-phase system, the two phases are in quadrature with each other (Fig. 3-18).

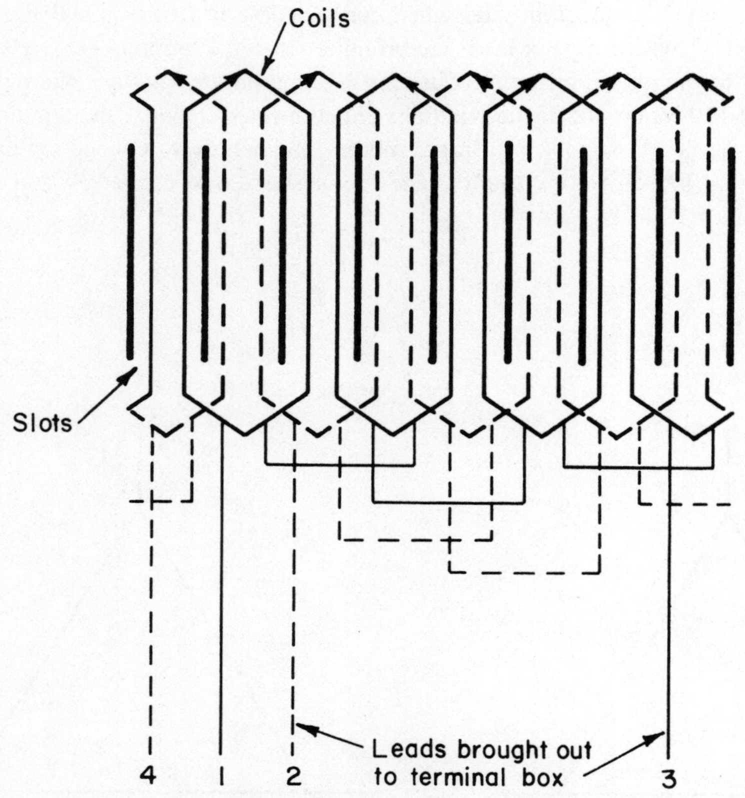

Fig. 3-18. Single-speed, two-phase, four-pole motor.

3.2.4. Single-Phase Stator Windings

Section 3.2.2 indicated that a squirrel-cage induction motor running on one phase had no starting torque. In practice, therefore, a second phase is established, and the motor is wound like a two-phase motor as shown in Fig. 3-18. The second phase, which is physically in quadrature with the main phase, can be wound with turns of very small wire to produce a winding of very high resistance. The main winding has a relatively low resistance and high inductance, which results in a phase difference between the two windings when voltage is applied to the terminals. The current in the starting or auxiliary winding, as the second phase is called, will lead the current in the main winding. This arrangement is used only for starting. A centrifugal switch or relay opens the auxiliary winding when the rotor reaches a certain speed; then the motor runs on the main winding only. This kind of motor is called a *split-phase motor* (Fig. 3-19 (a)).

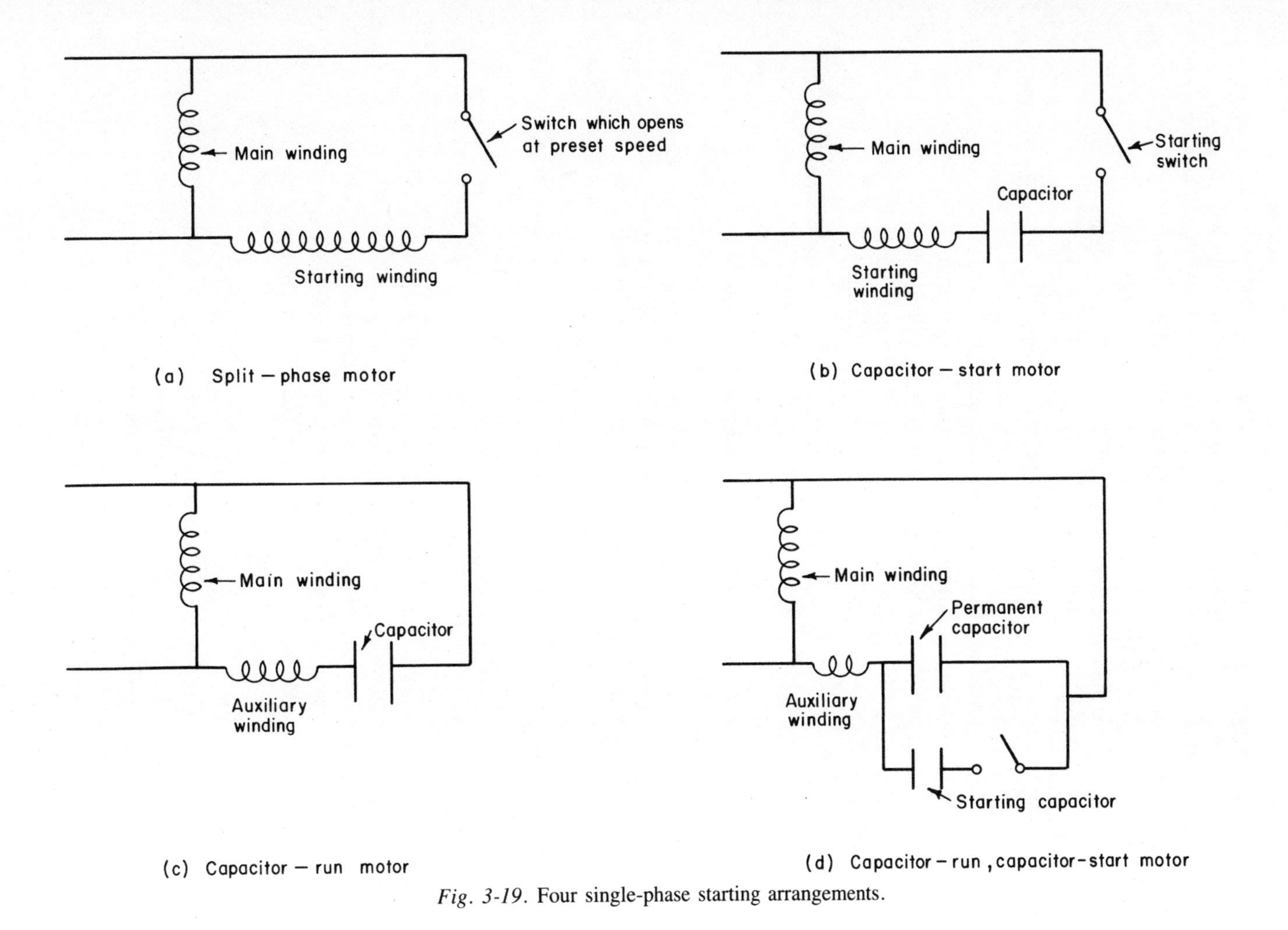

Fig. 3-19. Four single-phase starting arrangements.

If, instead of a high-resistance starting winding that at best results in a relatively small phase shift, the starting winding is designed to operate in conjunction with a capacitor, called a starting capacitor, the current in the starting winding leads the current in the main winding. This arrangement can give a large phase shift resulting in almost a true two-phase motor at starting. Again, the starting winding is disconnected by a starting switch when the rotor reaches a certain speed. This arrangement is called a capacitor-start induction motor (see Fig. 3-19 (b)). This motor has high starting torque characteristics. Electrolytic capacitors are used for motor starting, and they are rated only for intermittent duty.

In applications where not much starting torque is required, a capacitor connected in series with an auxiliary winding remains permanently connected during the operation of the motor. This is called a permanent-split capacitor motor (Fig. 3-19 (c)). The capacitors are usually ac oil-filled or metalized film capacitors. The permanently connected capacitor winding allows the motor to be designed for higher efficiency at full load, but the value of the capacitor in micro-farads is only a fraction of what is required for good starting. For many applications such as fans and blowers, not much starting torque is required. In general this motor runs much smoother and quieter than the previously mentioned single-phase motors because the motor can be designed to minimize the negative high frequency torque described in section 3-2-2.

If good starting and running characteristics are required, a two-value capacitor motor might be necessary. One capacitor is permanently connected to the winding, and the second one is only connected while the motor is starting (Fig. 3-19 (d)).

3.2.5. The Squirrel-Cage Rotor

The rotor consist of a laminated-steel core assembled on a shaft. The laminations are slotted, allowing conductor bars to pass end to end through them. At each end there are end rings that short circuit the bars.

The majority of rotors are die cast, which always refers to the bars and end rings (see Fig. 3-20). The material is either pure aluminum or an aluminum alloy. There are some cast copper rotors and some that use copper or brass rods assembled on copper or brass end rings. The reason these variations exist are cost, motor efficiency, starting torque, locked-rotor current, etc. Much of the motor performance is determined by the rotor resistance.

The steel laminations have a number of punched slots (usually one slot per bar). There are a variety of shapes of slots as indicated in Fig. 3-21; as a result, there are deep bar rotors, double cage rotors, etc. Although all these variations and combinations are very much of interest to the motor designer, it is important to users of motors as it permits many choices in motor characteristics.

(a)

(b)

Fig. 3-20. Die-cast rotors: (a) die-cast rotor bars and end rings. (b) Actual die-cast, squirrel-cage rotors. (Courtesy of LEESON ELECTRIC, Motronics Div., Little Falls, NY)

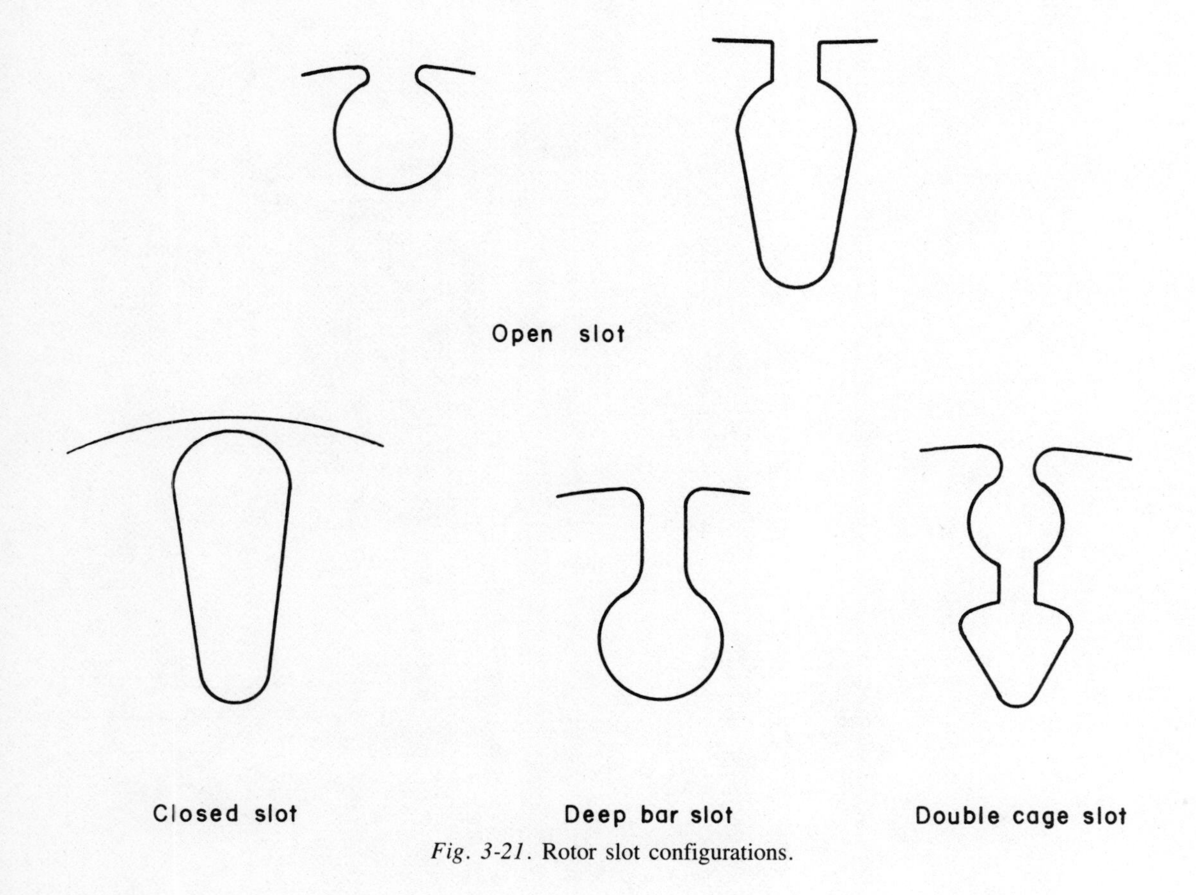

Fig. 3-21. Rotor slot configurations.

3.2.6. Performance Characteristics of Squirrel-Cage Induction Motors

The torque-speed characteristics of induction motors differ from those of dc motors and also differ from other induction motors with different designs. Fig. 3-22 shows a typical torque-speed curve and indicates the different torque points.

Figure 3-23 shows efficiency-torque and current-torque curves in addition to a torque-speed curve. In a typical motor, the efficiency should be close to maximum at the full-load point. Current increases with slip and is maximum in the locked-rotor

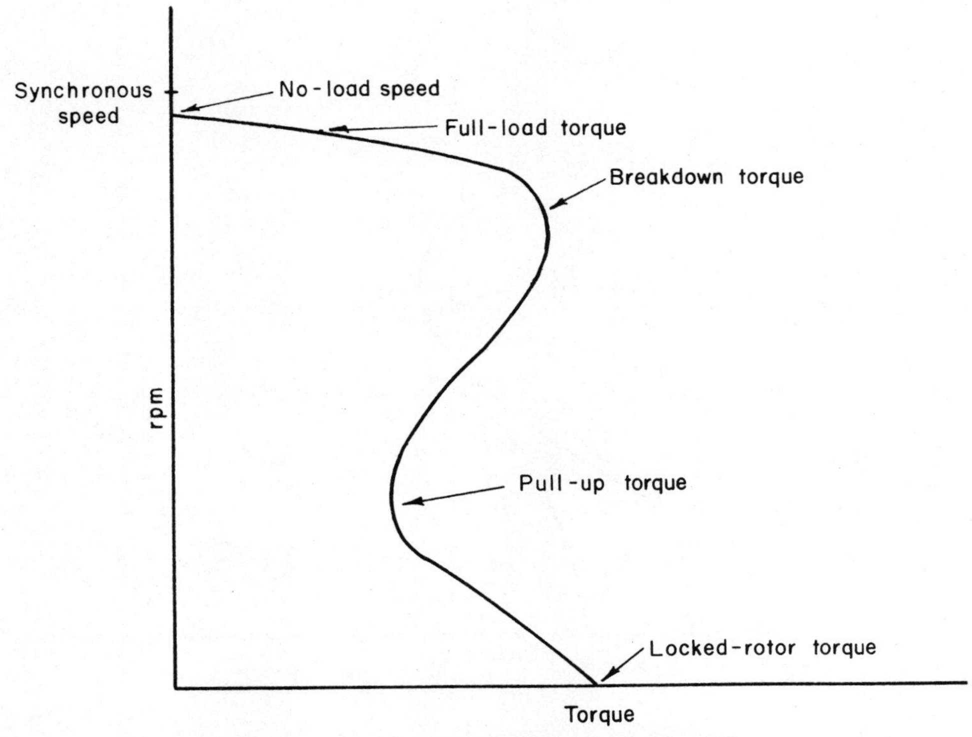

Fig. 3-22. Torque-speed curve of an induction motor indicating different torque points.

condition. Curves shown in Fig. 3-24 are those frequently displayed by manufacturers for a given horsepower rated motor. Power factor and watts input can be calculated from the data. Locked rotor torque and current might change somewhat with the position of the rotor.

Table 3-2 compares the different performance parameters for single-phase motors. Torque-speed curves can be engineered to meet all kinds of applications. Typical torque-speed curve of a torque motor is shown in Fig. 3-25. Sometimes these motors do not operate much above locked-rotor conditions. Although induction motors can and are specially engineered to specific applications, *NEMA* (National Electrical Manufacturers' Association) has developed standards to meet the requirements of definite-purpose motors for many important applications.

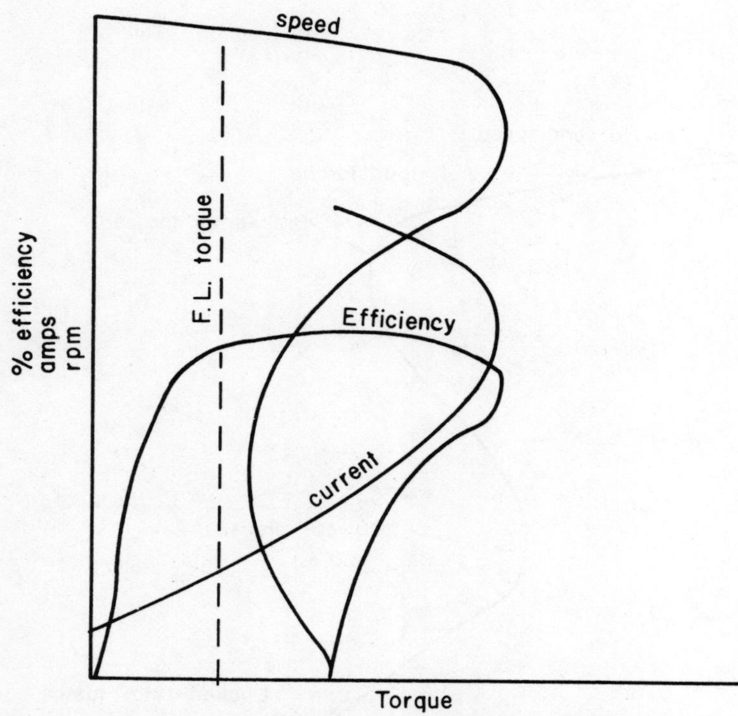

Fig. 3-23. Typical performance characteristics of an induction motor.

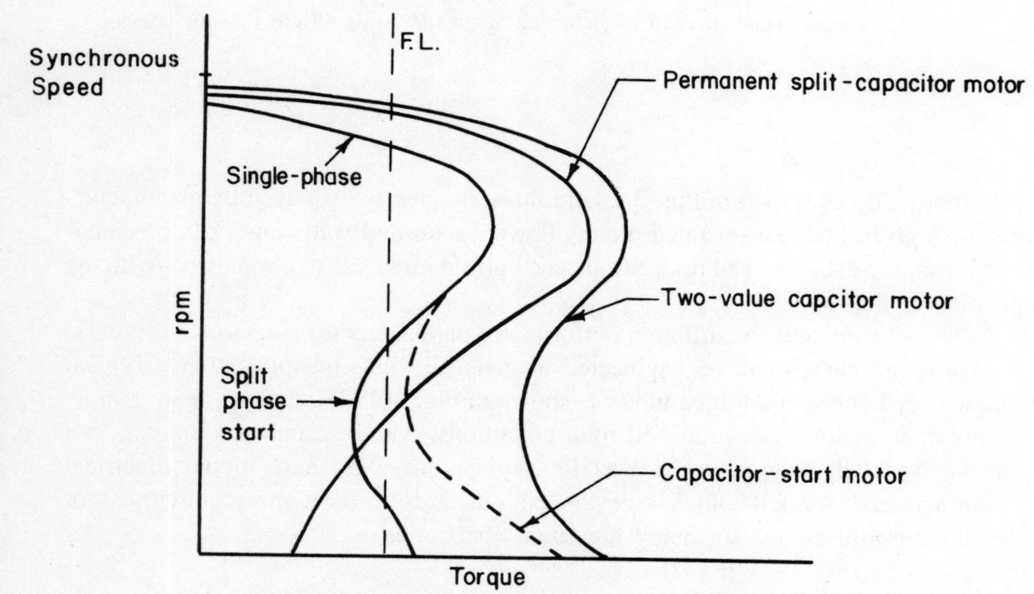

Fig. 3-24. Manufacturer's curves for a motor of a given power rating.

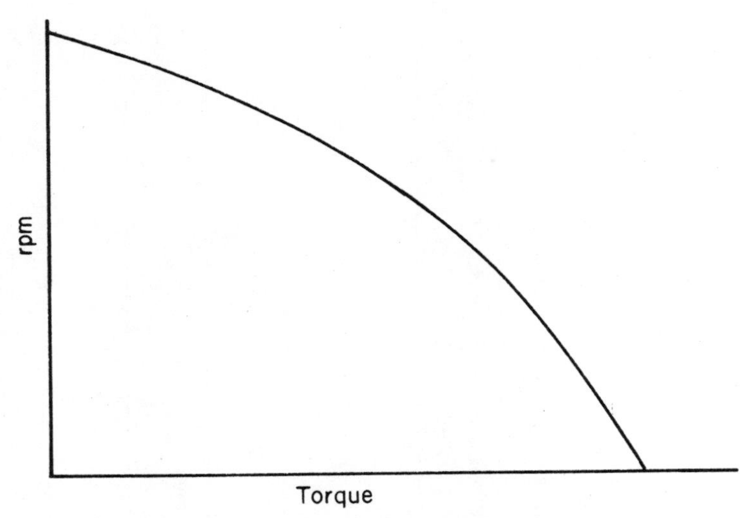

Fig. 3-25. Typical torque-speed curve for a torque motor.

To vary the speed-torque characteristics of a single-speed, squirrel-cage induction motor, either vary the voltage or frequency input or both. (See equation 3-9 for determining the synchronous speed of induction motors.)

Take care in choosing an induction motor while using voltage change for speed control. Polyphase motors with high slip characteristics are usually best suited for these applications. Typical torque-speed curves are shown in Fig. 3-26. Some torque motors, which are designed to operate at locked or very low speed conditions, can be used without danger of overheating. Single-phase, permanent-split capacitor motors can also be used. However, when using single-phase motors with starting windings, keep away from speeds at which the starting winding cuts in. Starting windings can easily be destroyed because they are designed for very short duty only. Solid-state electronic circuits are mostly used today for variable voltage supply.

Varying the speed of an induction motor by varying the frequency is becoming more common as the price of variable frequency power supplies is coming down (see Fig. 3-27). The response of the motor to different frequencies will vary to a large extent with the motor parameters. It will make a difference if the power supplied is in a sinusoidal or square wave shape. Generally the volts per hertz applied to the motor should remain constant. For instance, to a 240 V, 120 Hz, two-phase, variable frequency motor, you might apply 120 V, 60 Hz, two-phase or 60 V, 30 Hz, two-phase, and so on. If you increase the speed of a standard off-the-shelf motor, check with the manufacturer as to the recommended maximum speed that can be used.

Table 3-2. Relative Performance Characteristics of Single-Phase, Squirrel-Cage Induction Motors.

	Efficiency	Power Factor	Slip	LR.[1] Torque / FL.[2] Torque	Maximum Torque / Fl.[2] Torque	Relative Cost	Noise and Vibration
Split-phase	low	low	high	average	low	low	high
Capacitor-start	low	low	high	high	low	average to above aver.	high
Permanent-split capacitor	average	average	average	low	average	average to above aver.	average
Two-value capacitor motor	high	high	low	high	high	high	high

1. LR. = locked rotor
2. FL. = full load

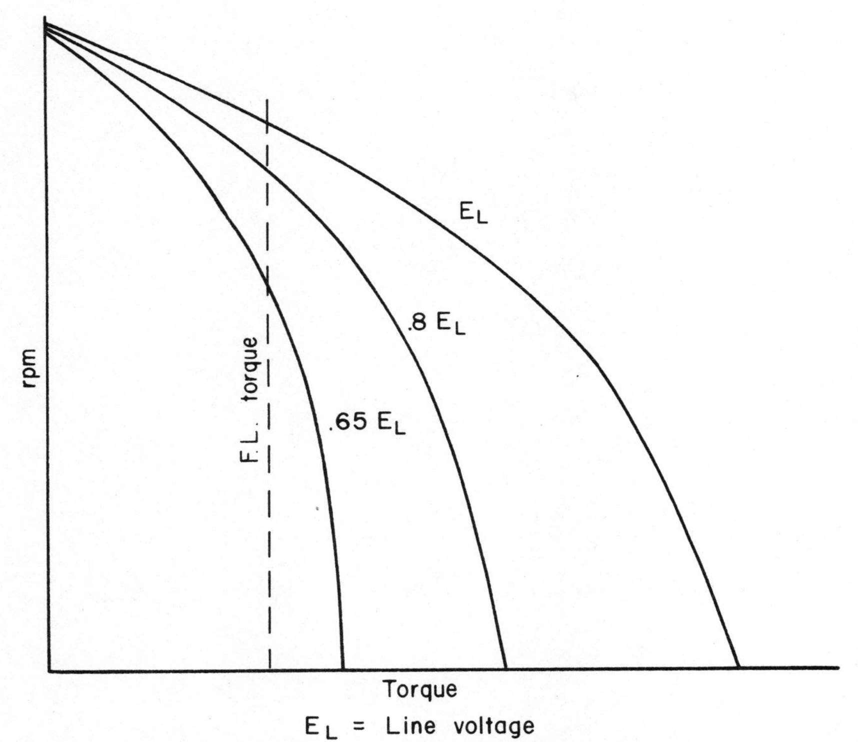

Fig. 3-26. Torque-speed curves for torque motor with various voltage inputs.

High-speed induction motors have been designed to run at 80,000 RPM and higher, and they are used in centrifuge and spindle applications.

Where several speeds are required, pole changing is very frequently used. For instance, if a fan is to run at 3450 RPM and 1750 RPM, a 2/4 pole induction motor might be used. The two-pole connection allows the fan to run at 3450 RPM and the four-pole connection operates the fan at 1750 RPM. There are two types of ratings commercially available for multispeed motors: constant torque and constant horsepower. Which one to use will depend on the nature of the load.

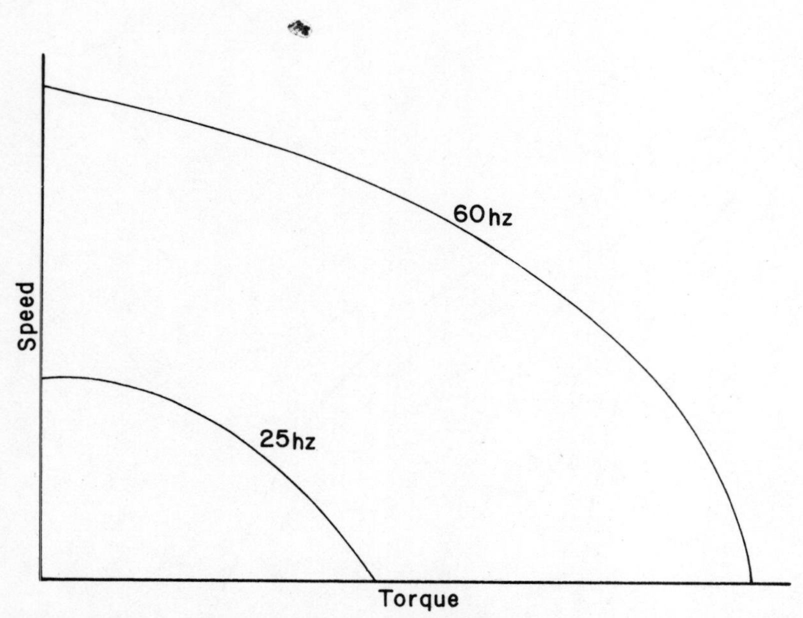

Fig. 3-27. Torque-speed curves of induction motor for 60 Hz and 25 Hz with constant V/Hz.

3.2.7. Shaded-Pole Motor

The shaded-pole motor is the lowest cost single-phase induction motor. One popular construction is shown in Fig. 3-28 where the main winding consists of a coil; the auxiliary winding, also called a shading coil, consists of one or two short-circuited copper strips per pole. Visualize the mode of operation of this motor by disregarding sections "a." Sections "a" are required for reasons of mechanical integrity, but magnetically the cross sections are so small that they will easily saturate.

When power is applied to the main winding, a current is induced in the shading coil, which is out of phase with the main winding. Physically the magnetic field created by the shading coil is also out of phase with the main field and in effect a second phase is created which is necessary for acceptable starting characteristics of the motor.

Typical torque-speed curves for this motor are shown in Fig. 3-29. Curve (b) would generally be more suitable for electronic speed control. Few shaded-pole motors are

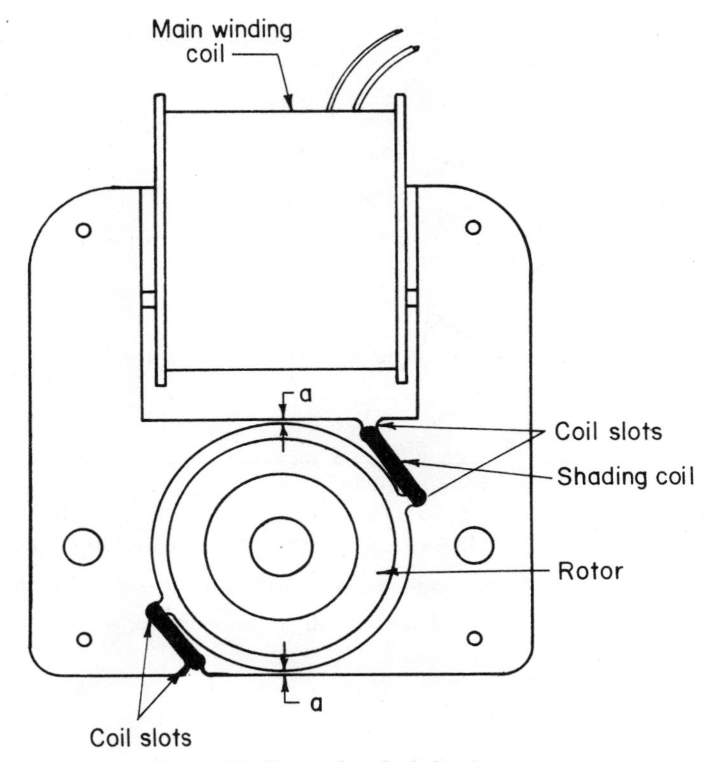

Fig. 3-28. Two-pole, shaded-pole motor.

rated above 0.08 hp, so low efficiency is not much of a problem. As price is usually the overriding issue, most of these motors are not as well designed and manufactured as they could be as far as efficiency and noise is concerned. Shaded-pole motors can be designed to operate very quietly.

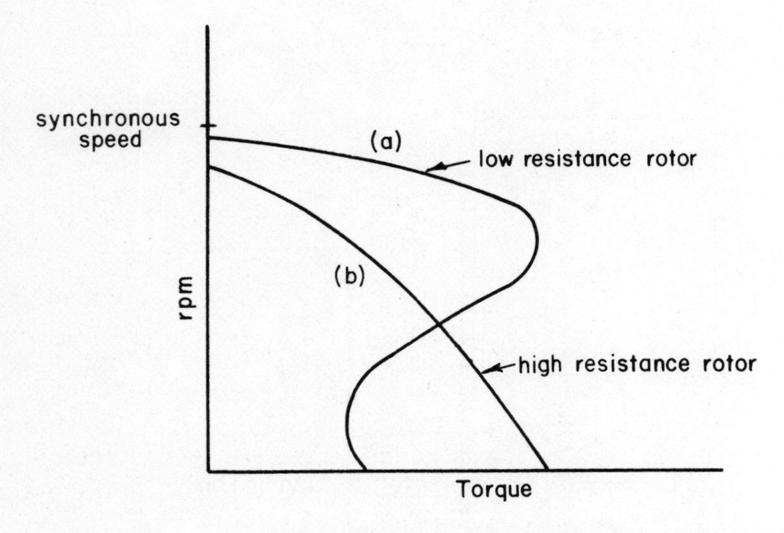

(a) Torque - speed curve with low resistance rotor

(b) Torque-speed curve with high resistance rotor

Fig. 3-29. Typical torque-speed curves for shaded-pole motor.

3.2.8. Rotor-Wound Induction Motors

Torque developed by the polyphase induction motor is:

$$T = \frac{9.55}{\text{syn. RPM}} \times \frac{I_2^2\, r_2 m}{S} \tag{3-11}$$

where $s = \dfrac{\text{syn. RPM} - \text{actual motor RMP}}{\text{syn. RPM}}$

T = Torque in Newton meters
I_2 = Current in rotor
r_2 = Rotor resistance
m = Number of phases
s = Slip (Slip is 0 at synchronous speed and 1 when the rotor is locked.)

Equation 3-11 shows that torque is a function of the rotor resistance. In the squirrel-cage motor, the rotor resistance is fixed by the design. In order to control the resistance, rotors can be wound with insulated wires and the leads brought out to the individually insulated slip rings. External rheostats are then connected to the rotor through brushes running on those rings. The resistance of those rheostats can be varied. Alternatively, fixed resistors can be switched in and out to adjust the torque-speed curve to suit. Because of the extra expense involved in manufacturing these motors, they are very seldom built in sizes of under 5 hp. A high resistance will limit the locked rotor current, which is an important factor in large motors.

3.3. THE AC COMMUTATOR MOTORS

3.3.1. Single-Phase ac Series Motors

If a motor similar to a dc series motor, as described in chapter 1 section 1.5 but with a laminated field core, is connected to an ac supply, the basic series motor characteristics will be maintained, even though the torque-speed curve will differ from the one that applies when the motor is connected to a dc supply of equal voltage. Alternating current creates an inductive impedance drop in the field winding not present on dc (Fig. 3-30). The ac motor operation also differs from the dc operation in

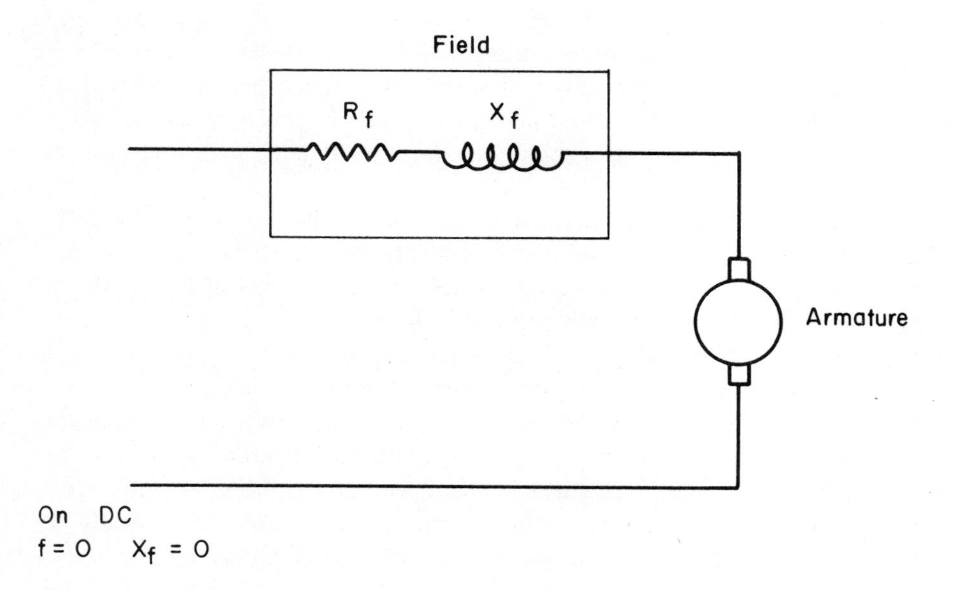

Fig. 3-30. Effect on field impedance of applying alternating current to a series motor.

that the supply line frequency produces a torque of double line frequency due to the sinusoidal nature of the supply voltage which goes through zero volts twice each cycle. The ac operation will therefore be less smooth and the motor will be noisier than the equivalent dc operation.

Originally these motors were designed to perform certain functions, such as driving a sewing machine on either ac or dc. Furthermore, the requirements might have been that on ac power, the motors perform satisfactorily operating from a 25 Hz supply. This requirement would have existed because at one time local electricity supplies were anything but standardized. Motors that meet these performance requirements are called *universal motors*. Most ac series motors are likely to be designed specifically for a 120 V, 60 Hz supply; 120 V, 50/60 Hz; 220 V, 50 Hz; or any other standard supply.

Typical performance characteristics for an ac series motor are shown in Fig. 3-31. The ac/dc characteristics of a small universal motor are shown in Fig. 3-32.

These motors are widely used in power tools, vacuum cleaners, sewing machines, food mixers and other appliances. Speeds are generally between 3000 and 20,000 RPM. The series motor not only varies in speed with change in load, but also varies considerably with supply voltage, as shown in Fig. 3-33. Therefore, speed control can be accomplished either by putting a variable resistance in series with the motor (see Fig. 3-34) or electronically with a solid state speed control. Where load-torque or voltage variations occur, mechanical or electronic governors can be used to maintain the speed of the ac series motor when constant speed performance is required.

In general, ac series motors have relatively poor commutation, in part due to the transformer EMF induced in the coil under commutation. Brush life might be quite limited. Universal motors are as a group noisier than other types of ac motors and they might cause EMI problems unless properly filtered.

However, with its salient pole field construction (Fig. 1-8) and the available means to automate the armature production, this makes it one of the lowest cost motors to produce. The motor can be operated at speeds above 3600 RPM from a standard 60 Hz supply without a variable frequency supply. Often this operation is very advantageous. It is also possible to design motors that operate on 115/220 V, 50/60 cycles by changing field connections. Alternating-current series motors are generally designed to turn in a single direction. Because of the relatively high audio noise associated with these motors, low-cost alternatives are constantly investigated, and they will have to come in the form of brushless motors.

Larger ac series motors often use a nonsalient pole field construction. A compensating winding is added in series with the armature in quadrature with the main winding to counteract the armature EMF. A diagram of such a motor is shown in Fig. 3-35.

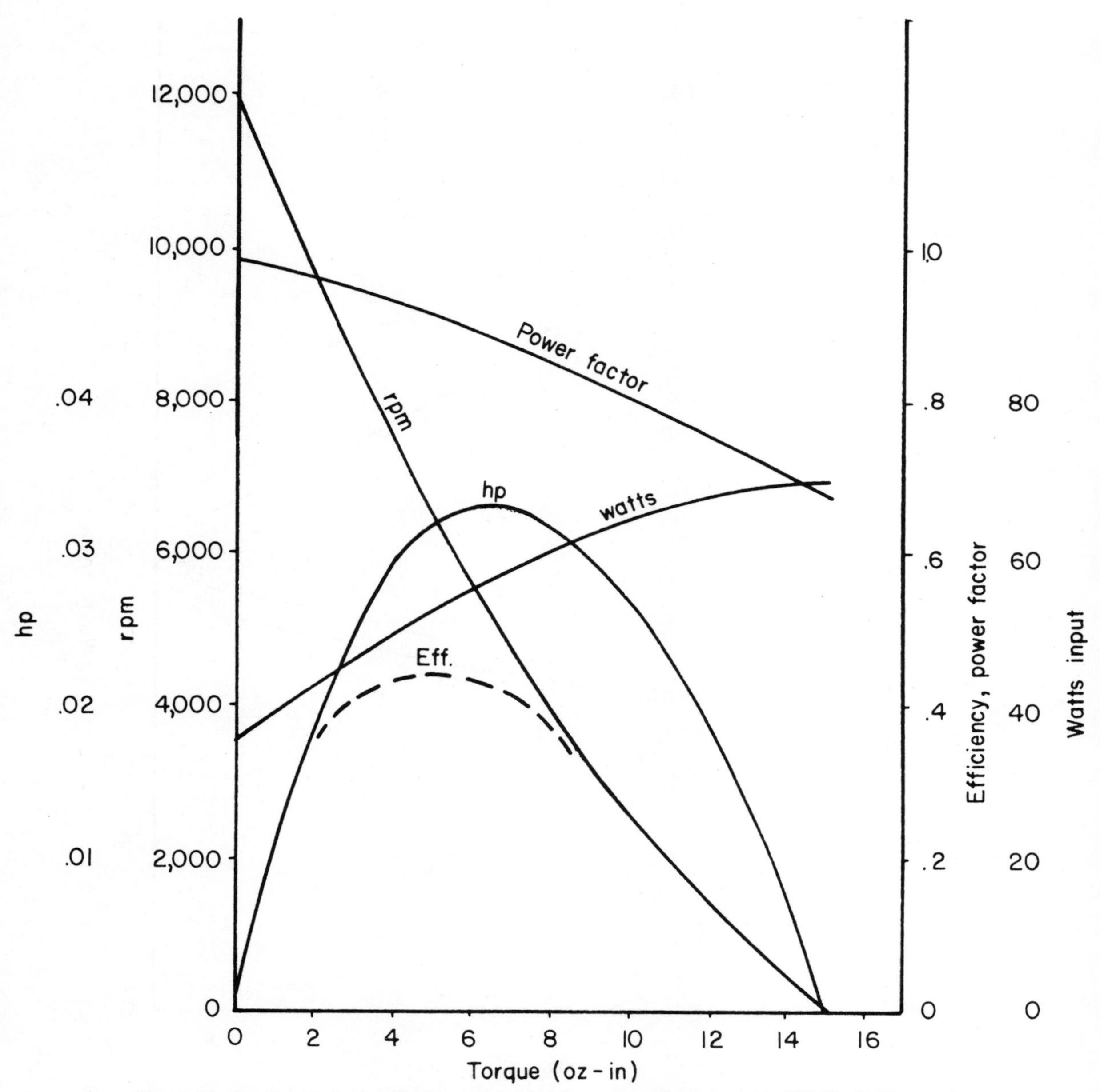

Fig. 3-31. Typical performance characteristics of a universal motor with 120 V, 60 Hz supply.

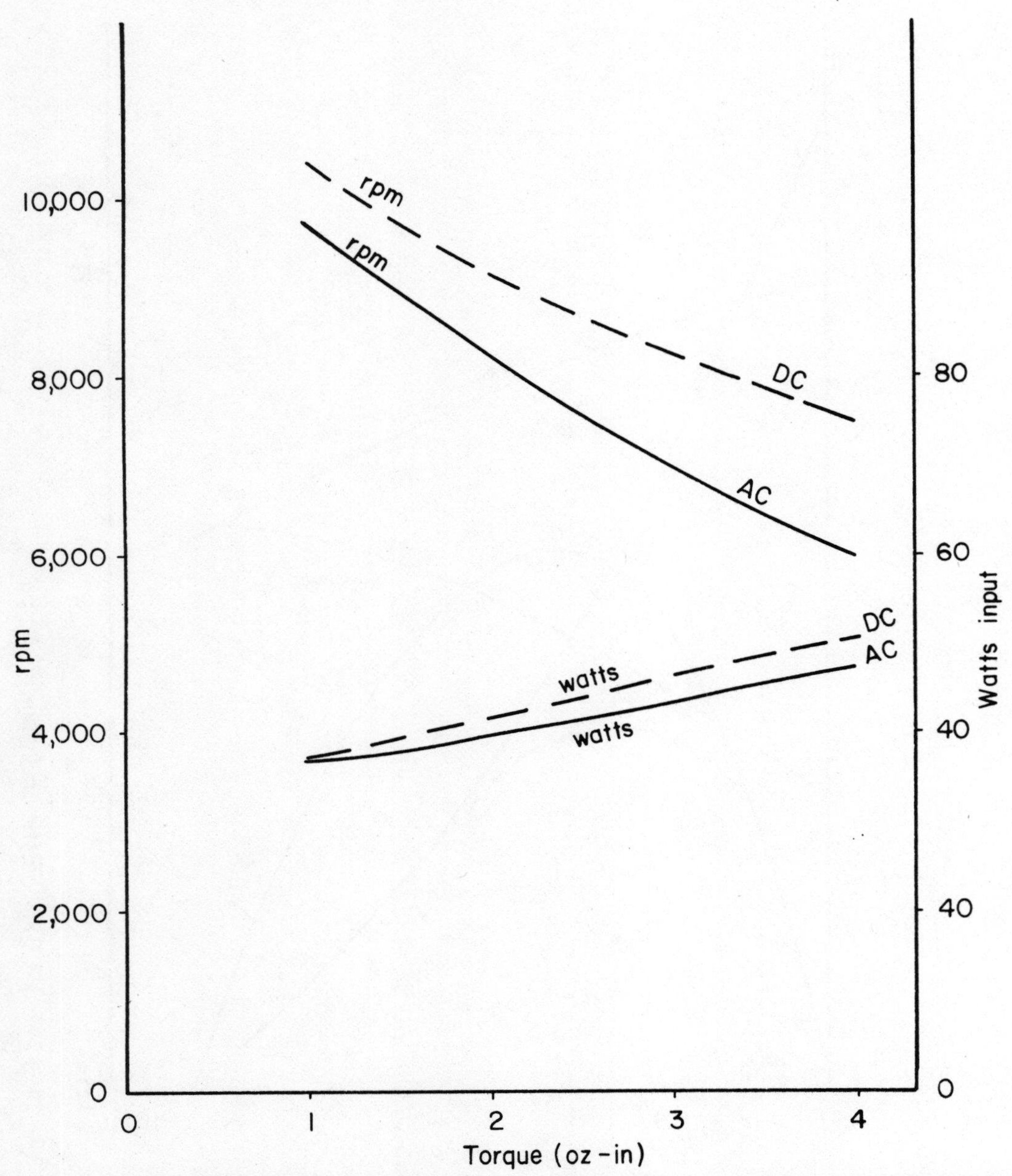

Fig. 3-32. Typical characteristics of small universal motors with ac supply of 220 V, 60 cycle, and with dc supply of 220 V.

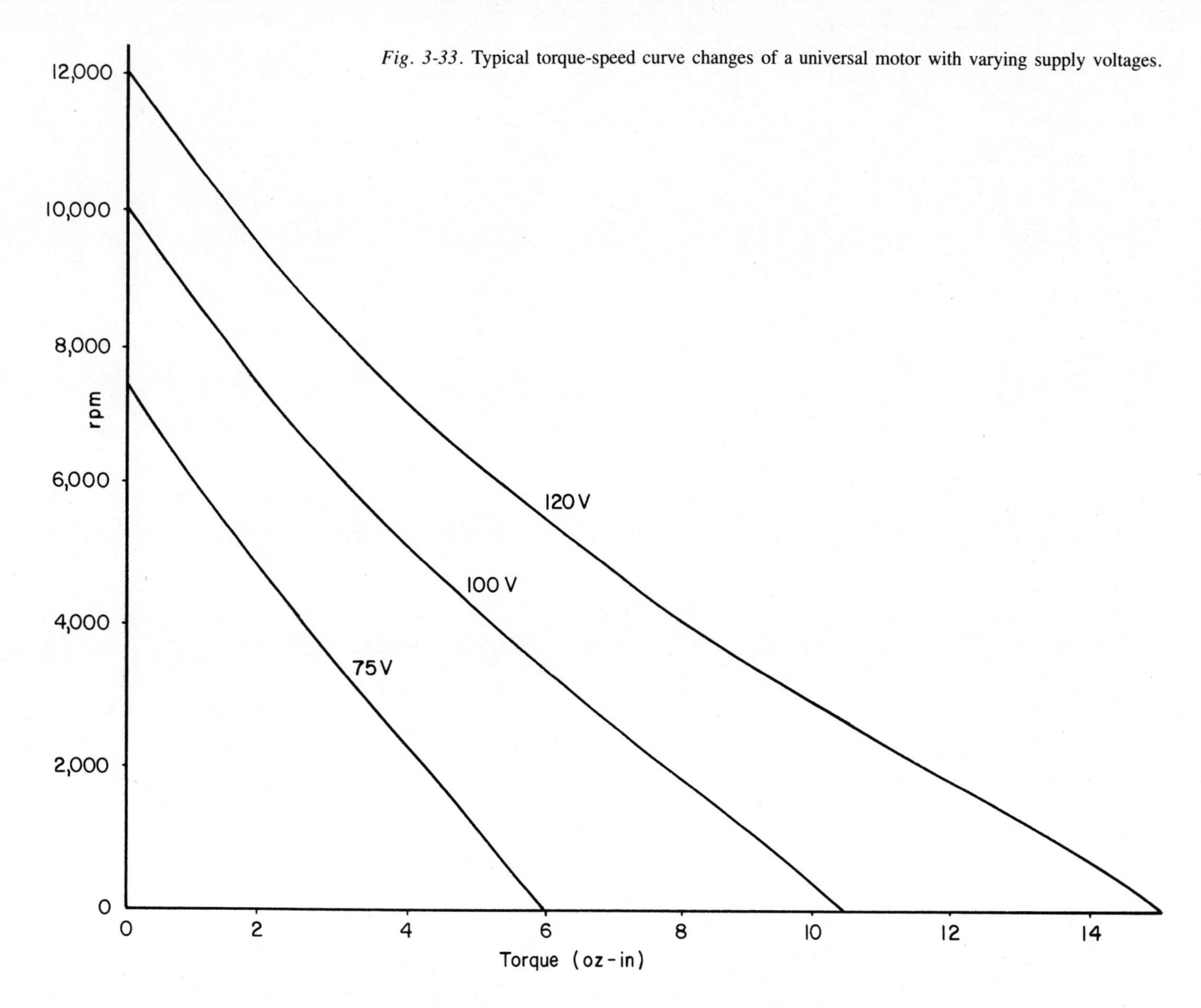

Fig. 3-33. Typical torque-speed curve changes of a universal motor with varying supply voltages.

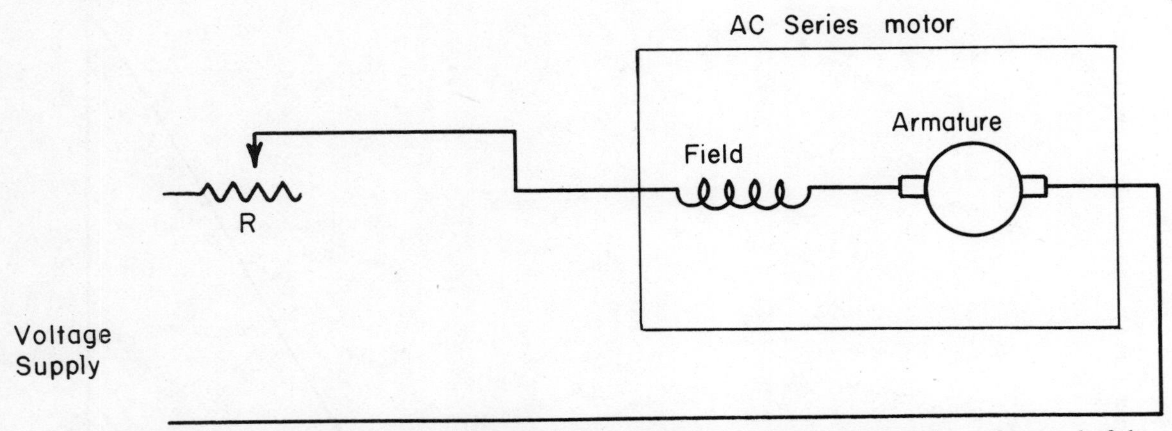

Fig. 3-34. Variable resistor in series with an ac series motor. Increasing the resistances reduces the speed of the motor and vice versa.

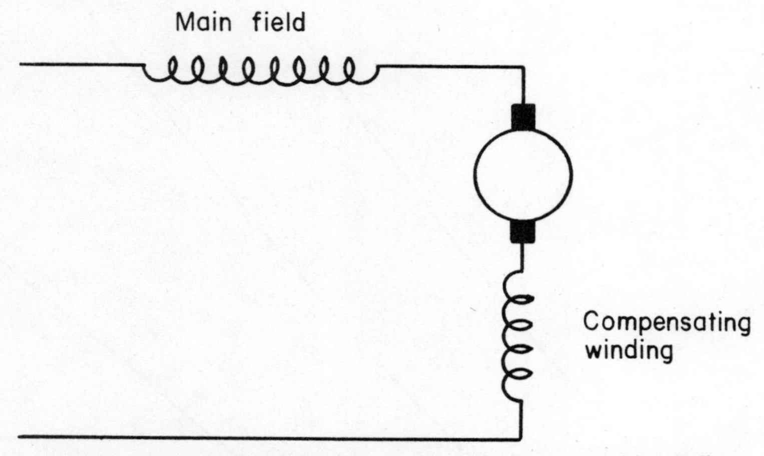

Fig. 3-35. Nonsalient-pole ac series motor with compensating winding.

3.3.2. Single-Phase Repulsion Motor

A series motor with a distributed-field winding reconnected so that the series field is connected across the supply and the armature brushes are short circuited, results in a repulsion motor as in Fig. 3-36. Current will be induced in the armature, the magnitude of which will depend on the brush shift.

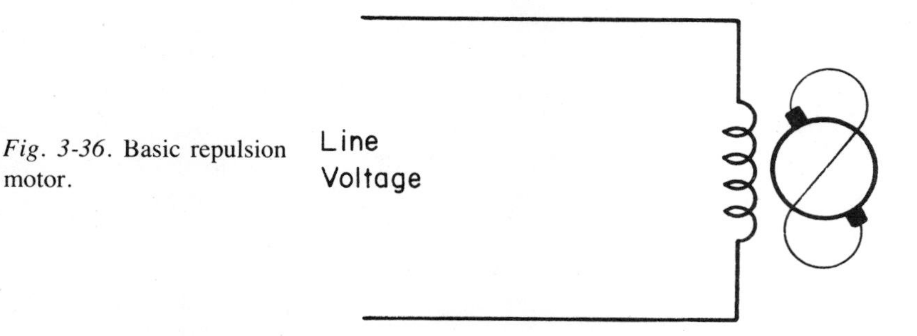

Fig. 3-36. Basic repulsion motor.

The following approximate relationship may be established for this motor by neglecting armature reaction:

$$T_L \approx \Phi^2 \sin 2\,\alpha \tag{3-12}$$

where T_L = Torque
Φ = Flux produced by the field
α = Angle of brush shift

Therefore, there is no torque produced in position when $\alpha = 0$ and when $\alpha = 90$ degrees. The reason for this is that when $\alpha = 0$, the brushes are shifted at right angles to the field axis, and the armature is nothing but a short circuited secondary of a transformer. When $\alpha = 90$ degrees, there is no current induced in the armature and the torque is 0. According to equation 3-12, it would seem that the maximum torque would occur at $\alpha = 45$ degrees but because of armature reaction, the maximum torque may occur at an angle closer to 20 degrees.

In general, the repulsion motor has better commutation than the series motors at speeds up to synchronous speed. At higher speeds however, the higher currents induced in the short-circuited coils are detrimental to the performance of the motor. A typical torque-speed curve is shown in Fig. 3-37. Speed control can be obtained by varying the supply voltage as with the use of a tapped transformer or by shifting the brushes.

As this motor produces a high starting torque, this has led to the repulsion-start induction motor. At a certain speed, the commutator bars are short circuited by a centrifugal mechanism that essentially becomes a squirrel-cage rotor. At this point, the motor will follow single-phase induction motor characteristics. Since low cost starting capacitors have become available, the repulsion-start induction motor has lost much of its attraction.

There are many more variations of ac commutator motors, such as squirrel-cage repulsion motors, Schrage motors, etc., all of them designed to improve the performance of the motor in some specific way.

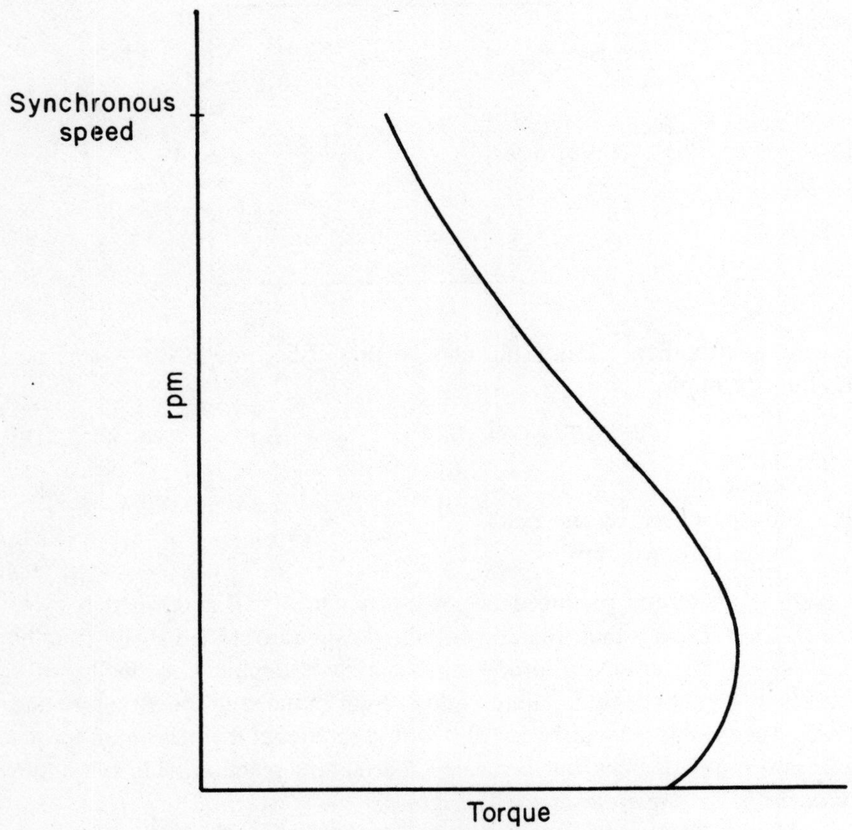

Fig. 3-37. Typical torque-speed curve for repulsion motor.

3.4. SYNCHRONOUS MOTORS

3.4.1. General Considerations

Synchronous motors are designed to operate exactly at synchronous speed that was previously given as

$$\text{Synchronous RPM} = \frac{120 \times \text{line frequency}}{\text{number of poles}} \tag{3-9}$$

Synchronous motors are used in a variety of applications, from subminiature motors for clock and timing applications to very sophisticated applications in robotics, computer peripheral equipment, record players, laser drives, recorders, etc.—wherever accurate timing is of utmost importance. Large synchronous motors are frequently used for their efficiency and the possibility to use the leading power factor at no or low load to improve the overall power factor of the load in a factory or mine and thus reduce the overall electric bill.

3.4.2. Mode of Operation

The method of creating a rotating field with a three-phase winding was explained in section 3.2.2 and illustrated in Fig. 3-10 and 3-11. If the rotor, in this case of salient pole construction, is an electro-magnet created by a dc current as shown in Fig. 3-38 and 3-39, and the rotor travels at the same speed as the field, then this motor performs as a synchronous motor. Figure 3-38 shows three different locations in time of a three-phase field and the corresponding position of the magnet. The N-pole of the magnet locks in with the traveling S-pole of the three-phase winding, and they both travel at the same speed. If a load is added to the motor, the rotor falls behind an angle δ as shown in Fig. 3-39. The maximum load that the rotor can develop is equal to the maximum tangential pull that can be developed between the rotor and stator. Beyond this point, the rotor falls out of synchronism and just comes to a standstill. Also there is no starting torque developed by this motor, and without other means of starting, the rotor would have to be driven up to synchronous speed.

The dc current to the rotor can be supplied much like the current to the armature in a dc motor except that the commutator is replaced by two slip rings on which ride the brushes. An alternative to brushes is to use a rotary transformer with the secondary mounted on the shaft. The current is than rectified.

A winding can be located close to the tips of the pole faces in order to make the motor self-starting. This winding acts like a squirrel-cage rotor winding. It also reduces hunting caused by sudden changes in supply voltage or load conditions. It is for this reason that these windings are called *damper* or *amortisseur* windings. See Fig. 3-40.

The motor starts like an induction motor, but an induction motor can not reach synchronous speed. The synchronous motor must be able to bring the rotor into synchronism. The maximum torque the motor can develop to pull in a load is called pull-in torque. A stated pull-in torque is a measured torque with only the rotor inertia being pulled in. With a large load inertia, the motor might not be able to pull in the load. Suppose the load is nothing but a disc; if the inertia of this disc is large enough, the motor might not be able to pull it into synchronism. The maximum torque at which the motor pulls out of synchronous speed is called pull-out torque. Generally the pull-out torque is higher than the pull-in torque. A typical torque-speed curve for a synchronous motor is shown in Fig. 3-41.

The effect of a change in field current on the power factor and line current for a given load is illustrated in Fig. 3-42. This is just one example of what can be accomplished with a change in field current.

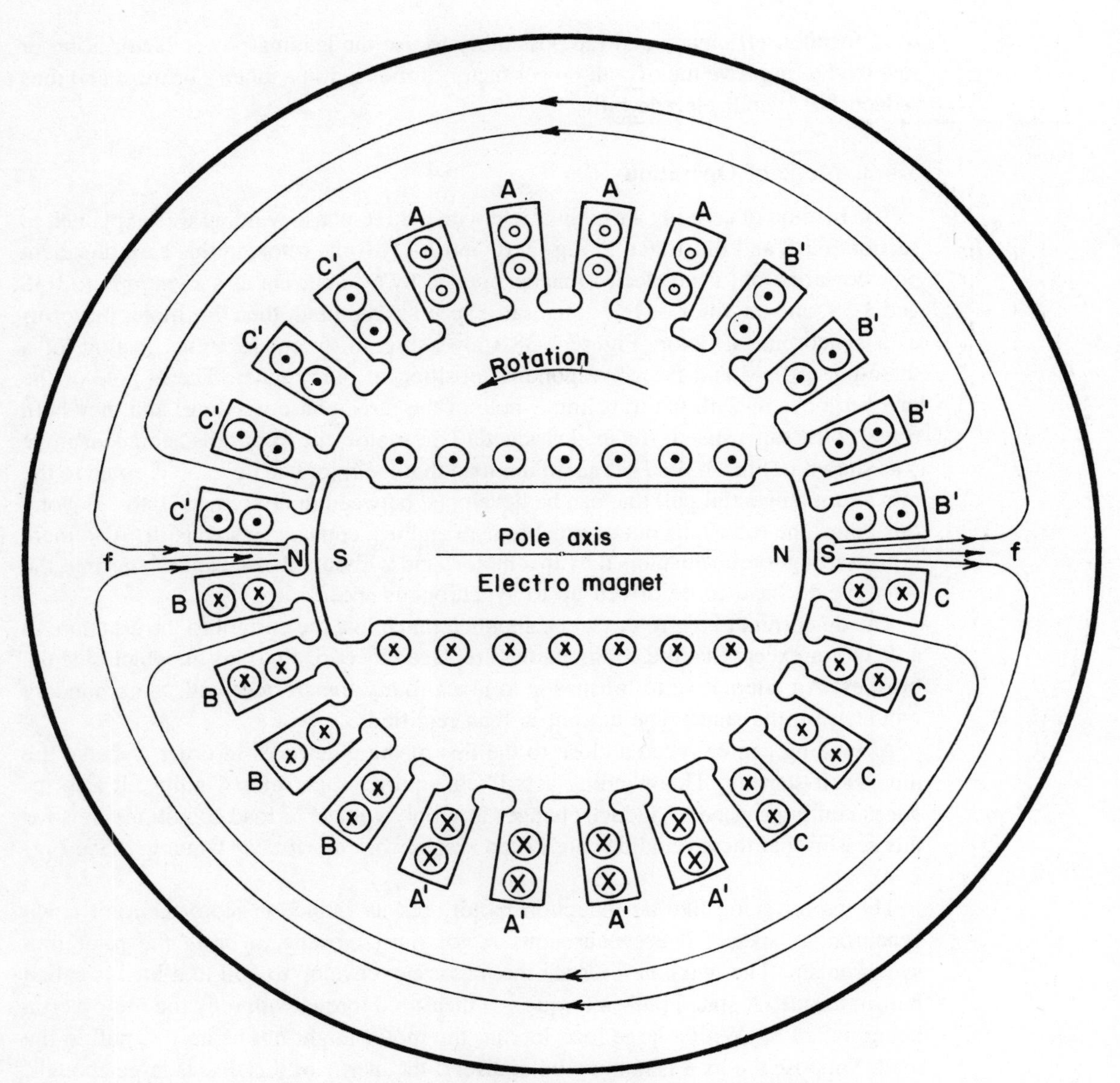

Fig. 3-38. (a) Synchronous motor action with no load.

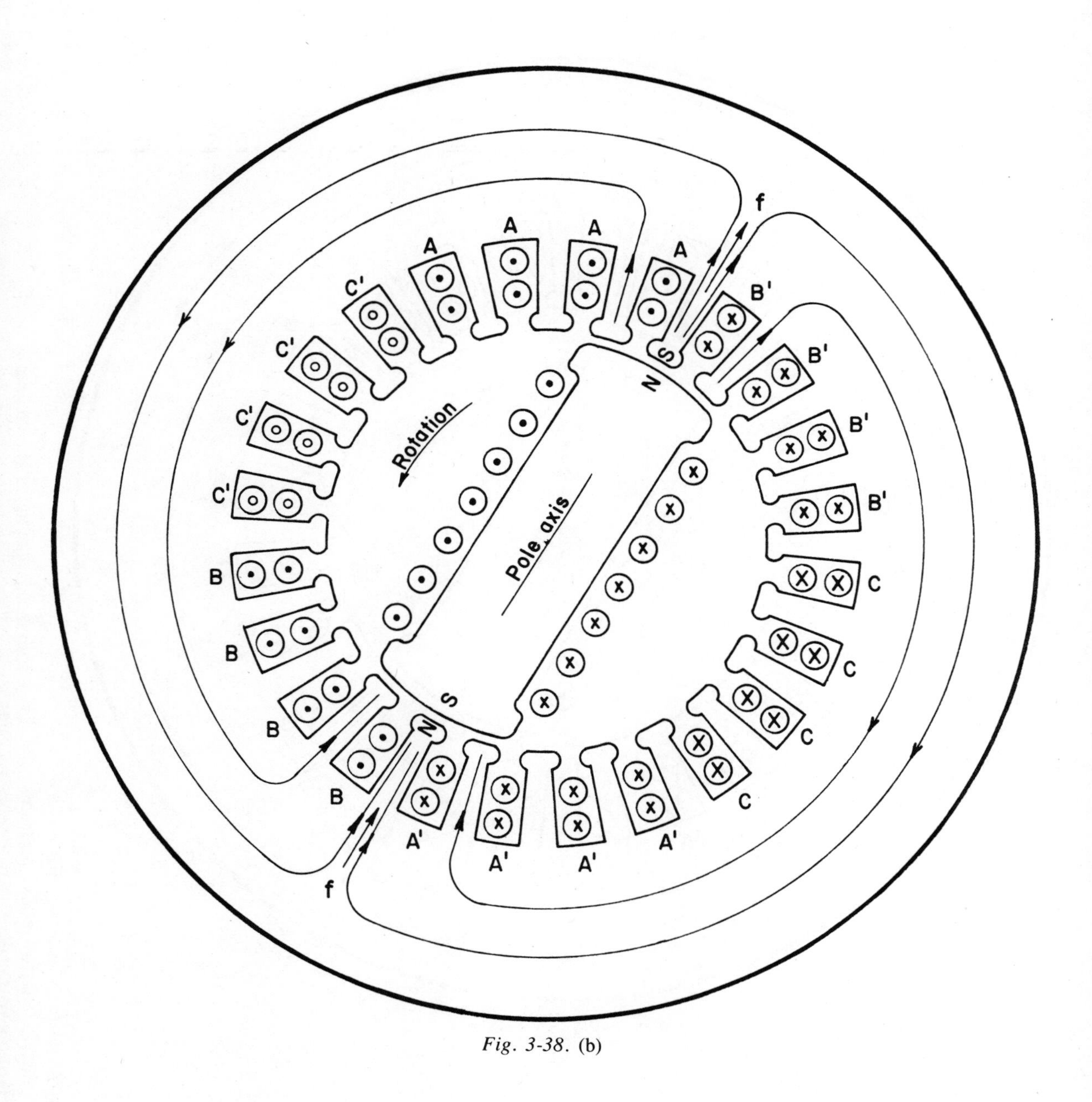

Fig. 3-38. (b)

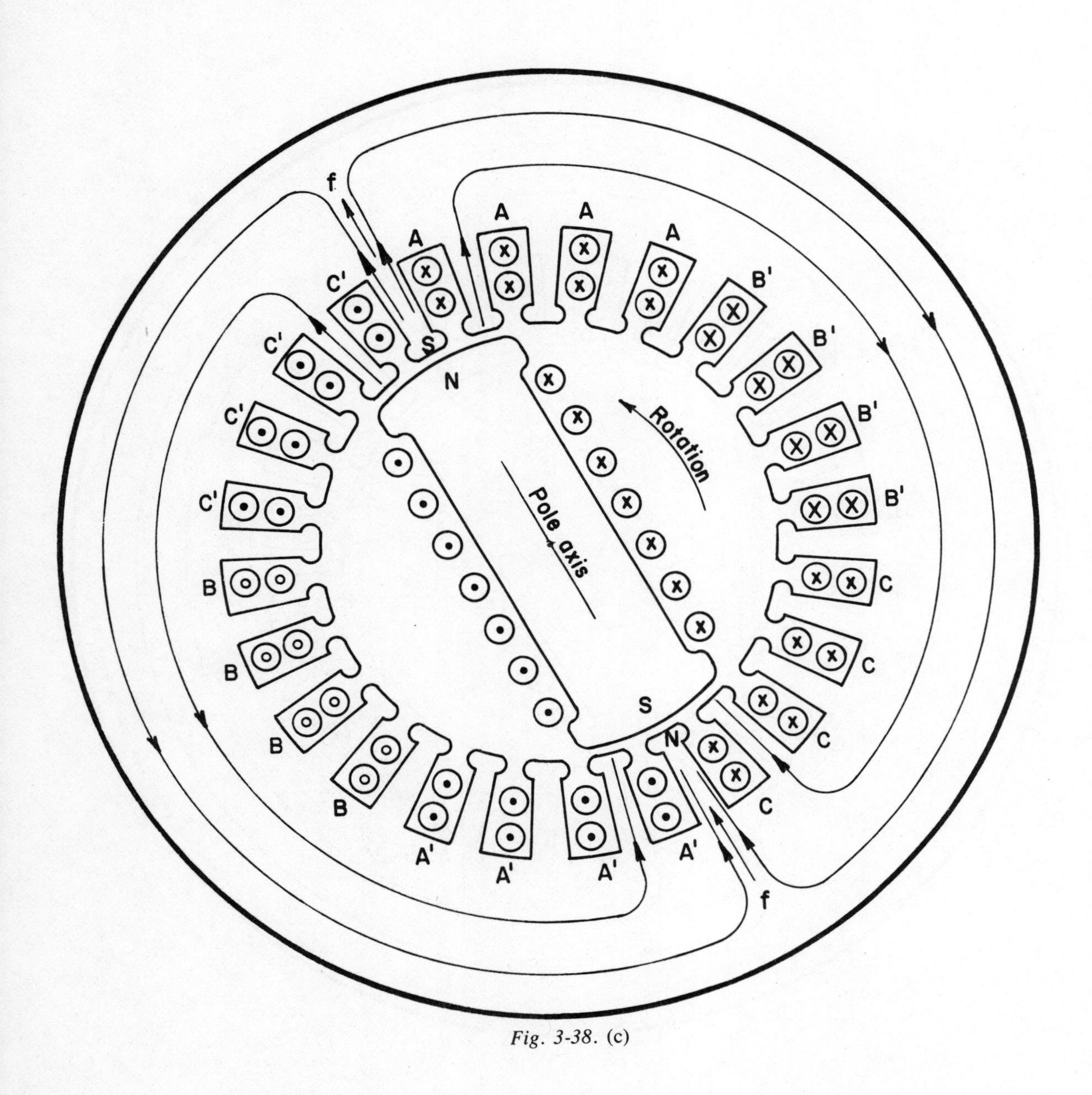

Fig. 3-38. (c)

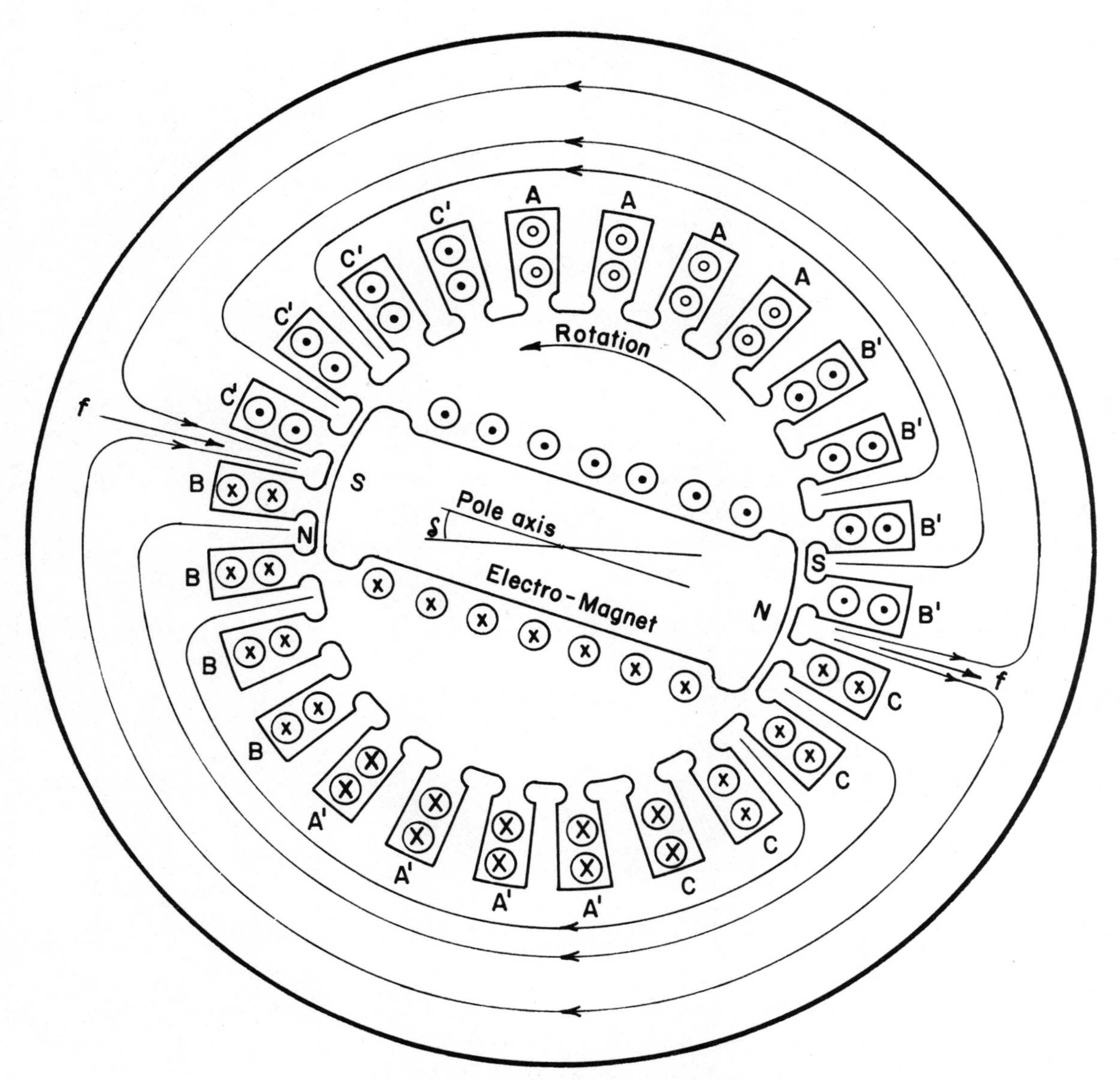

Fig. 3-39. Synchronous motor action with load.

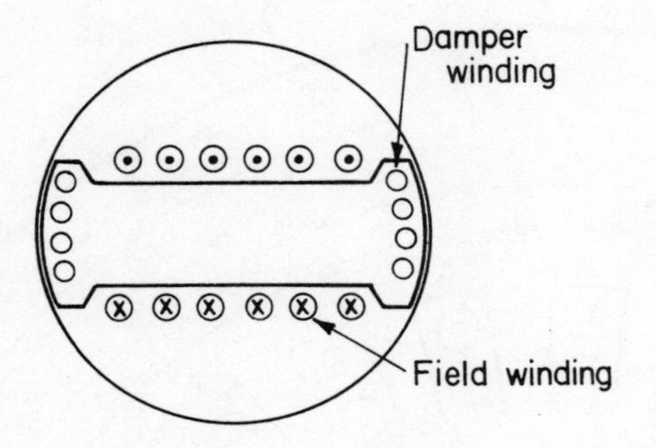

Fig. 3-40. Synchronous motor rotor with damper winding.

The wound rotor can be replaced by a permanent magnet. With a constant field, it is impossible to optimize the performance of the motor for different operating points. With a permanent-magnet rotor, the damper winding could be replaced by a separate induction motor rotor. Among other kinds of synchronous motors, are the hysteresis- and the reluctance-type synchronous motors.

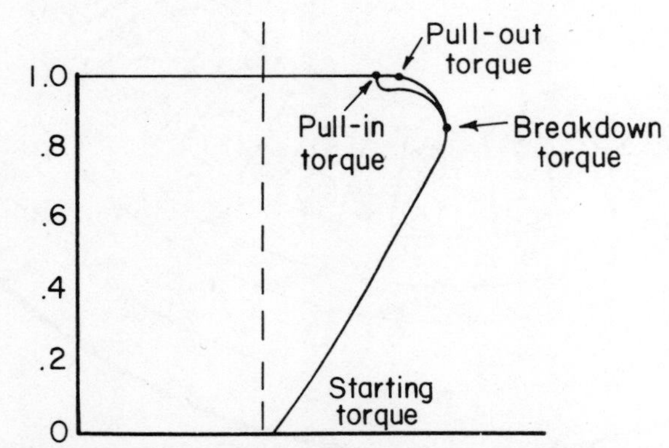

Fig. 3-41. Typical torque-speed curve of a synchronous motor.

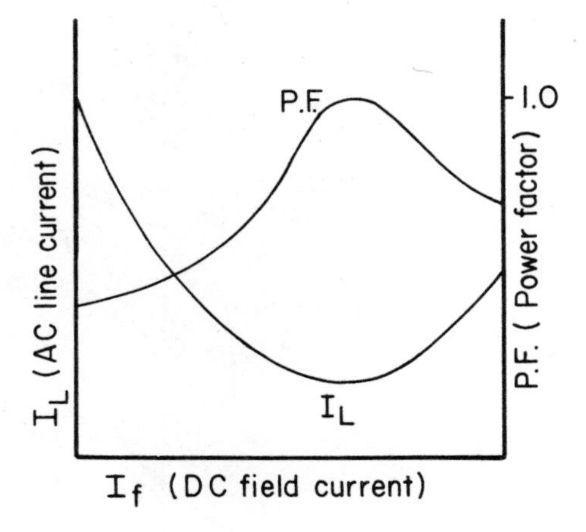

Fig. 3-42. Effect of field current on the power factor and line current with constant load.

3.4.3. Hysteresis Motors

If a revolving field such as illustrated in Fig. 3-10 and 3-11 is applied to a rotor made of a cylinder of hardened magnetic steel or certain permanent magnet alloys, poles will be induced in the latter by the revolving field. A torque will be produced when the resulting pole axis lags behind the magnetic axis of the revolving field. The lag is due to hysteresis. A hysteresis loop is shown in Fig. 3-43. The relationship between the two axis is illustrated in Fig. 3-44. The torque created by the hysteresis effect is proportional to the following:

$$T \approx PVW_h \tag{3-13}$$

where T = torque
P = number of poles
V = volume of the rotor cylinder
W_h = area of the hysteresis loop

The above equation indicates that the torque is independent of frequency and is basically constant from locked rotor condition to synchronous speed. At synchronism it behaves very much like a permanent-magnet synchronous motor. In actual practice, the torques are larger at other than synchronous speeds due to eddy currents induced in the rotor materials. Once maximum hysteresis torque is reached, the motor will pull out of synchronism but continue running at subsynchronous speeds. It was shown in equation 3-13 that the torque is proportional to the area of the hysteresis loop; this relationship calls for materials with large loops. The core materials used for fractional

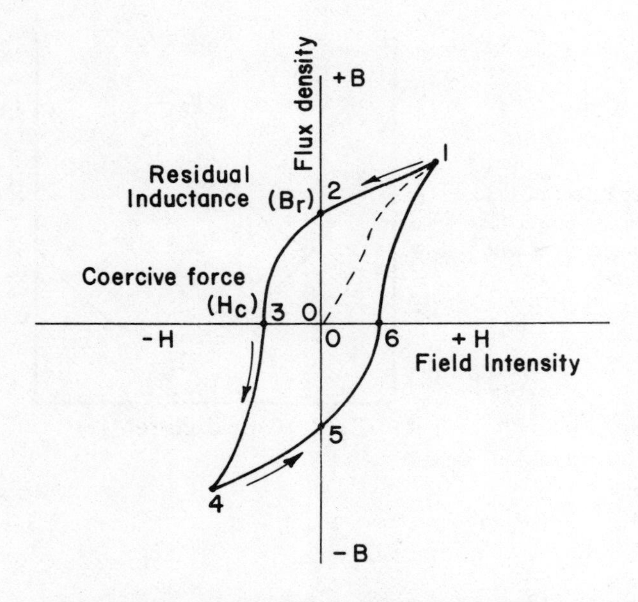

Above magnetic material cyclically magnitized shows two values of magnetic flux density (B) for each magnetizing force (H).

One B when the magnetic force is increasing, the other when it is decreasing.

The area contained in this loop is proportional to the energy loss from hysteresis.

Fig. 3-43. Magnetic hysteresis loop.

horsepower motors usually have a 15% to 40% cobalt content, some calcium, and the rest iron. Some carbon might be present. Alnicos have also been used for core material.

These motors are very smooth running and are able to pull-in inertia loads more readily than other types of synchronous motors. These motors have found a variety of applications in tape drives, printing machines, laser drives, recording equipment, etc.

Some of the core materials have excellent tensile and yield strength, making these

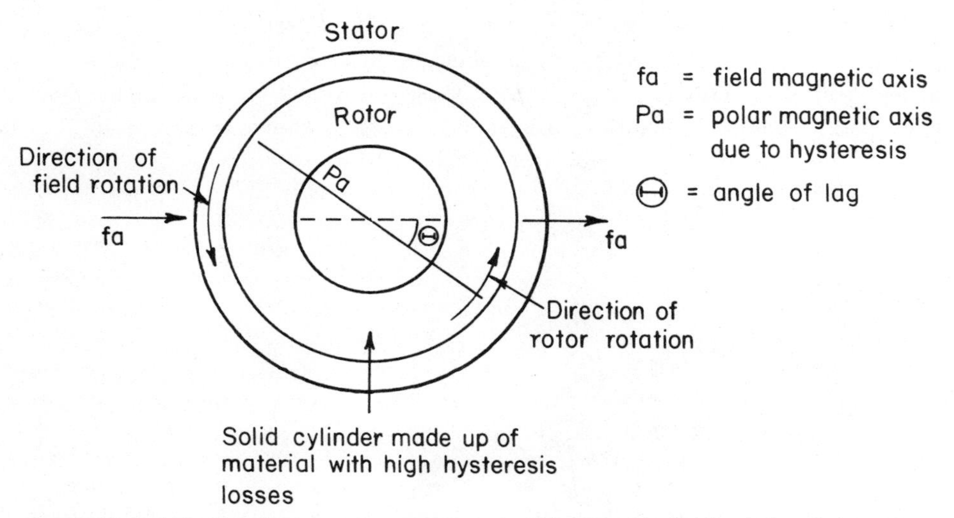

Fig. 3-44. Relationship between the rotating and polar magnetic field axis in a hysteresis motor.

motors suitable for high-speed applications. The fact that the torque is independent of frequency makes this motor attractive.

A typical torque-speed curve is shown in Fig. 3-45. Single-phase motors are generally of the capacitor-run type, and torque-speed curves can differ considerably depending on winding distribution, size of capacitor, etc. Multispeed motors such as 2/4 or 4/6/8 pole motors are common. Efficiency is generally low, which accounts for the fact that for the same speed and horsepower rating induction motors are often smaller than the corresponding hysteresis motor.

Speed control is accomplished with variable frequency control by maintaining the ratio of volts per cycle constant. Interest in this once promising motor all but vanished

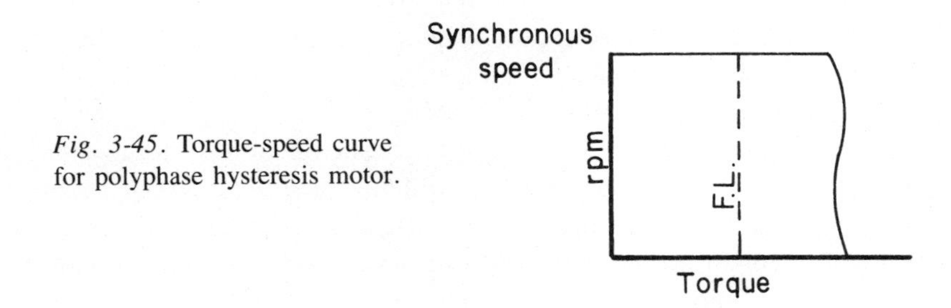

Fig. 3-45. Torque-speed curve for polyphase hysteresis motor.

with the often high cost and uncertain supply of cobalt. Alternative motors, such as stepper motors and BLDC motors, have taken the place of hysteresis motors.

Motors with subfractional ratings frequently use lower-cost, more attainable materials as core material. A picture of a hysteresis motor is shown in Fig. 3-46.

Fig. 3-46. Hysteresis motor. (Courtesy of ELECTRIC INDICATOR Company, Inc., Norwalk, CT.)

3.4.4. Reluctance Synchronous Motors

The reluctance motor might simply be an induction motor with some rotor teeth removed, making it a salient pole-induction synchronous motor. This construction results in a motor with characteristics similar to the salient pole motor described in section 3.4.2 but without the benefit of a dc field winding (see Fig. 3-47). Without a field current, it is basically an inefficient motor and is hardly ever used as an integral-horsepower motor. The typical torque-speed curve is shown in Fig. 3-41. The same limitations as to the acceleration of inertial loads described in section 3.4.2 apply to this motor. This motor is also likely to be quite noisy.

A variation to the removal of rotor teeth to accomplish a reluctance path is to provide a nonuniform magnetic path inside the rotor punching. The reluctance synchronous motor does have advantages as listed in Table 3-3, which compares this motor with the hysteresis synchronous motor.

As in the case of the hysteresis motor, speed control can be accomplished by varying the supply frequency and generally keeping the supply volts per cycle constant. It is important to consider the voltage waveform and steadiness of the frequency when using an electronic speed controller, such as an inverter to drive a synchronous motor, because these characteristics will have an important bearing on the amount of flutter produced by the motor. For certain applications even, standard 60 Hz line frequency might not be maintained accurately enough to avoid causing undesirable jitter in the motor.

Table 3-3. Comparisons of Hysteresis and Reluctance Motors.

	Hysteresis Motor	Reluctance Synchronous Motor
Phasing*	will not phase in at any particular angular position (however polarized hysteresis motors are available.)	will phase into synchronous speed at a number of fixed angular positions equal to the number of poles.
Noise and Vibration	very smooth running with a minimum of noise	usually noisier and might cause vibration
Hunting	more likely to hunt	minimizes hunting
Efficiency**	low	low
Relative Cost	high	lower cost
Multispeed (pole changing)	yes	no
Starting	same starting torque in any position	starting torque varies with rotor position
Inertial Load	able to accelerate high inertial load	acceleration of inertial loads limited

*Phasing referred to in this table means that the motor will phase into synchronous speed at fixed angular position or positions with respect to the motor.
**Refers to fractional horsepower motors.

Fig. 3-47. Rotor for reluctance synchronous motor-generator set. (Courtesy of ELECTRIC INDICATOR Company, Inc., Norwalk, CT.)

3.5. STEPPER MOTORS

3.5.1. Introduction

The idea of applying variable reluctance principles to electrical rotating equipment has been around for a long time. The old impulse motor was based on this principle, as were many rotary switches and of course the reluctance synchronous motor. What put the stepper motor into the important place it occupies today in the family of motors is the rapid development of electronic switching and sensing. Stepper motors today take up important, maybe even dominant, positions in such fields as robotics, motion control, disc drives, etc. As the relative cost of electronic components keeps on coming down, you can expect further development in the stepper motor field.

3.5.2. Mode of Operation

The motor basically consists of a wound stator and a slotted rotor. The stator core is made up of slotted steel laminations with a certain number of teeth. The rotor also consists of a core made up of slotted laminations, but with a different number of teeth. There are no windings in the rotor. The mode of operation is illustrated in Figs. 3-48 and 3-49.

The geometry of the magnetic circuit is shown in Fig. 3-48. The stator consists of six teeth and six coils, and the rotor has eight teeth.

Coils A and D are connected in series, as are coils B and E and coils C and F. Switching sequence of the winding is shown in Fig. 3-49. Initially switch Q is closed, coil A and D are energized and stator teeth a and d are lined up with the rotor teeth 1 and 5 respectively. For the motor to move, switch Q opens, de-energizing coils A and D, and switch R closes energizing coils B and E. This causes the flux path to go through stator tooth b through rotor tooth 2 following through tooth 6 and stator tooth e, completing the magnetic circuit by returning to stator tooth b. This makes stator tooth b an N-pole, rotor tooth 2 an S-pole, rotor tooth 6 an N-pole, and stator tooth e an S-pole. Opposite poles will have a tendency to line up. Rotor teeth 2 and 6 will do so with stator teeth b and e respectively, causing the rotor to move clockwise by 15 degrees. The same process can be repeated by de-energizing coils B and E and energizing coils C and F. Different rotor positions are graphically illustrated in Fig. 3-48 (a). An alternative explanation for the rotor action is that movement will be in direction of minimum reluctance, and the minimum reluctance is at points where rotor teeth and stator teeth line up in the positions as shown in Fig. 3-48 (a).

The motor is only one component of a whole stepping-motor system. Pulses are sent to a controller that activates the proper coil or coils and make the rotor move. Any limitation of the control system will limit the performance of the motor.

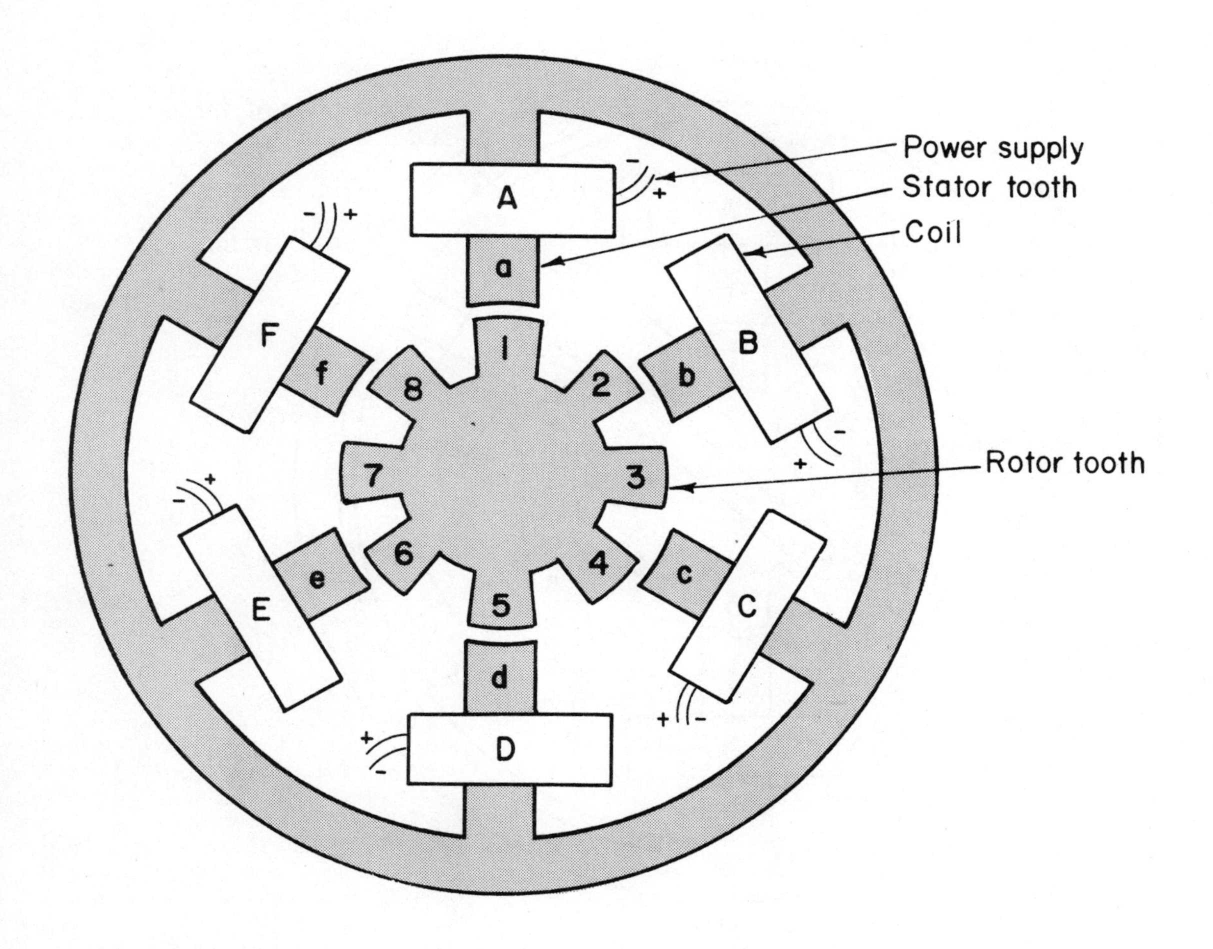

Fig. 3-48. (a) Mode of operation of a stepper motor: rotation of rotor as a consequence of switching power in stator winding.

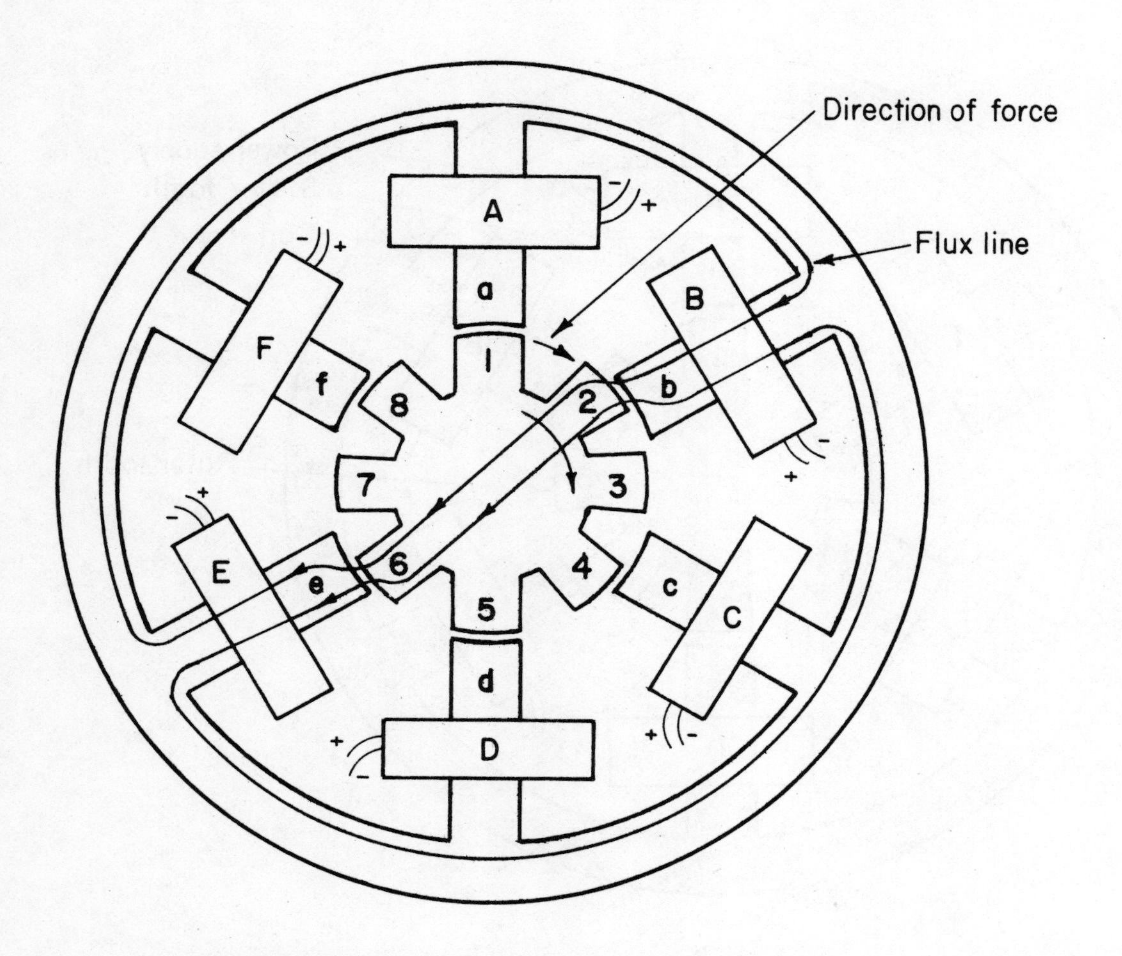

Coil A & D deenergized, coil B & E energized; force on rotor teeth 2 and 6 in direction of stator teeth b and e respectively.

Fig. 3-48. (b)

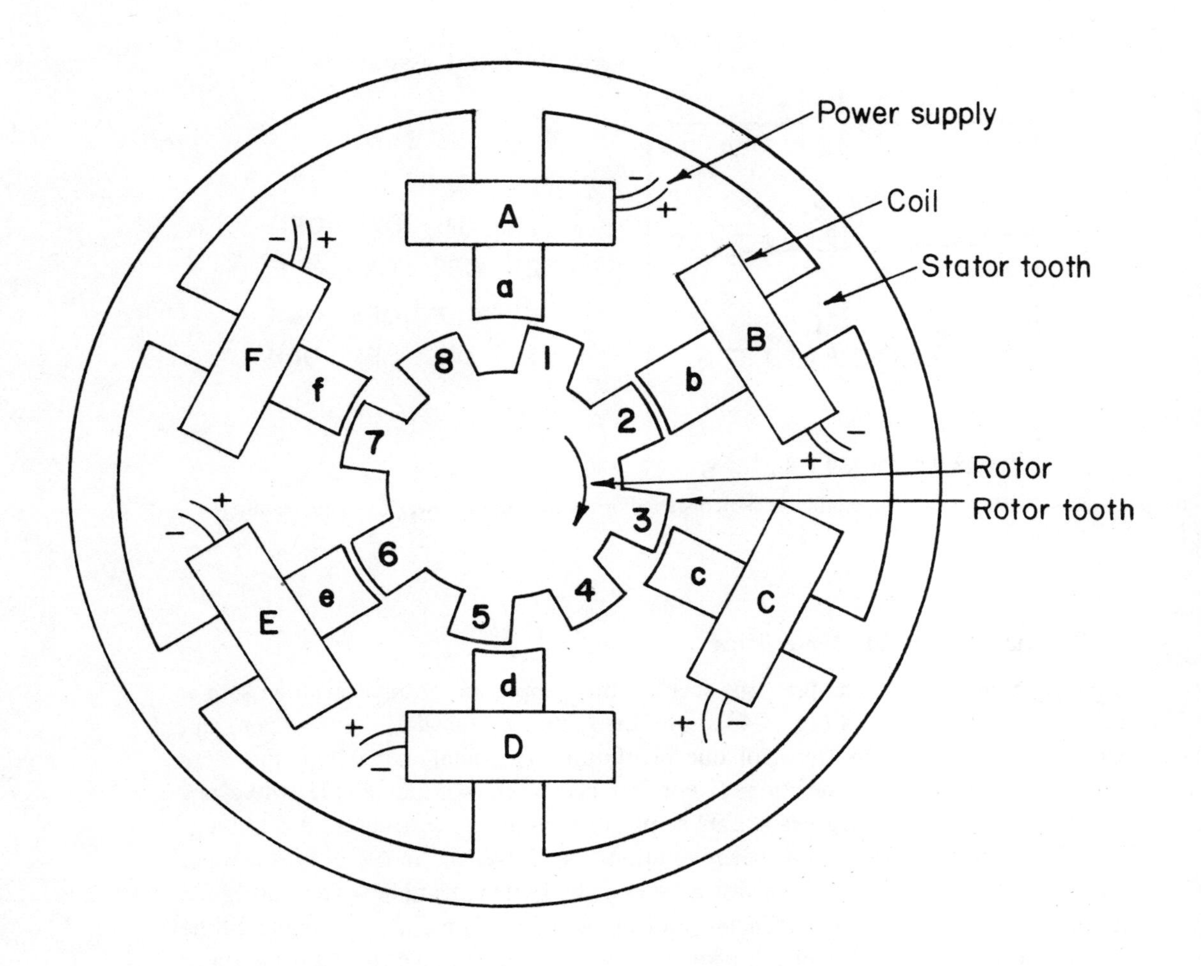

Rotor moved, one step completed;
stator tooth b lined up with rotor tooth 2,
stator tooth e lined up with rotor tooth 6

Fig. 3-48. (c)

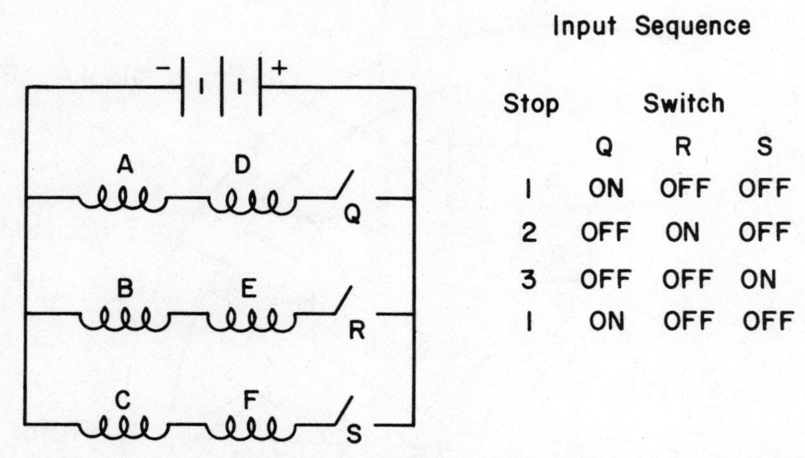

Fig. 3-49. Mode of operation of a stepper motor: switching of power in stator winding.

3.5.3. Basic Motor Characteristics

As you can see from the previous section, the stepper motor advances one step at a time. The illustration in Fig. 3-48 shows the motor advanced 15 degrees per step, which means it takes 24 steps for one revolution. The smaller the step, the more accurate the shaft can be positioned. For instance, motors are available where one step advances only 1.8 degrees or 200 steps per revolution for accurate positioning. The higher the number of steps per revolution, the slower the motor is likely to be, because as there is a limit of how fast power can be switched and how fast power can get into a coil because of the inductance of the winding. There is a mechanical time constant to reckon with because it takes time and power to move the rotor inertia or a combined rotor and load inertia. If the motor is going to step without errors, the system must be such that the rotor does not overshoot and miss a step.

It would seem that this is a very inefficient and not a very smooth way of moving a load, even though the motor can accurately position a load. A typical torque-speed curve is shown in Fig. 3-50.

In order to accelerate the stepper motor, it is often programmed not to start/stop every step, but the rotor is brought up to a final speed, generally referred to as slew speed, first with slow and then higher step rates. At the slew speed, the motor really runs in synchronism with a fast step rate. To stop at a certain position, the rotor is first slowly decelerated before coming to a standstill. Oscillations might occur before the load settles down in that position. To operate under such condition, these motors

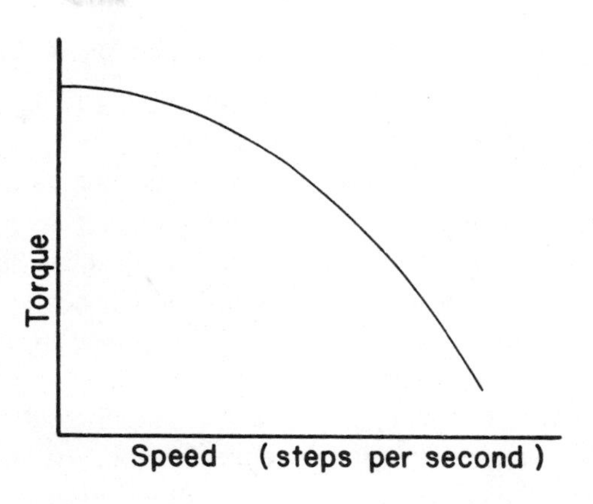

Fig. 3-50. Typical torque-speed curve for a stepper motor start/stop without error.

generally use an encoder to sense the shaft position and permit closed loop operation. The controlled acceleration and controlled deceleration of a stepper motor is commonly known as *ramping*. A sensor also might be mounted on the shaft to indicate the zero or initial position of the shaft. This arrangement permits the rotor to return to its original position or *return to zero position*. The closed loop system used in ramping and slewing stepper motors are similar to the systems described in chapter 6 for BLDC motors. Slewing makes the motor run smoother and more efficient. The effects of winding inductance, resistance, motor inertia, and electronic switching are pivotal in the operation of stepper motors, because these factors sharply limit the use of these motors. The above factors are discussed in some detail in chapter 5 in reference to BLDC motors but are equally applicable to steppers.

One important aspect of stepper motors is their holding torque. If in Figs. 3-48 and 3-49, the currents were turned off in all three sets of coils, there would be nothing to hold the rotor in position. If a set of coils remains energized after the rotor reaches its respective position, then the holding torque will be a function of the current passing through the winding. A permanent magnet is often added to the rotor to create a holding torque without the necessity of a continuous current in the winding. The disadvantage is that the holding torque created by the permanent magnet is an added load when turning the motor, this load makes its operation less efficient. Finally, as the lineup of the teeth is caused by magnetic forces only, which is not a positive stop, there is a possibility that the lineup is not exact, and a position error might occur. Where very close position tolerances are required attention must be paid to this particular aspect. The stepper motor speed also is limited by the limitations of the controller in much the same way as the performance of the BLDC motor is determined by its electronic system, which is discussed in chapters 5 and 6.

3.5.4. Summary of Stepper-Motor Limitations

The stepper motor is particularly useful in digital position systems. To this end, a given number of pulses are sent to a controller, and the motor will move the corresponding number of steps. For the motor to work properly, the moment of inertia of the load and total friction must not exceed the capability of the motor. The step rate is also limited by the design of the controller and motor. Before a stepper motor comes to a stop, some oscillations will occur before the load settles down. Stepper motors are limited in speed by high-speed slew rates beyond which the system can loose synchronism.

For many applications, the inherent cogging results in unacceptable performance. Development of stepper motor systems is continuing, and improved performance levels are continuously being reported.

4

AC and DC Speed Control

The previous chapters have acquainted you with the basics of dc and ac motor principles. The following chapters will discuss speed and torque control methods.

4.1. AC MOTOR SPEED CONTROL

Various methods have evolved for controlling the speed of small ac motors. Where precise speed regulation is not important and where output torque is low, the voltage applied to the motor can often be varied by a small amount. The result will be a change in slip speed, particularly in an induction motor. Obviously the speed will be unaffected in a synchronous type; the torque will suffer. To overcome the above problems, somewhat more sophisticated methods have evolved.

4.2. VARIABLE-FREQUENCY DRIVES

This type of speed control functions on the basis of changing the frequency of the ac voltage supplied to the motor. Speed control through frequency was first accomplished by driving an alternator with a variable speed dc motor; the alternator then drove the ac motor connected to the mechanical load. The electrical efficiency was quite low, but it worked and was used for many years until the advent of reliable electronic power components.

Now the ac frequency changer is normally implemented using SCR or power transistor techniques. In fractional horsepower synchronous motors, such as may be used in gyro, laser scanning, and similar low-power applications, the electronic drive shown in Fig. 4-1. is often used.

In this method, a clock frequency that can be fixed or variable is supplied to a logic circuit A. Typically the logic consists of cascade flip flops arranged to provide a quadrature square wave output at a_1 and b_1. These two signals are fed to drivers B, which are saturated switches (in some designs they might be linear amplifiers). The drivers raise both voltage and current to levels suitable for the motor. The motor is thus driven with 90 degree phase displaced voltage, and the speed will be dependent on the input frequency. If a wide speed range is required, the dc input voltage to the drives must vary to track the frequency to overcome motor losses and to maintain torque. The voltage must be proportional to frequency.

Depending on the particular motor design used, some trouble might be experienced in starting at higher frequencies. It is often necessary to start at a lower frequency and ramp up the frequency and voltage once the motor starts.

The use of square wave drive wave shapes will result in a poor form factor and can cause excessive heating in the motor. For this reason, the drivers at B in Fig. 4-1 are often linear amplifiers, and the input signal is sinusoidal. A unity form factor results and is the most efficient from the heating viewpoint. The synchronous motor is normally a low-efficiency device and, where high efficiency electrical to mechanical energy conversion is needed, does not offer many advantages.

In general, the ac motor is difficult to control because of the complex nature of speed and torque generation within the motor itself. Induction motors are next to impossible to control over wide ranges of speed and torque, except when used in the

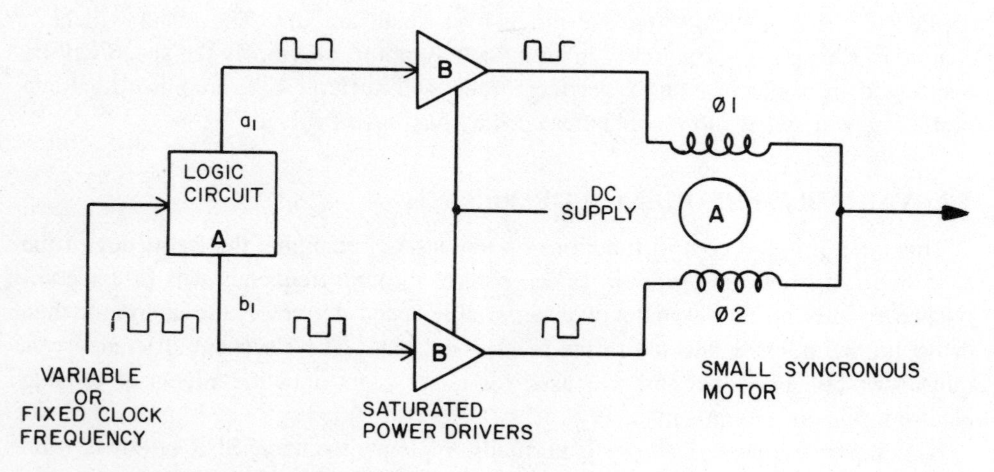

Fig. 4-1. Simple two-phase ac motor drive.

servo mode. In the servo mode, the motor is equipped with two windings similar to Fig. 4-1. However, the electrical phase, frequency, or both are varied in one winding while the other winding is fed constant ac voltage. As a consequence, direction and speed can be controlled over a fair range, but torque is low. This is similar to the Amplidyne system used in pen type recorders and plotters prior to the advent of efficient dc servos. In most fractional and integral horsepower applications, the designer is usually advised to avoid ac motors because of the cost and complexity involved. In almost all cases, the brush-type, permanent-magnet dc motor can do the job, but the problem of brush noise and wear must be considered. Additionally, EMI must be considered a source of potential trouble in some installations.

4.3. DC MOTOR DRIVES

Speed-control systems for dc motors can be broadly categorized as:

- Thyristor or triac types
- Linear-amplifier types
- *PWM* (Pulse Width Modulated) types

All three methods have advantages and disadvantages that must be sorted out by the user. In some cases, power levels mandate use of one or the other; in other cases, response time, speed accuracy, and even cost will place favor on one method over the other. It is beyond the scope of this book to aid in the decision-making process of the applications person other than to point out salient features of typical drive methods.

From the discussion of the PM (permanent magnet) dc motor in previous chapters, it would seem obvious that to control the speed of a motor, all that is needed is to vary the motor terminal voltage. This is quite true as is shown in Fig. 4-2 (a). Here a rheostat or other suitable variable resistance is inserted in series with the motor. The no-load speed will be proportional to the value of R. The loaded speed will be somewhat different, for as the value of R is increased the ratio of V_R to armature back EMF increases. Ultimately the system becomes constant current and behaves like a torque motor. This is a useful mode of operation in some applications, such as tensioning of film, tape, and similar materials. The drawback is, of course, one of excessive power dissipation in R. If the motor draws 1 A at 10 V and the supply voltage is 20 V, then $20 - 10 \times 1 = 10$ W dissipation in R. This would be unsuitable except for the smallest of toy motors. Figure 4-2 (b) implements the same scheme using an NPN transistor. Here the same dissipation problem occurs. The transistor is asked to dissipate the unused voltage term in the form of heat.

However, the transistor configuration is superior to the resistive loss approach because the transistor offers a low output impedance to the motor. Essentially, the constant current mode will be a problem unless the circuit is specifically designed for

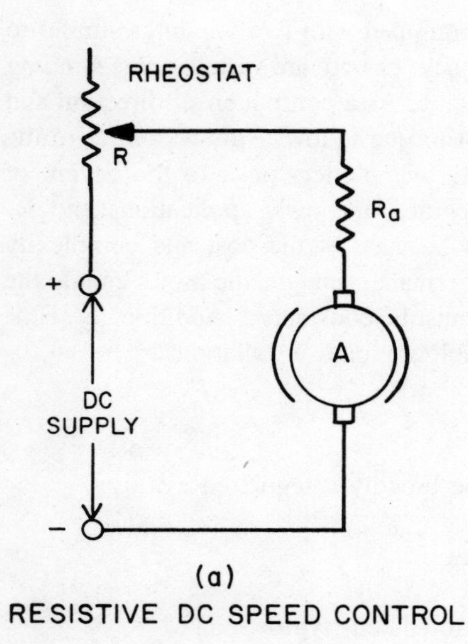

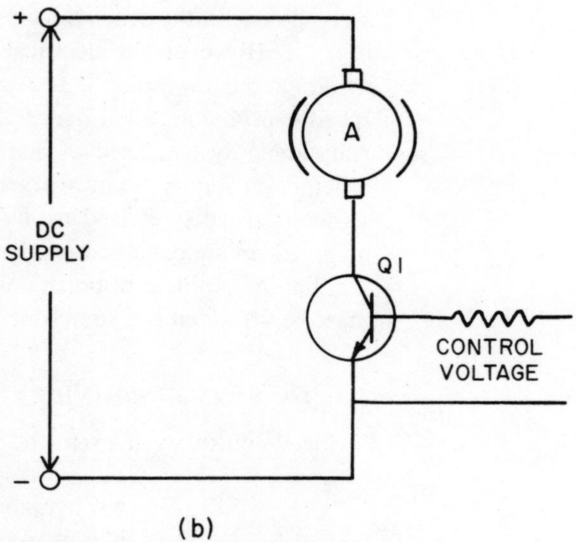

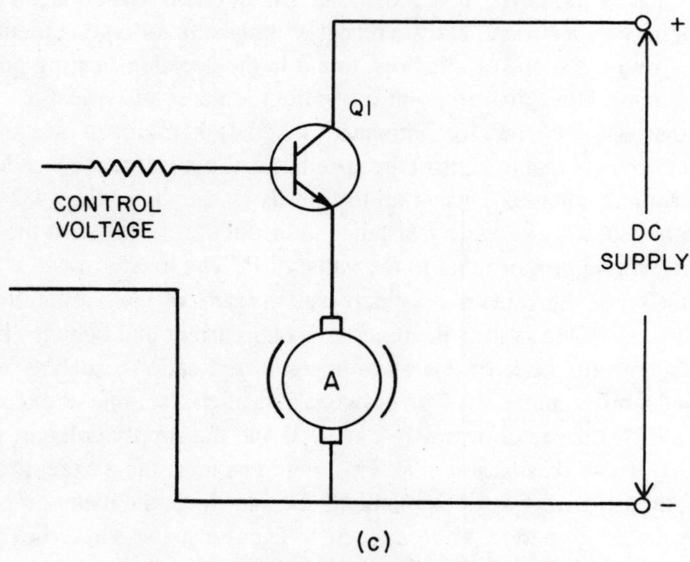

Fig. 4-2. Simple two-phase ac motor drive: (a) resistive dc speed control. (b) transistor speed control, collector load. (c) transistor speed control, emitter follower.

constant-current operation. The circuit shown in Fig. 4-2 (c) uses the transistor in the emitter-follower configuration and offers a lower output impedance than in Fig. 4-2 (b). This circuit is most widely used in the output stages of practical linear motor drive circuits.

4.4. THYRISTOR AND TRIAC DRIVES

The advent of the SCR (thyristor) in the 1950s brought about a major revolution in motor-control technology. The basic technique of phase-controlled rectification using mercury thyratrons or ignitrons had been around since the first decade of the twentieth century. These devices were cumbersome and often unreliable, prone to strange misfirings and other vexing problems. Their use was usually restricted to very large three-phase power conversion applications, such as railway and similar traction systems. Smaller thyratrons made their appearance in the 1930–1940s and were popular for speed control in integral and subintegral horsepower industrial applications.

The SCR made it possible to design small, inexpensive controls for subintegral sizes and eventually in excess of 1000 hp as we now have today. The SCR is a semiconductor gate controlled rectifier. See Fig. 4-3 (a). The SCR will block a positive voltage applied to the anode until a pulse of sufficient voltage and current is applied from gate to cathode. The SCR will then abruptly conduct from anode to cathode. Conduction will continue with zero gate voltage until the voltage is removed

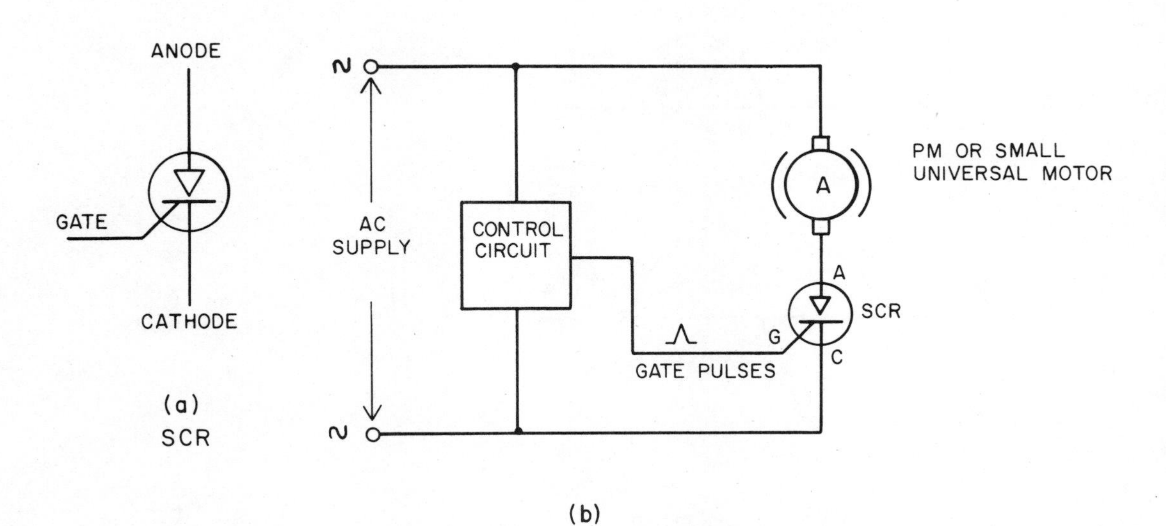

Fig. 4-3. SCR in motor control: (a) SCR device. (b) simple SCR control.

from the anode or the current through the SCR drops below a minimum holding value. The holding value is specified for each type of SCR but is usually in the range of several milliamperes to several hundred milliamperes. If an ac supply is used, the SCR will disconnect (or self commute) on the negative-going cycle of the ac supply as the voltage must swing through zero. In order to control the speed of the motor in Fig. 4-3 (b), the gate pulse to the SCR must be syncronized with the ac supply and applied to the SCR gate at the proper phase point. This is illustrated in Fig. 4-4.

Firing the SCR at points a, b, c will give varying conduction times, thereby controlling the voltage and current seen by the motor. The circuit in Fig. 4-3 (b) is referred to as a half-wave control because rectification and control occur only on the positive half cycle. The form factor is high, owing to the high peak-to-average current wave shape and will often cause excessive heating of the motor. The pulsating dc applied to the motor also causes rough motion at low speeds. The SCR is usually fired by means of very simple unijunction transistor devices or diac diodes using single time constant resistor-capacitor phase shifting to vary the firing angle. Because of the coarse output wave shapes, the best results obtain with motors of large electrical and mechanical time constants. In spite of the drawbacks the half-wave SCR control is very attractive in high-speed, low-power applications.

Improved performance is possible using three-phase SCR configurations because the resultant output is closer to dc. Yet another improvement can be obtained by using

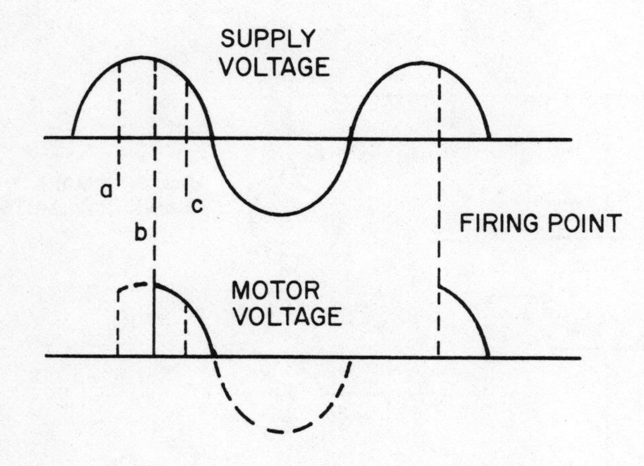

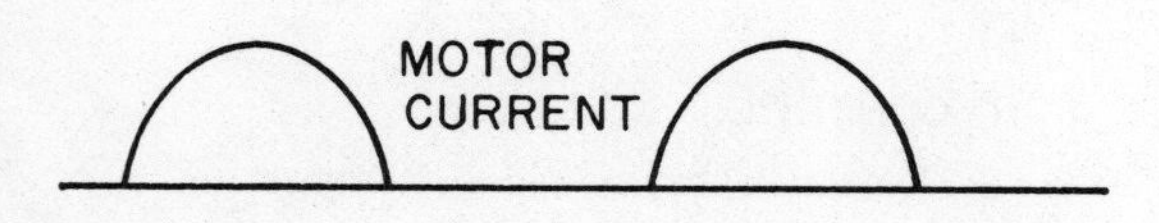

Fig. 4-4. SCR wave forms.

a full-wave SCR drive. Two SCRs can be connected in parallel in anticonduction and fired on alternate halves of the ac sine wave, producing output on positive and negative crests. Alternately, a center-tapped supply can be used (again two SCRs are required). In three-phase designs, six SCRs are often used. Most three-phase applications are integral horsepower on up to several hundred horsepower because of the savings in copper and improved conversion efficiency of three-phase circuits.

The triac is a device similar to the SCR but with the ability to fire on each half cycle. It can be viewed as two antiparallel SCRs. This device provides a simple means of implementing full-wave control systems. Most small household appliances such as blenders, mixers, fans, etc., as well as hand drills and other tools use triacs in conjunction with series-wound universal motors. Performance is usually quite good, with high starting torque. Controllers are available up to three or four horsepower using triacs along with back-EMF speed control loops. The speed regulation can be quite impressive, but low-speed operation can be poor. Often the speed range is restricted to values of less than 10 to 1 depending on the application. Almost all of the commercially available SCR and triac controllers used today in industrial applications are designed for use with PM field motors. This is a hard combination to beat when low cost and moderate performance are the criteria.

Reversible thyristor drives can be made that perform quite well. In this case the H-bridge configuration can be used as in Fig. 4-5. In operation, SCR A and SCR D

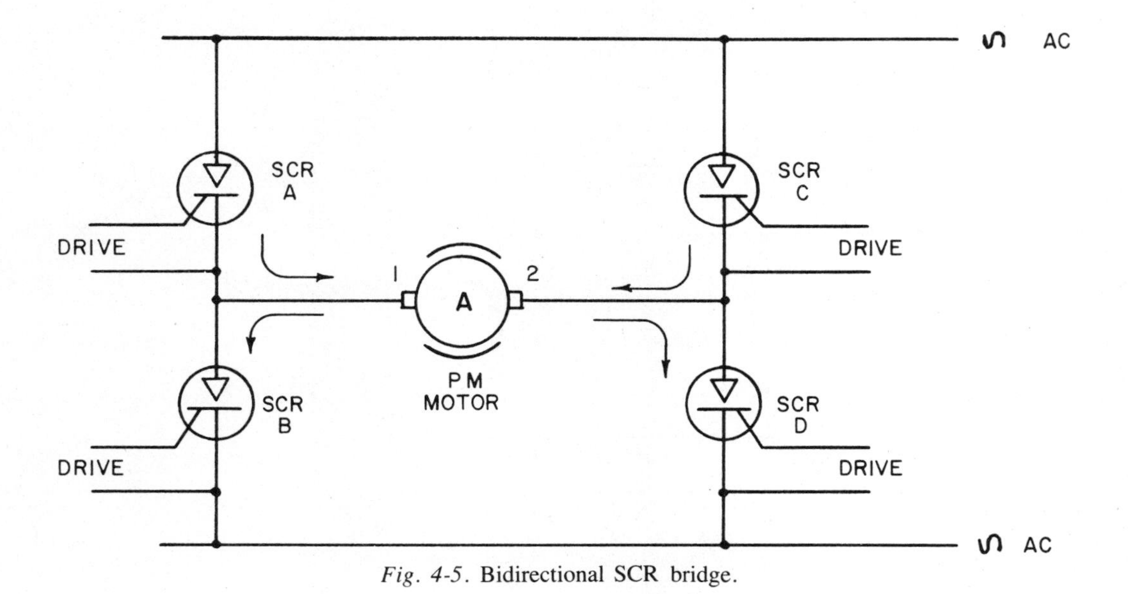

Fig. 4-5. Bidirectional SCR bridge.

are caused to fire, passing current through the motor from terminals 1 to 2. Firing SCR C and D causes flow through 2 to 1 reversing the motor direction. The control circuits must be designed to prevent A and B or C and D from simultaneously firing, which would place conducting devices directly across the power rails. It is possible to design regenerative drives having up to 80 percent or greater regenerative capability. However, the peak currents and phasing problems that result from such four-quadrant operation require complex and costly control circuits. Often you will find four-quadrant drives on hoist and elevator drives where overhauling by the load is part of normal operation. (See section 4-5 for more information on four-quadrant operation). In these cases, the motor is forced to reverse direction or *plugged* during part of a cycle and so acts like dynamic braking. Plugging requires a carefully designed current-limiting system to keep armature current within a safe value.

Simple control loops can be implemented around thyristor drives to provide speed and current regulation. Fig. 4-6 depicts a simple concept using a triac. In operation, the speed or velocity term is supplied by tachometer G. Current is monitored by resistor R_S. A current transformer can also be used. The control circuit compares the velocity and current values to fixed reference voltages and fires the triac to provide an equilibrium state. In most practical cases, the speed-control accuracy is rather good, with control accuracies of better than 1 percent. The current regulation is also good

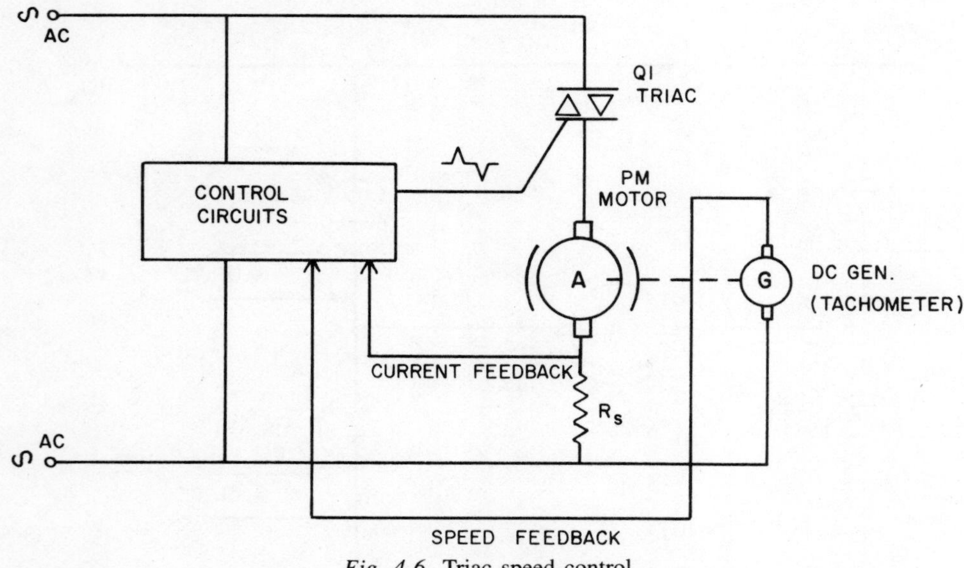

Fig. 4-6. Triac speed control.

and in some cases might be a multipoint current limit with a higher value for starting and a lower set point for run. There is a problem with this type of drive: because the current is pulsing at the power line frequency, the peak current values can get to be very high and cause heating and ultimately motor burn out. Current feedback must be augmented by time-out circuits or time-lag fusing to prevent temperature rise problems under locked rotor or other fault conditions.

Before leaving thyristor systems, the following points might be of interest to application engineers:

- The poor form factor output of SCR and triac drives require that the motor be oversized or SCR RATED. Oversizing often increases size and bulk.
- It is usually best to have a long mechanical and electrical time constant when using thyristor drives. The motor drive voltage is pulsing at the line frequency, and any additional smoothing provided by the motor and load is a benefit.
- The response time of the closed loop system will be slow as there is no control between line cycles. At 60 Hz, it amounts to 8.33 milliseconds for a full-wave, single-phase drive. The best response time is usually on the order of several hertz. These drives are not intended for use in servo applications requiring fast response.
- The voltage drop across a typical SCR or triac can reach 2 to 3 volts in some cases. Therefore, the power dissipation must be observed, and proper cooling attended to. This might require forced air in some installations.
- Electromagnetic interference is often a problem with this type of drive. The problem is caused by the fast DV/DT occurring during switching cycles, especially at low firing angles. A knowledge of the effects of this EMI on associated systems is often a necessity.
- When in doubt about the above, always consult the motor and drive manufacturer. Failure to do so can often result in poor performance, which may be wrongly blamed on the motor, control, or both.

4.5. LINEAR AMPLIFIER DRIVES

In most servo controls, bidirectional control is required. Figure 4-9 depicts a plot of motion (ω) versus torque. Four quadrants are shown, one for each possible mode of operation of an ideal servo system. Note that operation is possible in both clockwise and counterclockwise directions. Furthermore, this system could accept negative torque, such as that provided when reversing direction into an inertial load or when the system undergoes external torque disturbances. Four-quadrant operation can place very high load demands upon both amplifier and motor because of the large peak currents that will flow during reversal conditions.

Referring to Fig. 4-2 (b), notice the transistor controlling the voltage to the motor. Using two transistors as in Fig. 4-7 allows bidirectional motor control. By causing Q1 to conduct, the motor is driven with a positive voltage. Q2 in conduction will drive the motor with a negative voltage. Note that this configuration requires a split power supply. In small dc servo applications, this is not a problem because below a few hundred watts, the power supply cost is not severe. The linear, bipolar approach is very popular in servo applications requiring fast response and smooth control. Because of the electronic nature of the linear system, a great many synthesized motor types can be realized. It is possible to create synchronous, torque, stepper, and wide speed range motor configurations through proper choice of feedback and control techniques. Using microprocessor control, the possibilities are unlimited.

Major drawbacks to the linear approach are high power dissipation and very finite limits on operating voltage. Because the transistors must operate in their linear range, the power dissipated in the transistor will be:

$$V_s - V_m \times I_m = PW$$

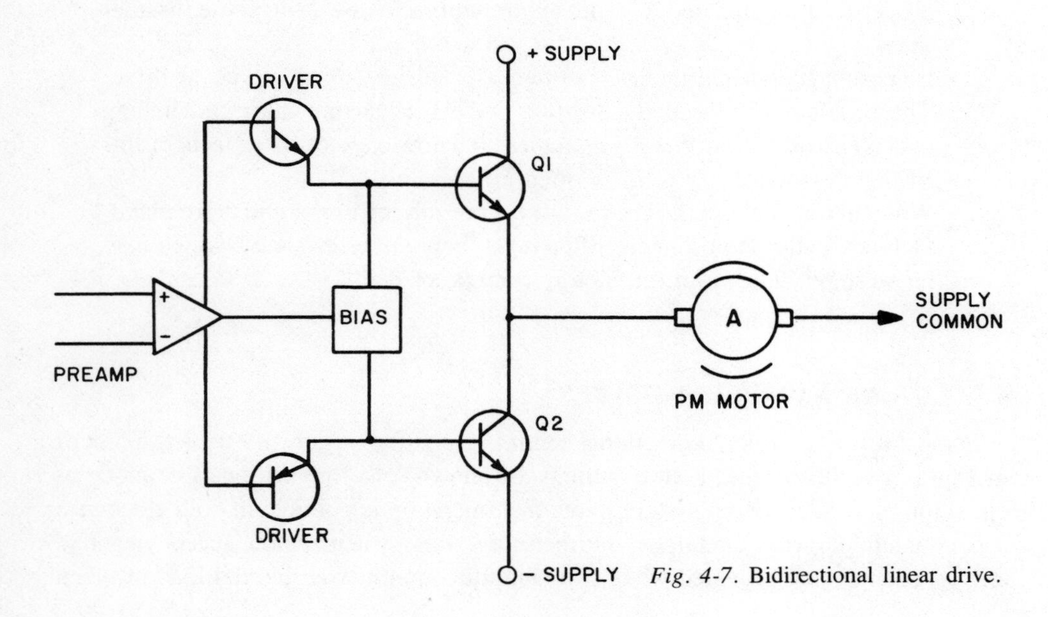

Fig. 4-7. Bidirectional linear drive.

where: V_s = Supply voltage
V_m = Motor voltage
I_m = Motor current
PW = Power dissipation

The maximum power dissipation of a transistor operating in linear mode is determined by the *SOA* (safe operating area) of the particular device. The SOA is characterized for all power devices. A typical curve is illustrated in Fig. 4-8.

The solid line represents the maximum current the device can handle under steady-state conditions. The designer must stay inside this area under all conditions of operation. The various broken lines represent safe transient operating levels. Note that under pulse operation, a higher current and voltage limit exists. The SOA is to be derated for elevated-temperature operation, so take care to consider maximum junction temperature of the device, and derate SOA accordingly.

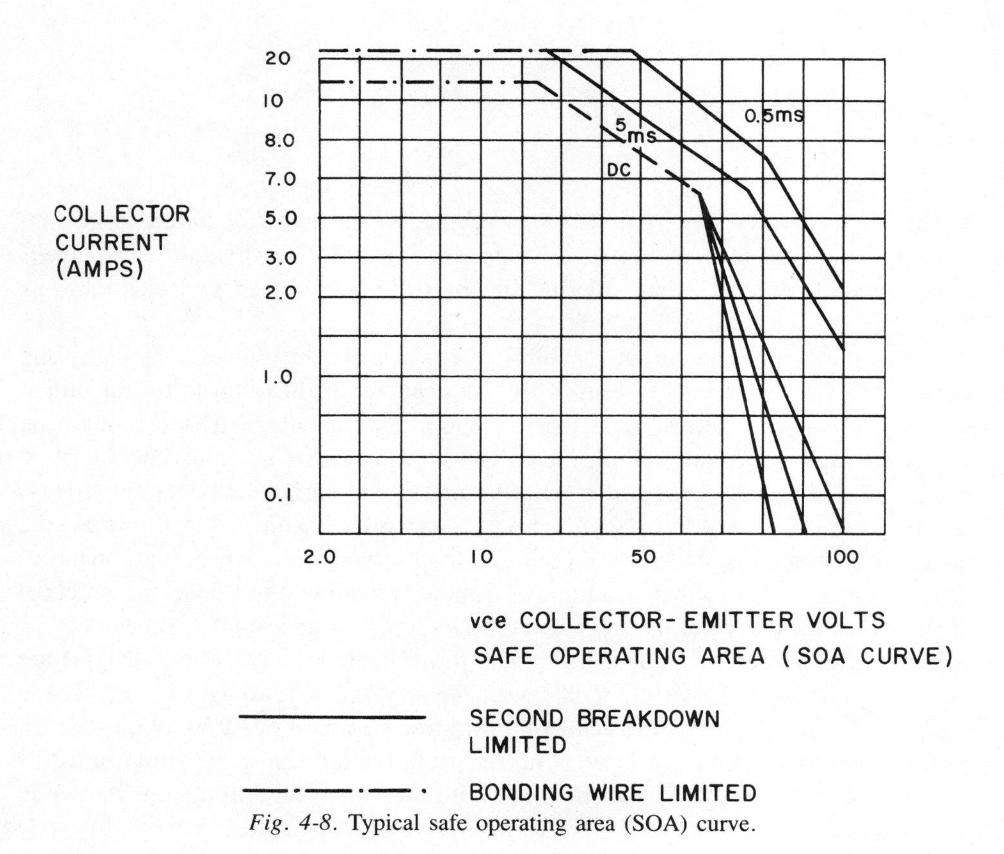

Fig. 4-8. Typical safe operating area (SOA) curve.

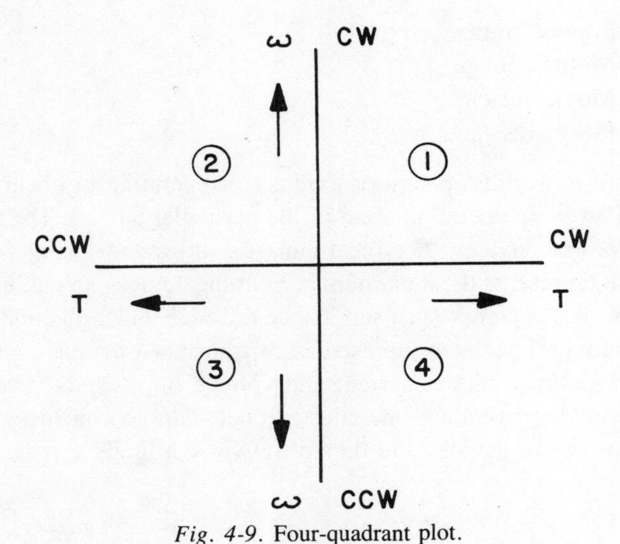

Fig. 4-9. Four-quadrant plot.

The SOA curve clearly imposes limits beyond which transistor failure is guaranteed to occur. The only way to increase output current capability at high V_{ce} voltage is to use parallel devices so that under maximum load current, each device assumes its portion of the load and is in a safe SOA region.

Linear amplifiers with output capabilities in excess of 300 W tend to be bulky and expensive. This drawback is caused by the need for paralleling sufficient output devices to ensure a safe SOA at the maximum current output. The maximum dc supply voltage is similarly limited by SOA considerations to values of 50–85 V maximum. Even under the constraints of limited power output the linear amplifier is still the practical choice for many high-performance applications. Most notably, the linear configuration is always used in closed-loop servo service where high linearity, fast response, and true four-quadrant operation is required. In almost all practical applications, the choice of motor is dictated by a few very important parameters. Cost is always paramount but rotor inertia, peak power handling capability, and size are first and foremost when designing fast response servos. Such fast systems are used in rapid-positioning applications such as laser-mirror positioning, film motion control, and computer tape drives. These applications often require response time of a few milliseconds at high angular velocity along with short stop and settling time thrown in for good measure. The motor then must behave as an incremental device. Obviously the basic parameter is then a low-inertia motor having high peak-power capability. It is not unusual to find average to peak current ratios exceeding 20:1. In a typical intermittent film pulldown system, the motor current is 2 A during slew or search mode and runs to peaks of 70 A during pull-down cycles. The pull-down cycles occur 24 times per second and require a 90-degree shaft motion over a maximum time of 14 milliseconds. Clearly, a very low rotor inertia is needed in a motor capable of handling very high peak currents. The armature inductance then becomes important because the electrical time constant is a determining factor in response time. Practical designs will use the basket wound cup rotor or the disc rotor type. Both types of PM motor can yield similar results but the disc rotor usually has lower K_T.

Applications such as tensioning require that the motor be capable of operating at near stall conditions or at best operate up to a few hundred revolutions per minute with heavy load. This does not usually require a low-inertia motor but rather one that can handle large armature currents under continuous duty. The standard-wound rotor PM motor is most suitable in this application because of high K_T, good cooling capability, and reasonable cost. The requirement often exists in some applications for a skewed rotor design to reduce torque cogging. The number of commutator bars has an effect on cogging in torque applications. Generally the more bars the better. A practical approach of 20 bars minimum with 40 preferred is common in most high-performance positioning systems.

Constant-velocity applications such as tape capstan drives require low values of cogging, run out, and resonance, which would be interpreted by the data system as wow and flutter or in digital systems as time displacement error. In such stringent uses the rotor balance, brush system design and rotor winding method are but a few important parameters to consider. In most practical cases, a four-pole magnet structure is preferred over a two-pole design. A skewed rotor with a 40-bar commutator set in a four-pole stator is the designer's first choice in a high-performance, constant-speed application. Good-quality bearings and brushes are a must.

4.6. FEEDBACK DEVICES; BASIC APPLICATIONS

In the discussion of motor control, the most common element other than the motor is a source of velocity or position information. Speed/position control cannot be implemented without some means of feedback to convey information on the quantity being controlled.

The following are common methods for deriving this data:

- Direct-current tachometer generators
- Motor back EMF
- Alternating-current pickups, often reluctance or induction generators

- Hall-effect pickups
- Optical shaft encoders
- Syncro devices; resolvers, LVDTs (linear variable differential transmitters), etc.
- Potentiometric devices

A dc generator is often put into the motor package as an intergal component. In some cases, the rotor is fitted with a second commutator, and the tachometer winding placed in with the drive windings. This latter approach must be viewed with caution because there can be mutual coupling effects that will adversely affect system stability. These effects are present with wide-bandwidth, high-gain loops. The dc tachometer generator quality should always be consistent with the final results desired. A high-performance constant or wide-range speed servo will only perform within the stability range allowed by the tachometer. Thus a precision tachometer having less than 1 percent output ripple is needed along with linearity better than 0.5 percent if instability problems are to be avoided. Of course, if the system gain or bandwidth is reduced, or if some lag due to electrically filtering the tachometer output can be tolerated, then a lesser device can be used. In many cases, an ac tachometer with suitable rectification and filtering works out quite well for velocity control. The dc tachometer allows true velocity feedback, permitting four-quadrant operation over a very wide speed range, although speed regulation accuracy is limited. The limitation is due to analog drift, which forces reliable speed regulation to not better than 0.5 percent over nominal temperature ranges. Figure 4-10 depicts the classic linear feedback configuration for velocity feedback.

The circuit in Fig. 4-10 shows a PM motor A connected to the output of a bipolar power amplifier. The feedback source is dc tachometer generator G. The polarity of the generator is such that for any value of dc tachometer voltage output, the polarity is opposite that of input voltage e_{in}. Summing junction n will be the algebraic sum of both control and feedback voltages. The drive amplifier preamplifier amplifies this error voltage, and the power section PA supplies the amplified voltage to the motor at the required current level. With zero e_{in}, the motor will be stationary assuming no dc offset voltages. If the motor shaft is externally forced in one direction, the tachometer voltage (being of opposite polarity,) will be amplified and fed to the motor, thereby resisting the external force. The result is very high shaft rotational stiffness that is a function of the loop gain. As e_{in} is increased from zero either positive or negative, the motor will turn in the appropriate direction and velocity as dictated by the amplifier gain modified by the amount of feedback applied by G. This simple loop is capable of excellent performance but, being dc in nature, will suffer from analog drift degradation. Assume that with e_{in} of 0.1 V, the output at A is 20 V. This yields a closed loop gain of 20/0.1 or 200. If the dc tachometer output is also 0.1 V for the same speed

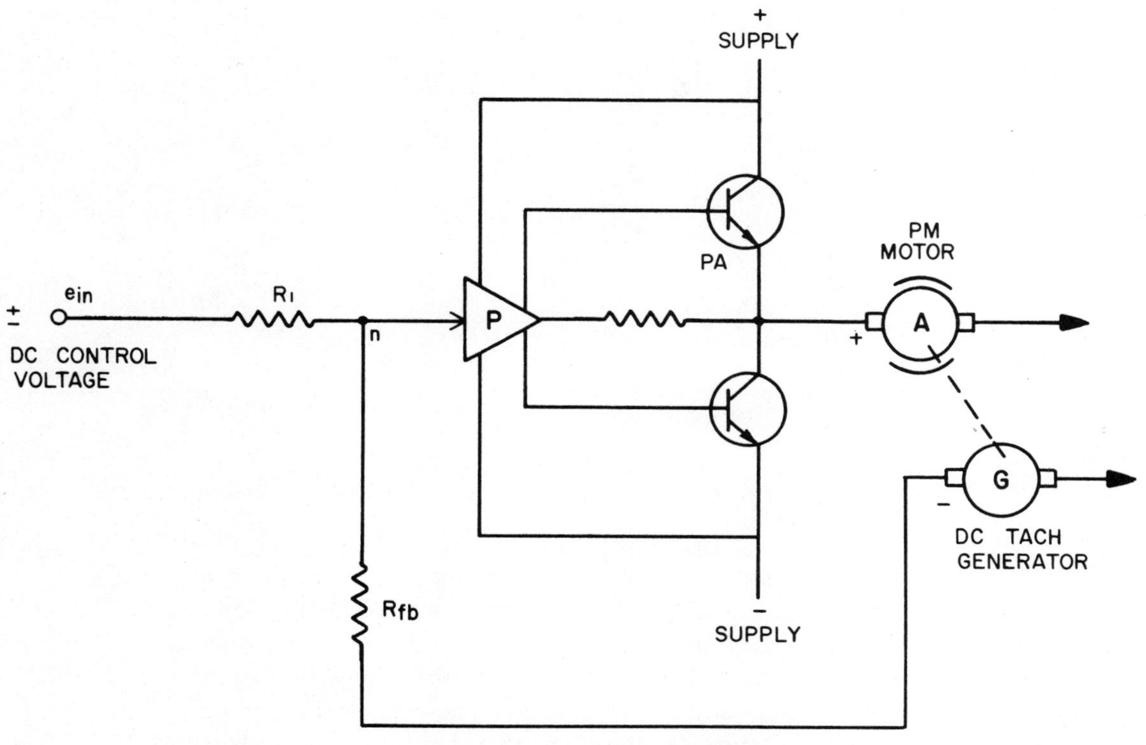

Fig. 4-10. dc velocity loop.

and a 2 mV change in tachometer output occurs, an error of 2/100 × 100 or 2 percent will be evident in the speed. Motor and amplifier parameter variations will not be evident because they are attenuated by the value of the feedback factor. Tachometer errors, however, are directly evident as speed change.

The use of motor back EMF to regulate speed can also be used in lieu of a dc tachometer generator. In this case, the motor voltage is sensed, amplified, and fed back to the amplifier. This method is not very practical in bidirectional servos but can sometimes be used in small, unidirectional, low-cost applications such as cassette tape players and other consumer products.

Where very accurate speed control is required and dc loops are not capable of being compensated for temperature, etc., the ac digital loop is preferred. The source of velocity error feedback can be an ac generator, optical shaft encoder, or Hall-effect magnetic sensor. Figure 4-11 shows each of the above in simple terms. In Fig. 4-11 (a), the simplest pickup is a ferrous gear in proximity to pickup P. Voltage induced in the pickup coil will have amplitude and frequency as a function of the angular velocity of the gear teeth. Electronic processing of the signal will result in either an analog

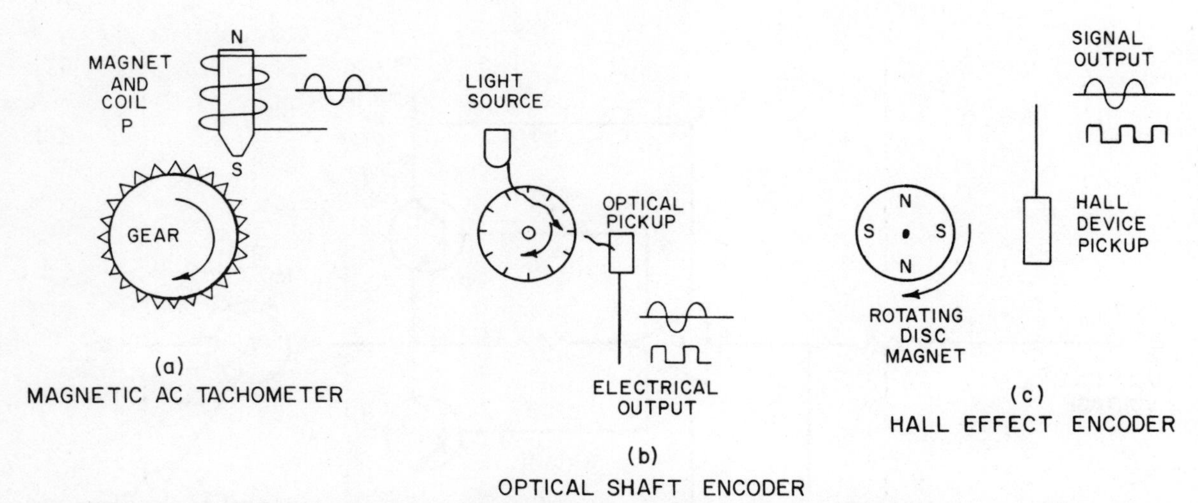

Fig. 4-11. dc velocity loop components: (a) magnetic ac tachometer. (b) optical shaft encoder. (c) Hall effect encoder.

dc voltage or a series of pulses at the rotational rate. Conversion to dc is rarely used as the signal carries no directional data. A two-phase generator could be used to derive direction data, but the complex electronics needed tend to outweigh any advantages gained. The optical encoded in Fig. 4-11 (b) is the most widely used system at the present time. The light source is usually a *LED* (light emitting diode) and the pickup is of the photo-transistor type, but some designs use photo-voltaic devices. Two basic types exist: incremental and absolute. The incremental type is illustrated in Fig. 4-11 (b), and the output is one pulse per slot per revolution. An absolute encoder will output a series of binary numbers per increment of revolution. Absolute encoders are often used for angular displacement readout and are rarely used for velocity control. The incremental encoder can be configured with up to 5000 pulses per revolution and can be equipped with dual sensors to provide two-phase output for simultaneous direction and velocity sensing. The chopper disc can be of almost any material that transmits light, but glass with photographically deposited opaque lines or metal discs with laser or other high-accuracy milled slots are common today. Plastic is available for low-cost applications.

A variation of the incremental encoder is shown in Fig. 4-11 (c) where a rotating magnet in conjuction with a Hall effect device provides a pulse output. The Hall device is basically a low-resolution approach since physical limitations as to the number of magnet poles restrict the pulses per revolution to low values, usually not greater than several hundred. The three methods just described have one important characteristic in common. They are discrete-cycle output devices. The accuracy of the output cycles are a function of the manufacturing process and can, within reason, be made as accurate as needed within cost limitations.

Another method of feedback is the *syncro* or *resolver,* which is an externally excited ac generator. The output can be processed to provide both velocity and position data. Modern resolvers, either rotational or linear types, are capable of excellent accuracy but require fairly complex phase demodulation circuitry to provide usable output. At present their use is mostly relegated to positional feedback on machine tools, but lately some are finding their way onto motors as velocity transducers. Originally, these devices were restricted to low speed operation, but new materials and electronics are raising speed limits to ever higher values.

Potentiometers are often used in simple positioning servos where maximum rotation of only a few revolutions is required. A typical applications is remote control of valves, gates, and other mechanical functions often requiring high torque and slow speed. Figure 4-12 depicts the typical dc positioner.

The feedback element G in Fig. 4-2 is a potentiometer mechanically connected to the motor shaft, or output shaft if a gearbox is used between the motor and output. The output of device G is therefore a dc voltage of sign and magnitude as a function of shaft position. The input signal from e_{in} is similar. The two signals e_{in} and e_{fb} are summed as in Fig. 4-10. The motor will turn in such direction as to reach a zero equilibrium output from amplifier P. As long as there are no major time lags in the system, the servo will null in order to match e_{in} and e_{fb}. It is obvious that errors in the way of dc drift will affect the final null points. When control of the velocity between set points is required, it is customary to use a dc tachometer in a second loop to stabilize motor response characteristics.

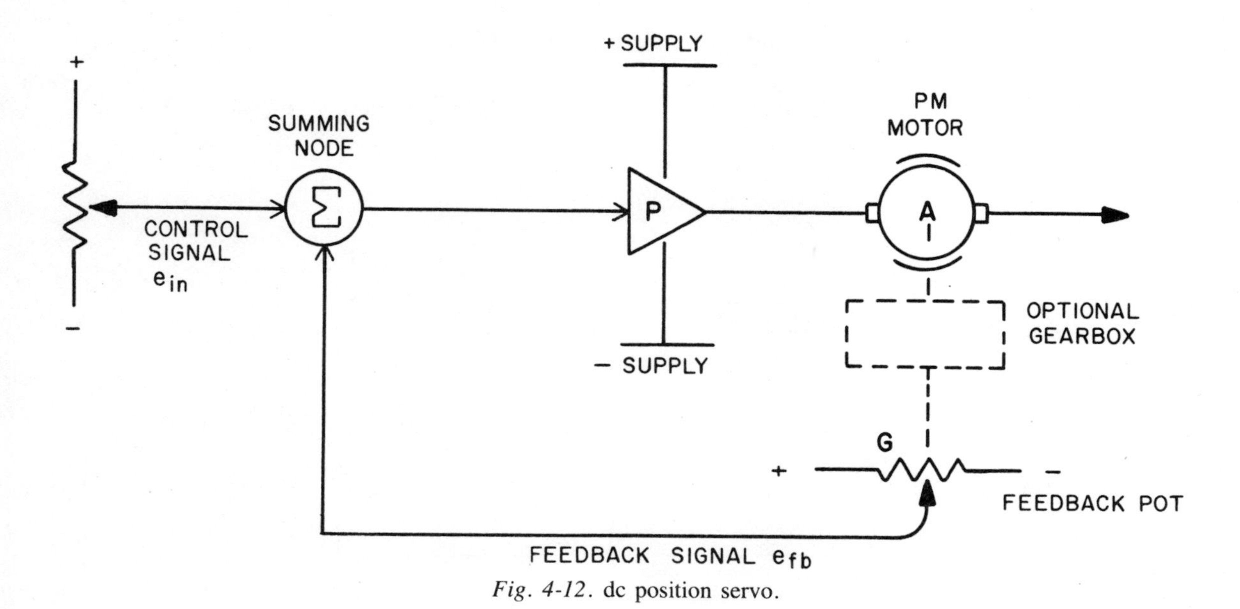

Fig. 4-12. dc position servo.

4.7. BASIC PHASE-LOCKED LOOPS

The digital shaft encoder also can be used in similar applications. However, because the output of a digital feedback element consists of discreet pulses, some signal processing is required. In most systems, binary counters are used to convert the pulse-by-pulse output to a numeric value that can be processed. In simple constant-velocity loops, the method in Fig. 4-13 is often used. Here the feedback loop is somewhat more complex because both analog and quasi-digital techniques are used to create a *PLL* (phase-locked loop). In Fig. 4-13 the input clock f_{in} is compared to the encoder output f_{vel} in phase comparator ωC. The comparator output consists of pulses of fixed amplitude but having a duty cycle as a function of the instantaneous phase error between the two signals. These pulses are integrated in low-pass filter ($\int$), resulting in a variable dc voltage to power amplifier P. It can be seen that for specific loop conditions, the motor speed is directly proportional to f_{in}. In practice, however, the configuration of Fig. 4-13 suffers from some very severe limitations. The simple phase detector might be a flip flop or one of the integrated circuit devices currently available. The output must be integrated to provide a dc level for the amplifier, and some residual clock is always present. If the integral is such that the time lag is long, then difficulty in locking will occur. Furthermore, the system can slip phase or lock onto harmonics of the input clock. This can occur because the typical switched-phase detector is forced to operate in both the time and frequency domains. Thus if you were to analyze the comparator in each domain, only one stability point can occur, this point being where the simultaneous combination of both frequency and phase of the two inputs are right for lockup. When used in systems where the input frequency is fixed and the mechanical load swings are small, the simple PLL of Fig. 4-13 can be used quite effectively.

An improved digital PLL is depicted in Fig. 4-14. In this configuration, a binary

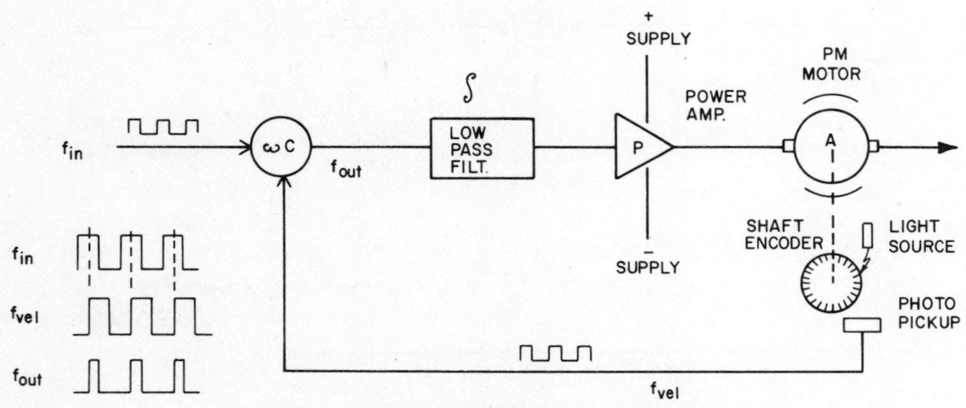

Fig. 4-13. Elemental PLL (phase-lock loop).

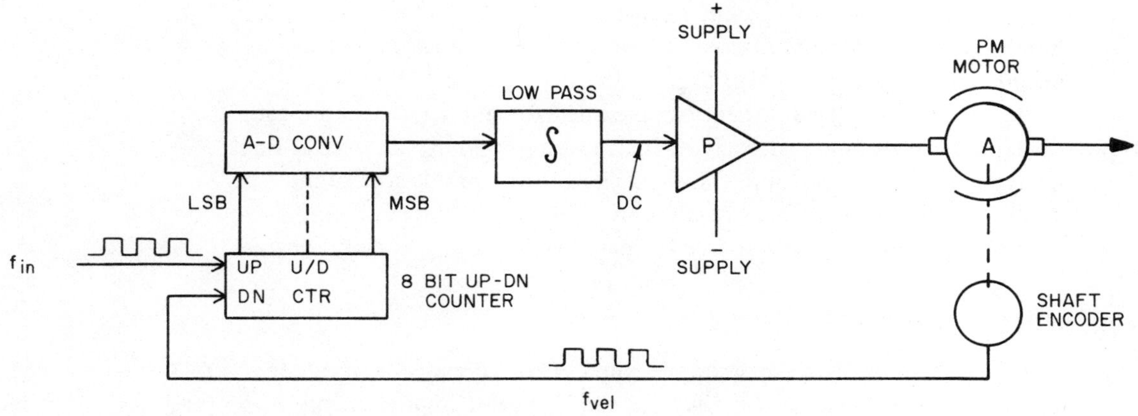

Fig. 4-14. Digital-integrator PLL.

counter and *DA* (digital-to-analog) converter is used as a digital integrator to provide the analog derivative of the two clock values f_{in} and f_{vel}. The output of the A-D is the integrated difference between the reference signal f_{in} and the feedback signal f_{vel}. At final-lock equilibrium, the LSB of the counter will alternate bits. The higher bits will be in a stable value, which produces the approximate dc value for correct speed. Thus the LSB could be viewed as containing the phase difference and the higher order bits the frequency values. Such PLLs are very easy to implement and offer excellent speed stability.

To implement positioning features, the counter can be made longer (more bits) so that a discrete number for finite shaft angles is generated. A great many variations on the circuit of Fig. 4-14 are possible. A complete analysis of PLL design is beyond the scope of this book, and you are invited to review the excellent treatment offered in general literature.

When considering the use of PLL techniques for speed and position control the following points should be remembered:

- The motor inertia and mechanical load combine to produce a pole in the loop equation. Always consider the effects of load change on the stability of the overall system. Furthermore, mechanical resonances in both motor and load will have a far-reaching effect upon system performance.
- The overall performance of a closed-loop system will depend upon the quality of the feedback element. If precise control of speed is required with low instantaneous speed error, then accurate, high-quality encoders must be used. Attention must be paid to disc runout, mounting stability, and other mundane factors. Good mechanical practices are a must.
- It is often advantageous to mount feedback devices on the rear of a motor

unit. This will protect the pickup device from possible output shaft deflection effects. This is particularly the case with high-resolution optical-shaft encoder using small air gaps.

- Wide speed range PLLs present complex design parameters that are often difficult to determine. Extensive bench testing is advised before a final design is realized. Each application has its specific problems that must be sorted out before satisfactory results can be obtained. The motor and drive manufacturers are the best source for data leading to a successful design.

4.8. NONLINEAR PWM DRIVES

The previous sections of this chapter presented the basic methods of motor control with emphasis on the linear servo drive. In recent years, improvements in power transistor design have made the switch-mode or pulse-width modulated drive an attractive alternative to the linear amplifier. Figure 4-15 illustrates the simplest PWM output stage. This single-transistor speed control is often referred to as a *chopper* type. The basic feature of the chopper is that the transistor Q1 operates in saturated mode. This means that the transistor has only two basic states, either on or off. In the on state, the motor is fed with full supply voltage minus the collector-emitter drop of Q1 (V_{ce}). In most cases, V_{ce} falls in a range of several hundred millivolts to several volts. During the off condition, the motor is fed no voltage because Q1 is not conducting. Transistor Q1 is driven from a signal source of fixed frequency having a variable duty cycle. Thus, speed control is obtained by varying the on and off times of the transistor. The motor constants of inductance and inertia are relied upon to integrate the resulting current pulses to an average value. The diode CR is needed to keep current flowing in the armature during the off period. This prevents decay of the current, which would result in starting from zero current at each on cycle. The result is improved power transfer at lower average current. The chopper base frequency is chosen to keep the average armature current variation to around 10 percent or so. The actual frequencies found in practice vary from 1 to 50 kHz depending on motor inductance, size, and power level.

The primary advantage of the chopper is power efficiency. In Fig. 4-2 (b) is a linear circuit controlling the speed of the motor. If the following conditions are assumed:

$$\text{Supply voltage} = 50\ \text{V}\ (V_s)$$
$$\text{Armature voltage} = 25\ \text{V}\ (V_a)$$
$$\text{Armature current} = 10\ \text{A}\ (I_a)$$

Then the transistor dissipation in Fig. 4-2 (c) will be $(V_s - V_a) \times I_a = (50 - 25) \times 10$ or 250 W. The transistor dissipation for 50 percent operating *DC* (duty cycle) in the chopper for the same conditions, assuming V_{ce} saturation of 2 V, I_a peak of 20 A, will be I_a peak × V_{ce} or 20 × 2/DC = 40/2 = 20 W. Obviously a power savings of 230 W results in the chopper configuration. In the above example, switching losses were omitted, but in properly designed PWM systems the transistor losses resulting from turn-on and turn-off times will usually represent less than 10 percent of the total power dissipation. A notable feature of the PWM configuration is more freedom from failure caused by SOA limits. Because the transistor switches through the linear region very rapidly, the peak SOA values can be used to advantage. The voltage limitations of the linear amplifier are essentially bypassed in PWM systems because transistors capable of switching several hundred volts at tens of amperes are now available. Advances in power *FET*s (field-effect transistors) and similar devices has further raised the power-level capability of PWMs.

The simple circuit of Fig. 4-15 is a single-quadrant drive capable of controlling the

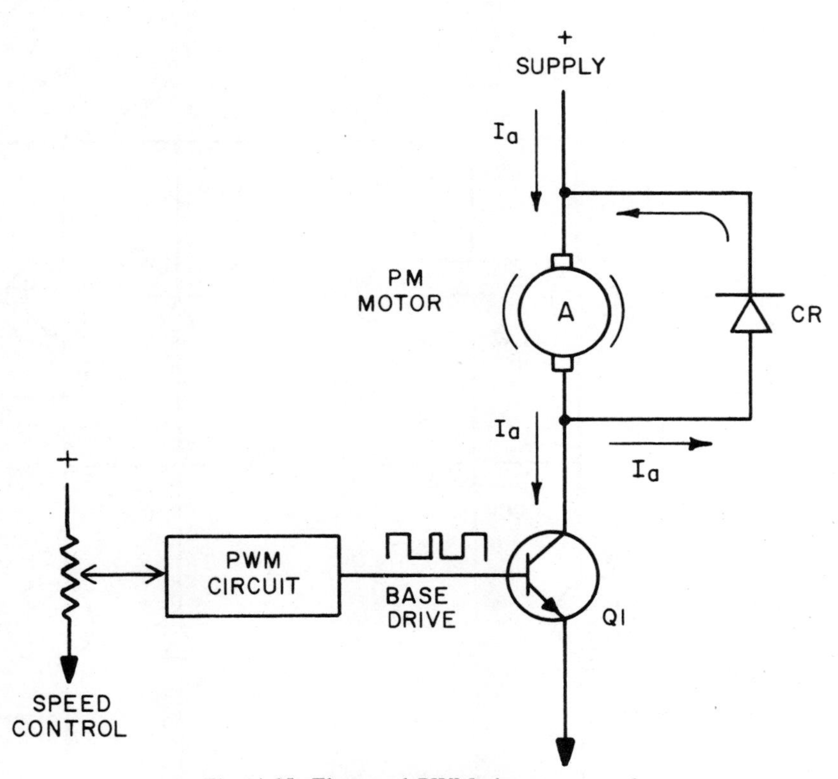

Fig. 4-15. Elemental PWM chopper control.

motor in one direction only. Of course, the motor terminals could be reversed for direction change. This is often done in practice to save cost, especially in small consumer applications. In order to achieve bidirectional or four-quadrant control, the circuit of Fig. 4-16 is commonly used. This circuit is often referred to as a full bridge or H configuration. Operation is quite simple: Q1 and Q4 conduct to provide clockwise flow, Q2 and Q3 conduct for counterclockwise rotation. The control circuitry is not so simple because the transistors must be turned on and off in proper sequence, taking into account the transistor switching time, etc. The diodes CR1–CR4 serve the purpose of commutating armature current during transistor switching. The control circuits must prevent simultaneous conduction between Q1, Q3 and Q2, and Q4, which would otherwise destroy the transistors. A typical control circuit block diagram is shown in Fig. 4-17. A triangle generator A running at frequency F_o produces a bidirectional triangle wave having equal amplitudes each side of zero volts. The triangle wave is input to amplifier B along with the error voltage from amplifier C. The error voltage will cause a baseline shift of the triangle wave if the error voltage is greater than zero. The shifted triangle is sent to voltage comparators D and D′. The

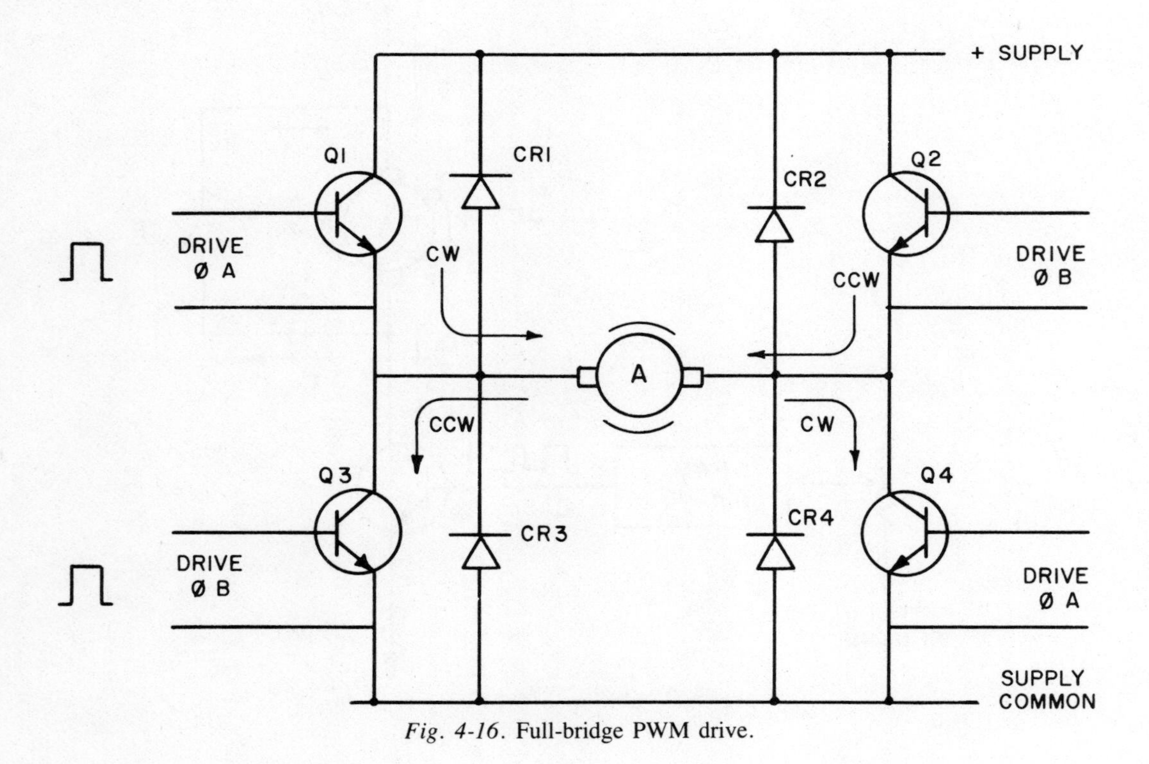

Fig. 4-16. Full-bridge PWM drive.

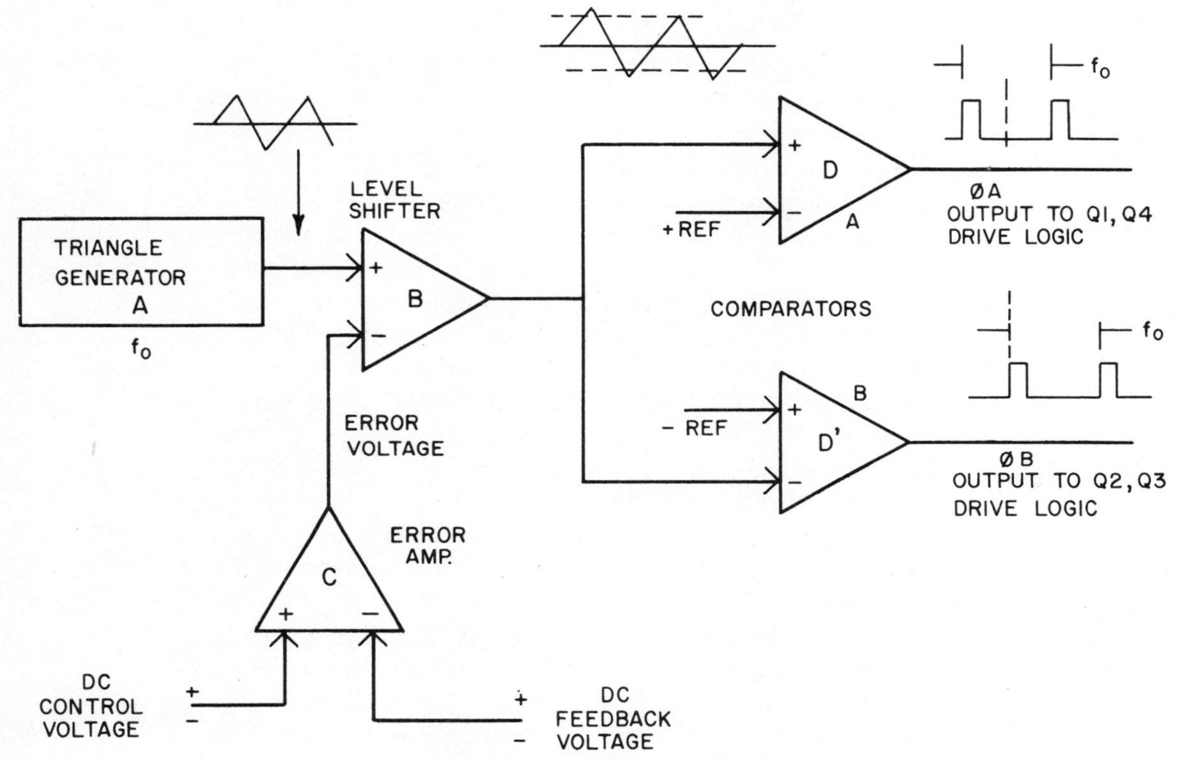

Fig. 4-17. Elemental PWM control circuit.

two comparators are dc biased with positive and negative levels respectively. With no level shift to the triangle, the comparators will output narrow pulses each half cycle of ramp frequency F_o. Under zero signal conditions, the two outputs, phase A and B, are used to drive transistors Q1–Q4 through suitable drive logic and level shifters. The motor therefore receives current pulses of equal magnitude but of opposite sign. Because the pulses cancel in the motor, no motion occurs. Now if the input to the shifter B increases from zero, the pulse width in one phase will approach zero, and the other will increase in value, causing motor rotation in the desired direction. In this manner, bidirectional operation is achieved. The system is symmetrical and is capable of excellent linearity when proper feedback methods are used. Of course, the actual circuit design is a bit more complex than the above, but the elements are similar. There are H-bridge PWM drives available with power outputs to several kilowatts, and larger designs are now available in the tens of kilowatts. The basic PWM bridge is also used as the driver in contemporary brushless motor drives as is explained later in this book.

4.9. ELEMENTAL CURRENT LIMITING

The previous sections of this chapter discussed methods of effecting speed control. An equally important motor variable to control is current, because it is the current which produces output torque. Current limiting in linear amplifier drives is usually straightforward and is needed to: (a) limit armature current to a safe value under fault or operating extremes, (b) to modify the motor operation profile as in the case of torquing applications, or (c) to limit transistor current to safe operating values. Fig. 4-18 illustrates the usual method of limiting current in a small system application. Note that this configuration consists of two feedback loops. One serves to implement the velocity control, and the other provides current feedback. The voltage dropped across R_s, as a function of armature current, is fed back to the amplifier input in such manner as to be the algebraic difference of the e_{in} control signal. Thus an increase in current causes a reduction in amplifier input drive voltage. By selecting a proper value for R_s and correct signal processing at node a, the current profile can be modified to necessary values. It is possible to use time constants and two or three step levels at node a to provide high start current tapering down to a lower run value or provide for a higher value at stall than run or many other profiles. Commercially available linear drives are usually strappable for various current limiting features.

Current limiting in PWM amplifiers is not as straightforward as in the linear case. The current profiles are often pulse in nature and do not lend themselves to simple processing. Also the motor terminals are not ground referenced as in Fig. 4-18. The typical circuit shown in Fig. 4-19 permits current sensing at the points shown. Note that current monitored at R_{sa} and R_{sb} is similar to that used in the linear system of Fig. 4-18. Alternately, a current transformer in position 3 could be used to monitor peak

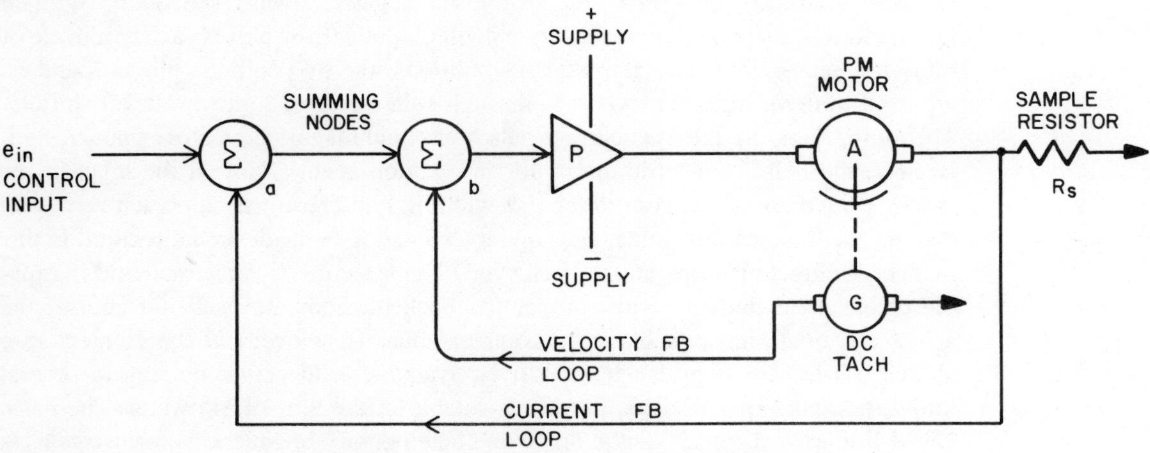

Fig. 4-18. Linear-control current limiting.

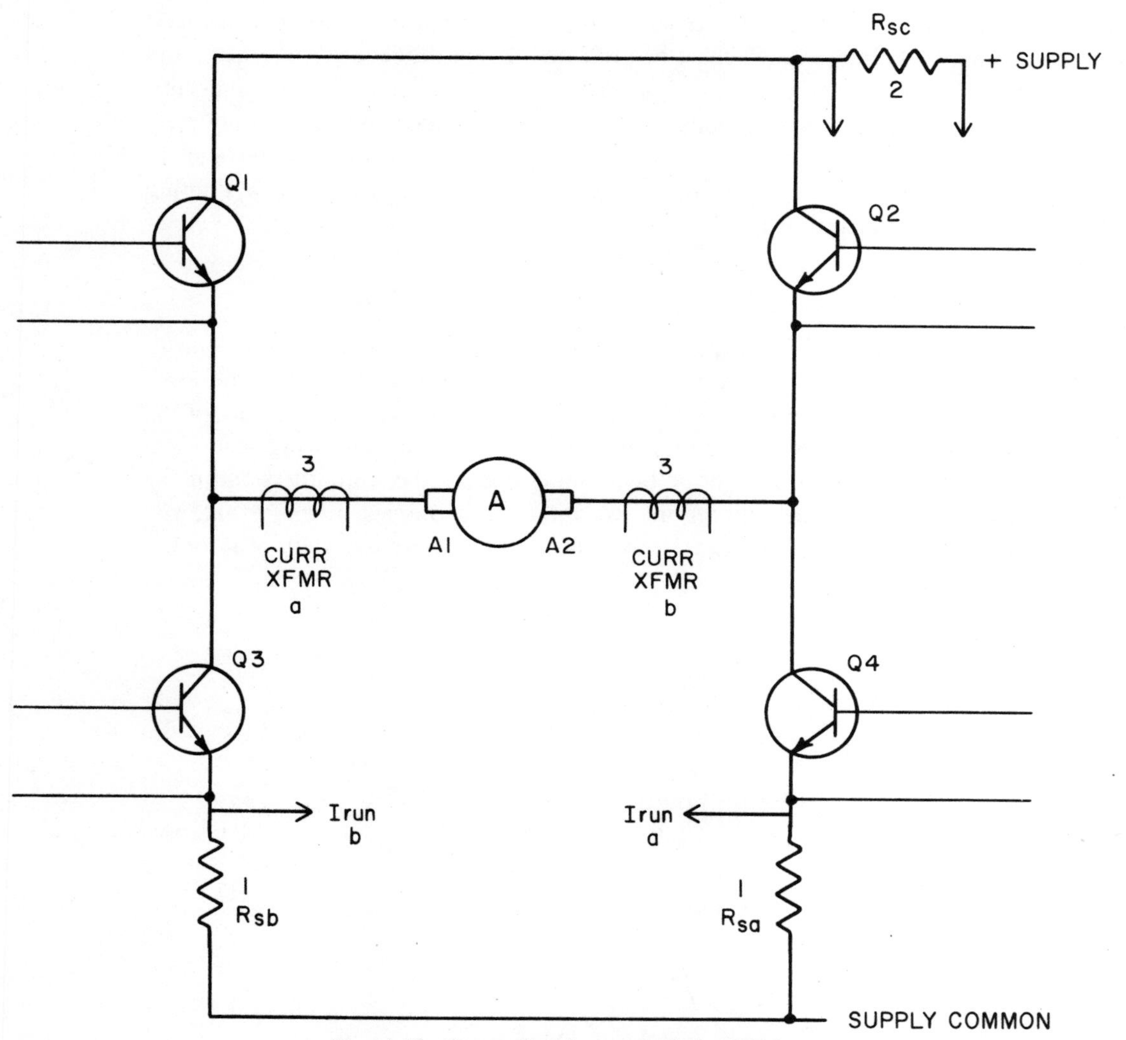

Fig. 4-19. Current-limiting methods in PWM.

switched values. Resistor R_{sc} monitors total system current and is often used to fire an electronic circuit breaker to cut off supply voltage should armature terminals A1 or A2 be accidently grounded. In some designs, all three methods are employed, each providing its own special function within the systems.

With the exception of very small drive systems having limited power capability, the need for some form of current limiting is mandatory. In large systems, operator safety is a primary consideration with the need for protecting semiconductors the next priority. Finally the motor itself must be protected from excessive current that could damage the armature windings or, in fast servo applications, cause stator demagnetization. The designer or applications person should consider current limiting with great care. Semiconductors usually try to protect any line fuse that may be installed to prevent excessive current. It is best to protect the semiconductors with active limiting and thus extend their useful lives.

4.10. SUMMARY

The aim of this chapter is to acquaint you with the basic elements of motor control. No attempt is made to analyze the theory of drive systems, particularly not the PLL. Sufficient material exists to help the aspiring designers with their task. Many of the basic circuit configurations described in this chapter are in the following section on brushless motors. Thus, you might be better able to grasp the similarities and make sense out of the differences between the two motor technologies. In any event, you are invited to pursue the study of drive concepts by means of the wealth of information now in print.

5

Brushless Motors

5.1. INTRODUCTION

For almost as long as dc motors have been around, there has been a desire to replace them with a motor having similar performance characteristics, but without brushes and commutators. Brushes require replacement, commutator surfaces wear and have to be turned, arcing cannot be permitted in certain hazardous locations, and the system imposes severe speed limitations on the motor. With development of electronic switching devices, it seemed natural that these might replace the mechanical switching components that are part of the conventional dc motor. The motor was built with a multipole, permanent-magnet rotor, a wound field stator, electronic switching circuits, and an absolute sensing system that duplicated the torque-speed and torque-current characteristics of a conventional dc permanent-magnet motor. This motor was called, naturally, a brushless dc motor. With closer analysis, you will see that it was a dc motor in name only.

Certain design considerations remain the same in both motors. Winding inductance is to be kept at a minimum for better commutation. For the conventional dc motor, the solution is an increased number of armature coils to improve commutation. This solution is not a very practical one in an electronic commutator because of cost considerations. An alternative, the moving-coil version of the dc motor, has an equivalent with the toothless version of the brushless motor for low inductance, low electrical time constant, and minimum magnetic drag. Although the moving coil also drastically reduces armature inertia, this is not the case with the toothless BLDC motor. However, the smoothness of operation is greatly improved.

While commutator and brushes make up only a small fraction of the cost of a conventional dc motor, the cost of an electronic package for a brushless motor might rival or even exceed the cost of the motor components. Although, the electronic commutator might at first seem less cost effective, it does vastly increase the versatility of the motor.

The brushless dc motor was originally thought of primarily for servo applications and robotics, but it appears that the bulk of the applications will be elsewhere. Brushless dc motor systems start to make their way into air conditioning equipment (now using induction motors), pumps, laser and disc drives (synchronous and stepper motors), and high-speed applications such as centrifuges and spindle drives (now universal and induction motors). Brushless dc motors also are starting to appear in slow-speed, direct-drive applications where gear backlash is unacceptable and in any applications that require speed control. These varied applications show the versatility of the system. It not only replaces dc motor drives, but ac motor drives as well, because it frees the user from the tyranny of line frequency or costly power supplies.

Brushless dc motors are generally supplied in one of three ways by the manufacturer:

- As a complete motor and electronics package
- As motor only, including sensing systems. This option is very frequently made available for customers who design their own drive system
- Motor only without electronic drive or sensing system. This option is mostly supplied to manufacturers of electronic control systems

Start thinking of drive systems with a different set of criteria than you are accustomed to with present-day conventional motors.

When costs are considered, it is the cost of the system that counts. A low-cost motor might require a very much more expensive drive system and power supply. The same applies to performance. The efficiency of the system counts, not those of individual components.

Often these motors are preferred over conventional dc motors because of their long life and low maintenance requirements. A word of warning on this point: although motor life will depend on the bearing life, there has been a tendency to make motors smaller and let them run at higher temperatures. So-called high-temperature greases are available, but they still do not last very long at the temperatures present with motors using H and F insulation. The high temperature shortens bearing life considerably. Because of the requirement of an absolute sensor, the replacement of a bearing might require a resetting of the sensor.

5.2. BRUSHLESS DC MOTOR SYSTEM

The brushless dc motor is much like the polyphase, permanent-magnet synchronous motor, but without the self-starting arrangements mentioned in chapter 3. It also differs from the conventional permanent-magnet synchronous motor in that the current into the windings is electronically switched in a manner similar to the switching in a stepper motor. This switching is often called commutation and serves a function similar to the commutation in a conventional dc motor by means of a commutator and brushes.

The brushless dc motor system consists of the following:

5.2.1. The Motor. The motor consists of a rotor on which permanent magnets are mounted, always arranged in pole pairs. These magnets supply the field flux.

The stator contains the stator winding and is designed in such a way that if the current reaches the right coil or coils at the right time, interaction with the field flux occurs and torque is produced. In addition there are the usual bearings, end caps, a housing, etc.

5.2.2 The Sensing System. In order for the coils to be switched in the correct sequence and at the correct time, the location of the rotor field magnets must be known. Locating magnets requires an absolute sensing system that can be magnetic and consist of Hall sensors, or it can be optical and use encoders or a variety of other arrangements. This function can be very critical in the operation of this motor.

5.2.3. The Electronic Commutator and Control. The function of the electronic commutator is to switch the right currents in the right stator coils at the right time and in the right sequence by taking the information supplied by the sensor and processing it with preprogrammed commands to make the motor perform in the way it was intended to perform.

The electronic control consists primarily of power devices such as Darlington amplifiers or FETS that can handle the motor currents and the control circuits. The control circuits handle very small currents and switch the power transistors. Microprocessors are rapidly becoming a part of these electronic control circuit.

5.3. MODE OF OPERATION

For a cross-sectional view of a typical brushless dc motor see Fig. 5-1. Suppose a dc voltage is applied to a three-phase, wye-connected stator and the currents are switched with mechanical switches in a certain mechanical sequence as indicated in Fig. 5-2 (a to f) and tabulated in Table 5-1. The resulting flux vectors are shown in Fig. 5-3, which also illustrates how this particular switching sequence causes a counterclockwise field rotation. If the switching sequence were reversed, the field rotation would reverse and be clockwise. Figure 5-2 (a to f) also shows that two phases are energized at all times and that the currents actually reverse in each phase of the

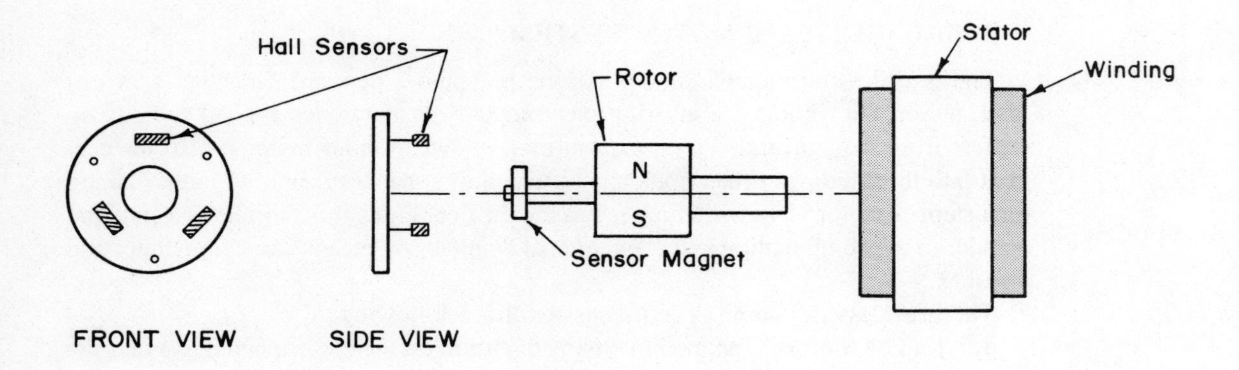

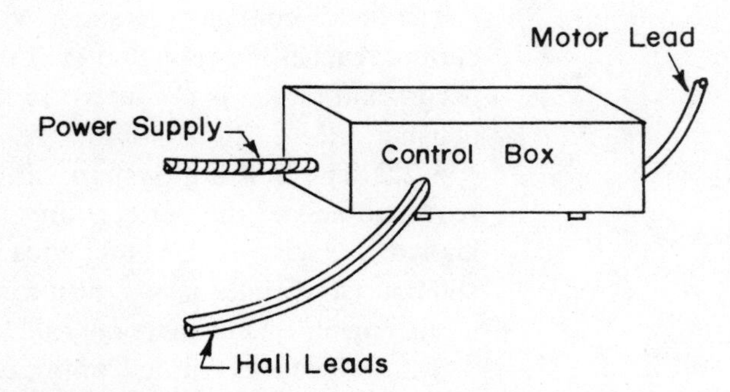

Fig. 5-1. A typical BLDC motor system.

Table 5-1. Three-Phase, Full-Wave BLDC Motor Switch Positions and Current.

Switch Position			Direction of Currents in Windings	Figure
r	s	t		
+	−	o	a to b	5-2 (a)
o	−	+	c to b	5-2 (b)
−	o	+	c to a	5-2 (c)
−	+	o	b to a	5-2 (d)
o	+	−	b to c	5-2 (e)
+	o	−	a to c	5-2 (f)

+ is switch connected to positive side of power supply
− is switch connected to negative side of power supply
o is switch in open position

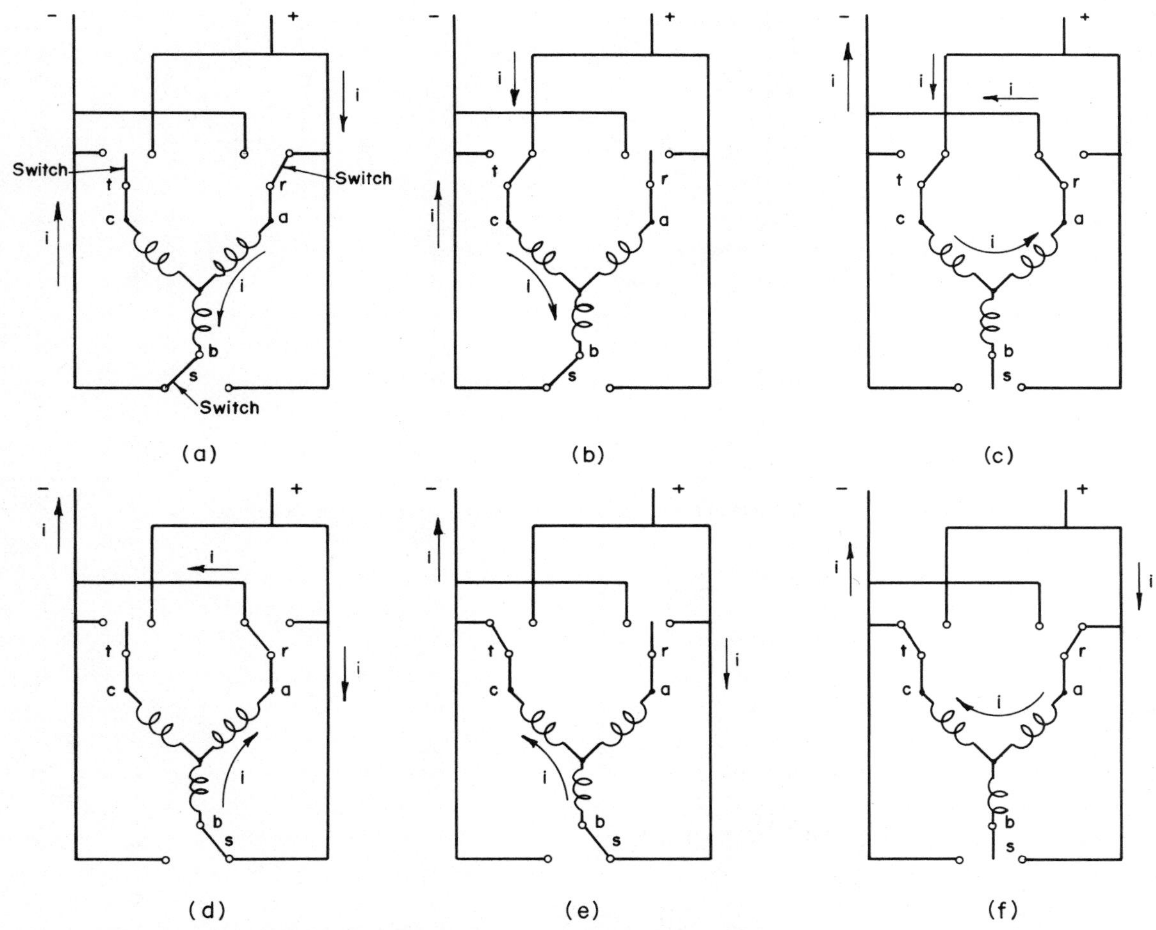

Fig. 5-2. Six switch positions showing the mode of operation of a three-phase, full-wave, wye-connected BLDC motor.

winding during one complete sequence cycle. This characteristic is more typical of an ac motor than a dc motor.

In practice, the switching is done electronically and the switching timing is done by an absolute position sensor, which accurately senses shaft position and tells the electronics when to switch. When the shaft rotates, a back EMF is generated in the winding of Fig. 5-3. Depending on the magnetization and shape of the magnets and the winding distribution, e_b can have a variety of shapes. A typical one is a sine wave as shown in Fig. 5-4. Also shown are the periods during which conduction occurs. This mode of operation is called a full-wave operation because conduction occurs during both the positive half as well as the negative half of the back EMF wave. With

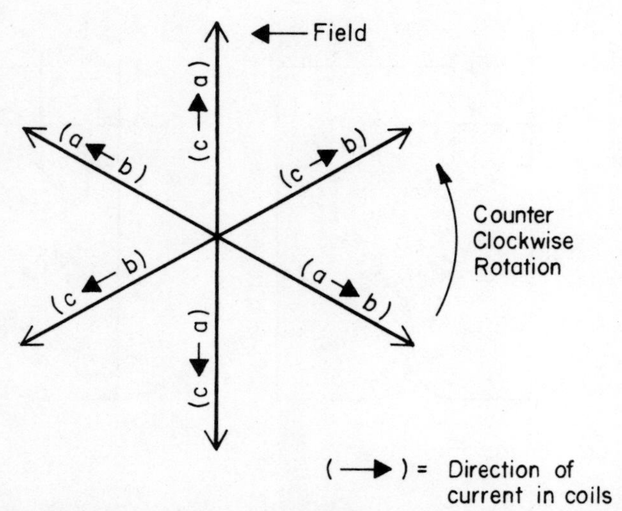

Fig. 5-3. Resultant flux vectors from currents in Fig. 5-1 three-phase, fullwave, BLDC motor.

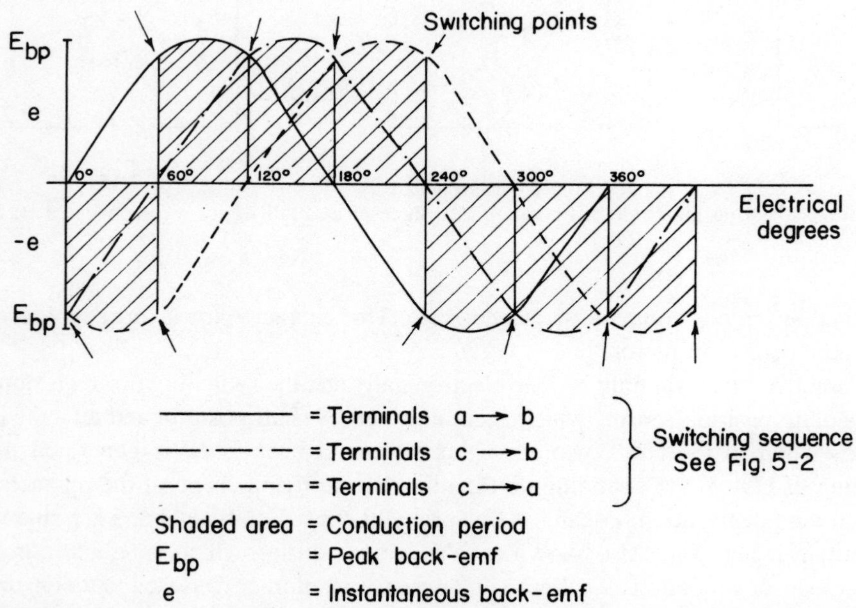

Fig. 5-4. Instantaneous e_b values and conduction periods for a three-phase, full-wave BLDC motor.

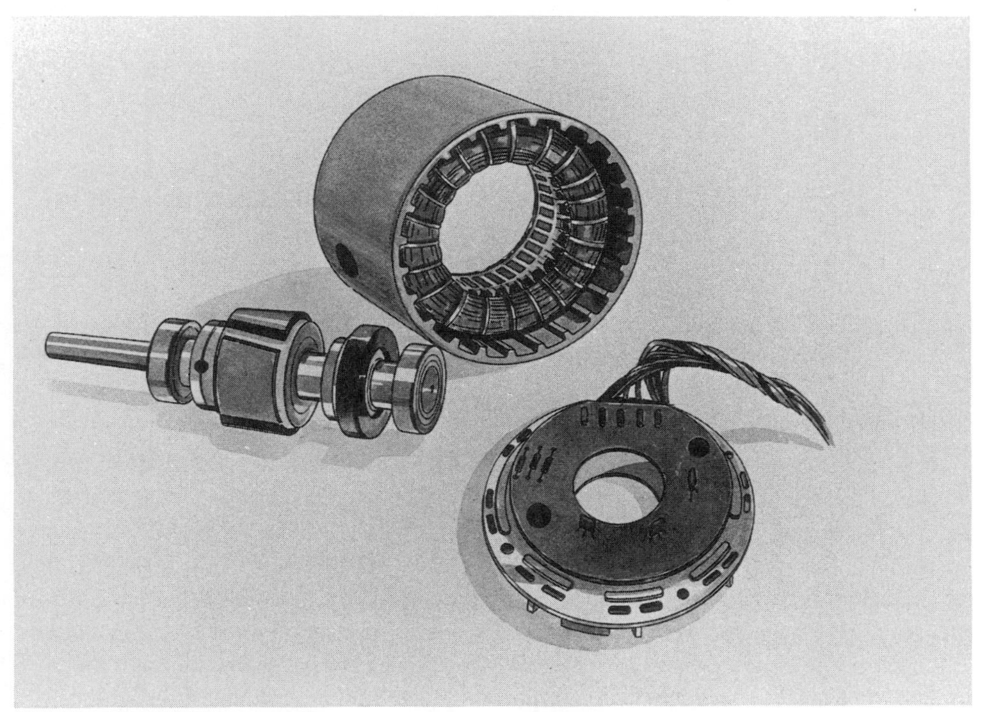

Fig. 5-5. Principal BLDC motor components. (Courtesy of LEESON ELECTRIC, Motronics Div., Little Falls, NY)

the supply voltage E_{DC} larger than e_b, a current will be flowing during the conduction period, which is largely in phase with e_b. This approach meets the basis requirements for generating torque.

The mode of operation of the brushless dc motor is the interaction of a permanent-magnet rotor and a rotating field, which is created by electromagnets consisting of coils connected in a certain winding pattern that are being switched in a certain sequence at a time determined by the rotor position. This of course can be accomplished in many different ways. A BLDC motor showing the wound stator, a permanent magnet rotor, Hall sensors and sensor magnet is shown in Fig. 5-5.

5.4. WINDING AND SWITCHING PATTERNS

5.4.1. Three-Phase, Full-Wave BLDC Motor Operation

The previous section analyzes a BLDC motor with a three-phase winding, wye-connection and full-wave switching sequence. This operating mode is very common. As is pointed out in section 5.3, only two phases are energized at any one time.

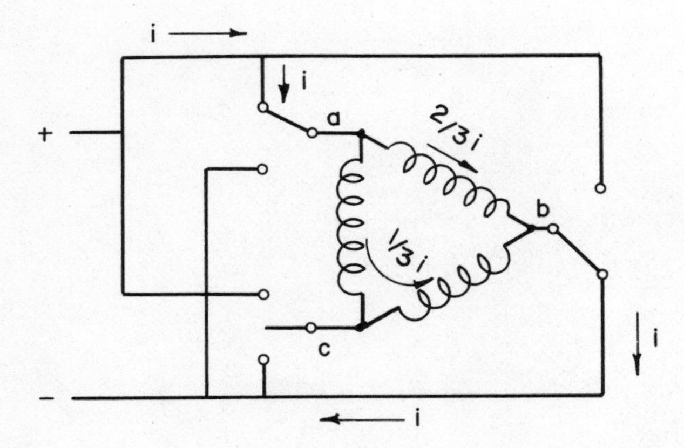

Fig. 5-6. Sketch showing one switch position for a three-phase, full-wave, delta-connected BLDC motor.

An alternative is a three-phase, delta connection in which the switching sequence would be identical to that of a wye connection, however, the current distribution differs. As can be seen in Fig. 5-6, two thirds of the line current goes through one phase, a–b in this particular instance, and one third of the line current flows through the other two phases, which are in series. You can follow the same switching procedure as in Fig. 5-2 and derive a rotating field as was the case with the wye connection.

Which of the two windings is preferred? Both types are used, even though the wye connection is more often used. Sometimes wire size can determine which of the two windings is more suitable. For similar voltage ratings, there are 1.73 times as many turns per phase in the delta winding than the corresponding wye winding. The difference is that of 2 1/2 times smaller gauge wire size for the delta connection that often makes it easier to wind a low-voltage motor, while the opposite is true for the high voltage motor. The wye might also be preferred where it is difficult to magnetically balance all three phases accurately. The delta is a closed winding, which permits internal circulating currents with winding unbalance.

5.4.2. Three-Phase, Half-Wave BLDC Motor Operation

Occasionally it is desired to have a three-phase motor with a switching arrangement where the phase currents will not reverse. This switching arrangement is used primarily for economic reasons because switching is simpler, and the cost of the electronic package is lower.

For this condition, a wye connection is used with the neutral playing an important role in the switching process as illustrated in Fig. 5-7 (a, b, c) and 5-8. The neutral can simply be grounded. There is a current flow in one phase at a time as shown in Fig. 5-7. The conduction period occurs only in the positive part of the back EMF cycle as shown in Fig. 5-8. Also shown is the current shape that would result if switching time were zero and there were no inductance in the winding. This is of

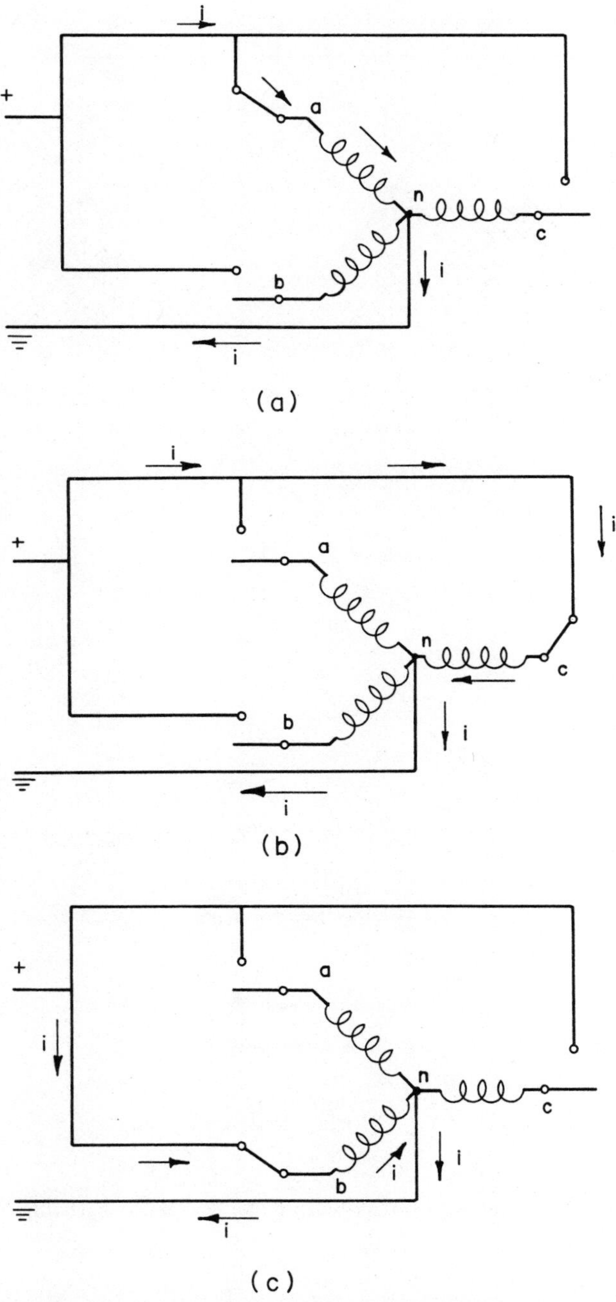

Fig. 5-7. Three switch positions showing the mode of operation of a three-phase, half-wave, wye-connected BLDC motor.

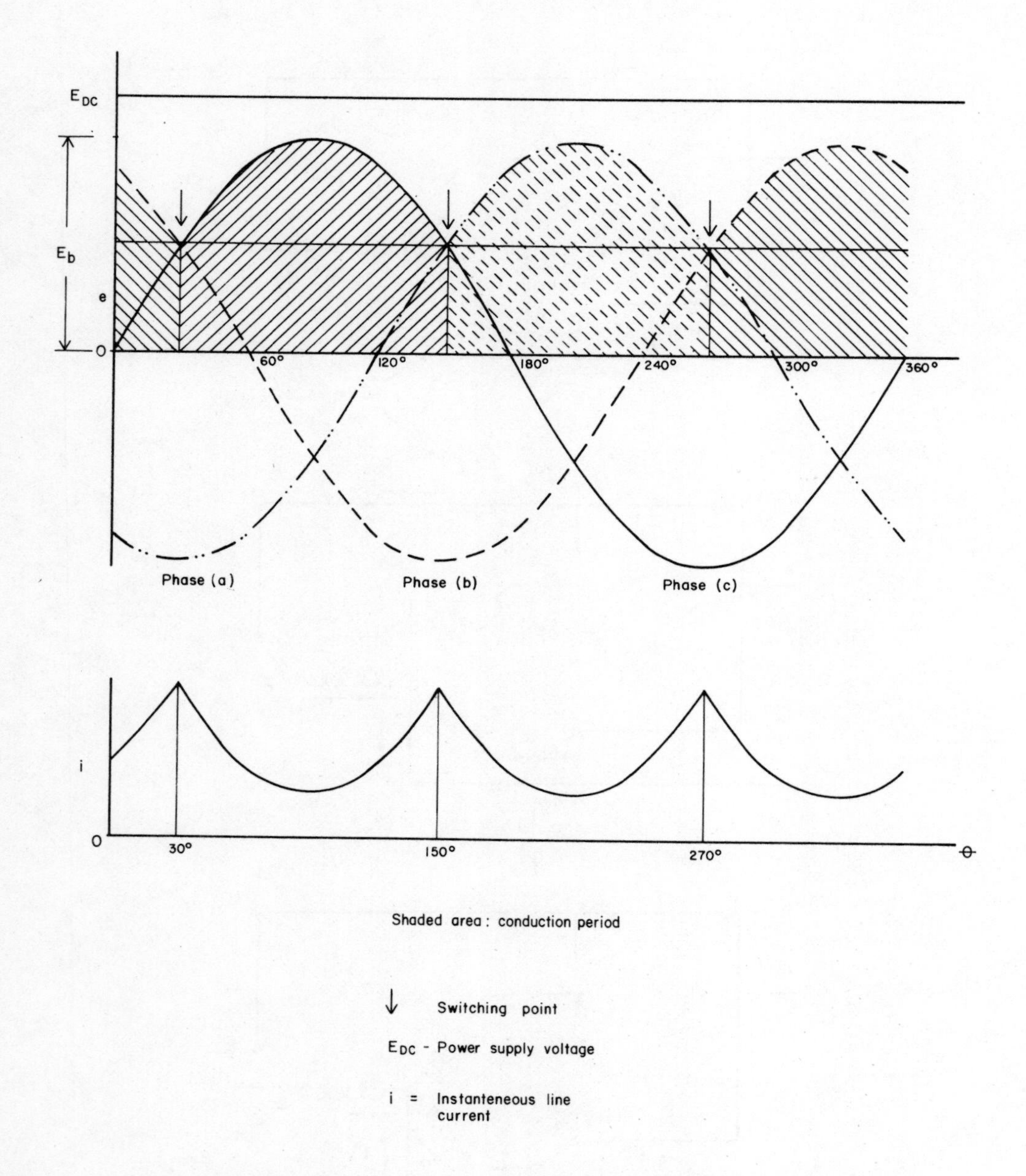

Fig. 5-8. Idealized three-phase, half-wave motor operation neglecting inductance.

course never the case, therefore, the current usually looks quite different. What stands out in this design is the under-utilization of the motor material.

5.4.3. Two-Phase, Full-Wave BLDC Motor Operation

A two-phase, full-wave BLDC motor mechanical switching arrangement is shown in Fig. 5-9 (a to d). The advantage of this system over the full-wave, three-phase system is that only two three-position switches, rather than three three-position

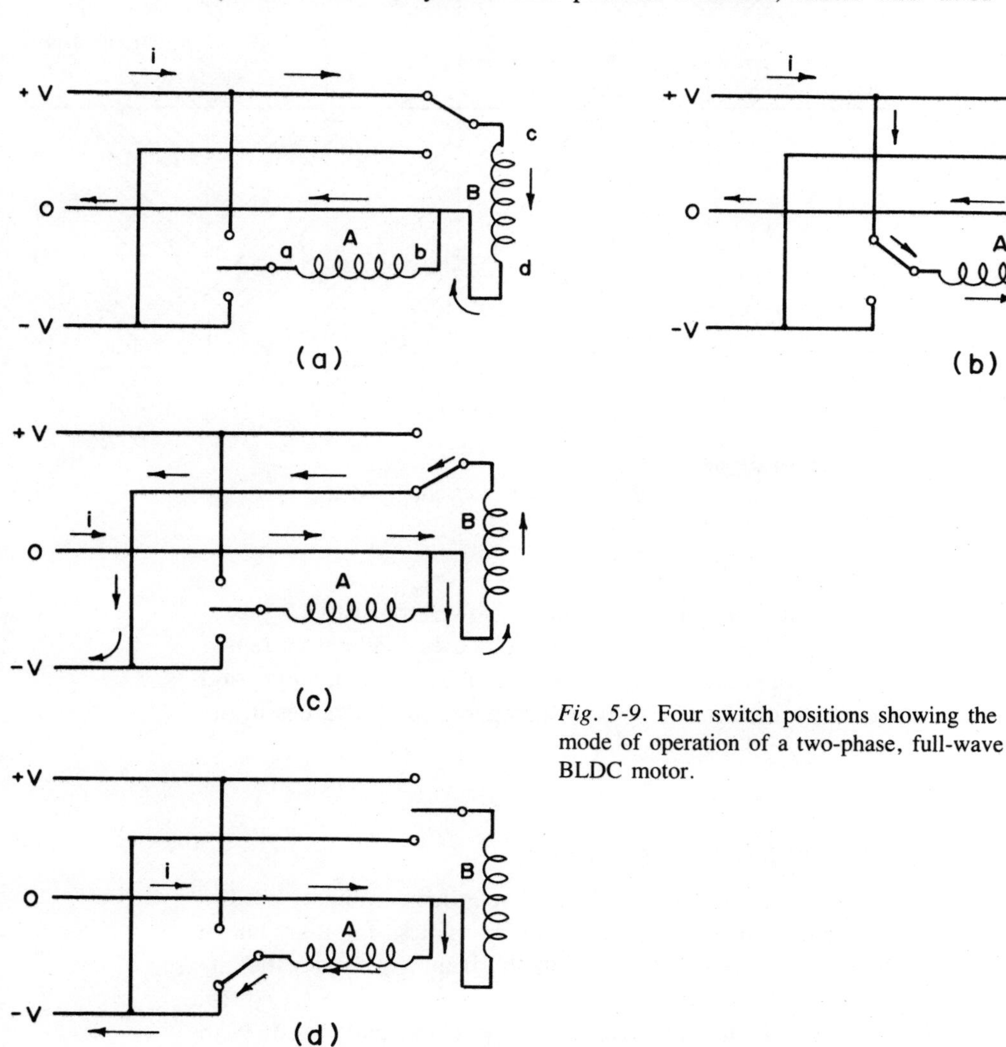

Fig. 5-9. Four switch positions showing the mode of operation of a two-phase, full-wave BLDC motor.

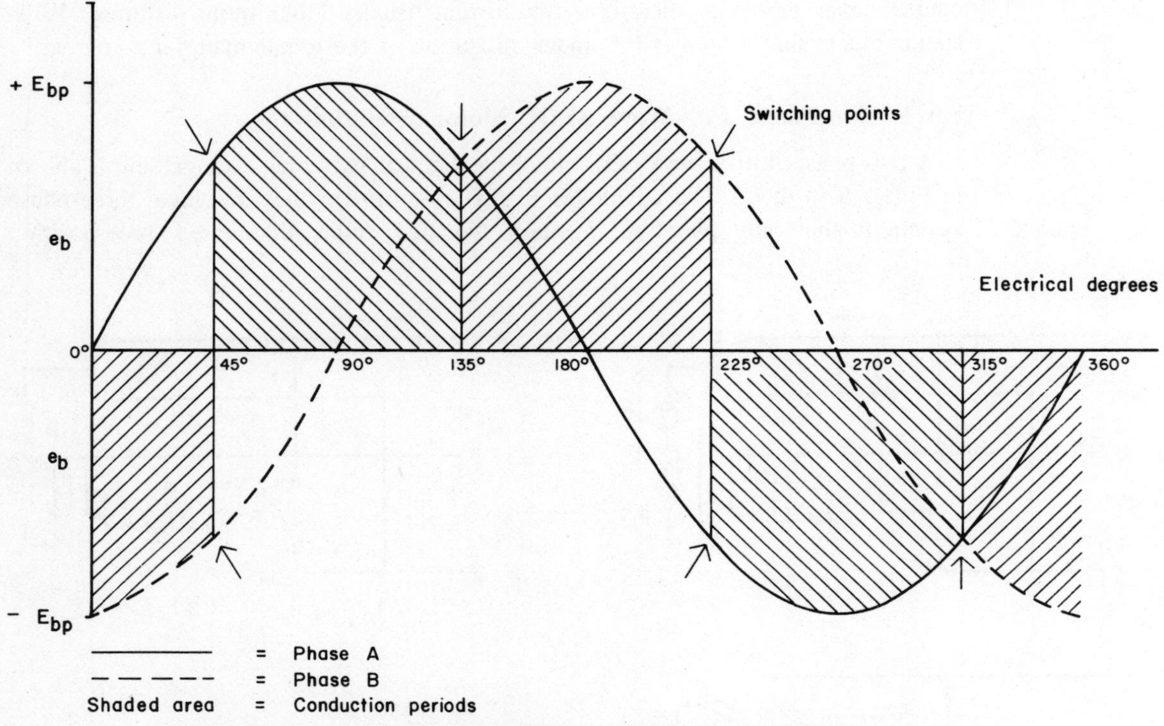

Fig. 5-10. Two-phase, full-wave switching points and conducting periods.

switches, are required. The equivalents are four and six power transistors, respectively, in electronic circuits. However, only one of the two phases conducts current at any time, using only half the stator winding during this period. The conduction period is 90 electrical degrees as illustrated in Fig. 5-10 as compared to 60 degrees in the three-phase motor.

5.4.4. Four- and Six-Phase BLDC Motors

The windings discussed in previous sections of this chapter are commonly used in polyphase ac motors. The four- and six-phase windings are not so familiar, but in BLDC motors they are extensively used because of their advantages in specific circumstances.

The four-phase, delta-connected, full-wave BLDC motor is frequently used. With this winding configuration, full advantage can be taken of all the coils in every switch position as can readily be seen in Fig. 5-11 (a to d). This permits higher power output

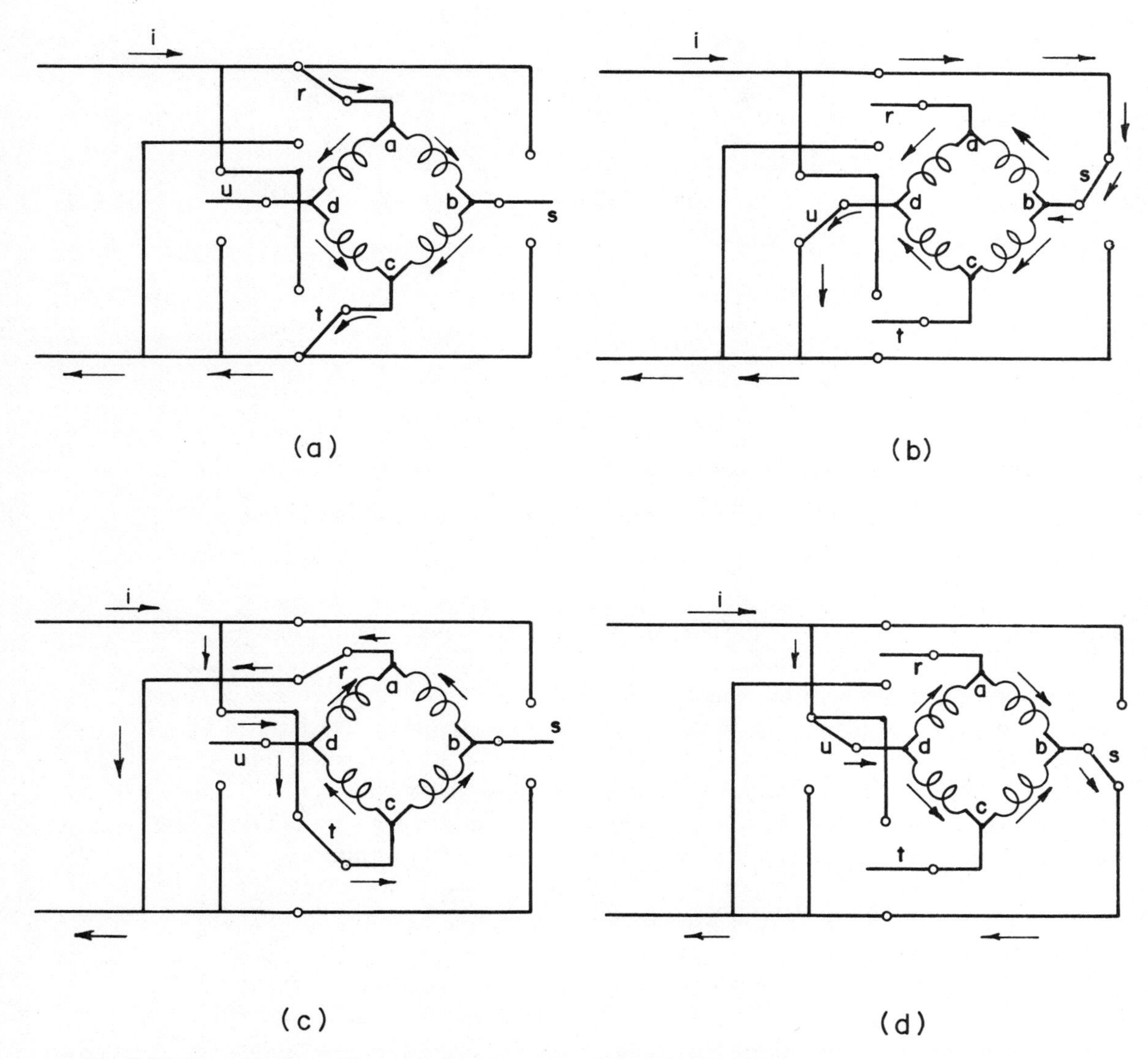

Fig. 5-11. Four switch positions showing the mode of operation of a four-phase, full-wave BLDC motor.

Table 5-2. Four-Pole, Full-Wave BLDC Motor Switch Positions and Current.

Switch Position				Direction of currents in windings	Figure
r	s	t	u		
+	o	−	o	a to b b to c a to d d to c	5-11 (a)
o	+	o	−	b to a a to d b to c c to d	5-11 (b)
−	o	+	o	c to d d to a c to b b to a	5-11 (c)
o	−	o	+	d to a a to b d to c c to b	5-11 (d)
+ is switch connected to positive side of power supply − is switch connected to negative side of power supply o is switch in open position					

than an equivalent full-wave, three-phase winding for a given bldc motor. Table 5-2 lists the different switching positions.

A four-phase, half-wave BLDC winding is shown in Fig. 5-12 (a to d). As can be observed, only one of the four windings is energized in any one switch position, making inefficient use of motor space. However, it calls for a simple and low-cost electronic package, which might justify the use of this configuration.

The six-phase, full-wave delta winding in Fig. 5-13 (a to f) makes very efficient use of the motor winding. This design minimizes inductance and permits smoother motor operation than does the four-phase, full-wave winding. On the other hand, the six-phase winding requires more electronic components making this a high cost BLDC motor option.

Other winding combinations are possible. Fig. 5-14 shows the voltage distribution of six coils operating 30 electrical degrees apart for smoother operation. This design would use six sensors instead of the three sensors used for regular full-wave, three- and six-phase windings (six-phase, grounded-neutral systems).

Among other alternatives are designs that use two three-phase windings, the windings are switched independently to obtain smoother operation.

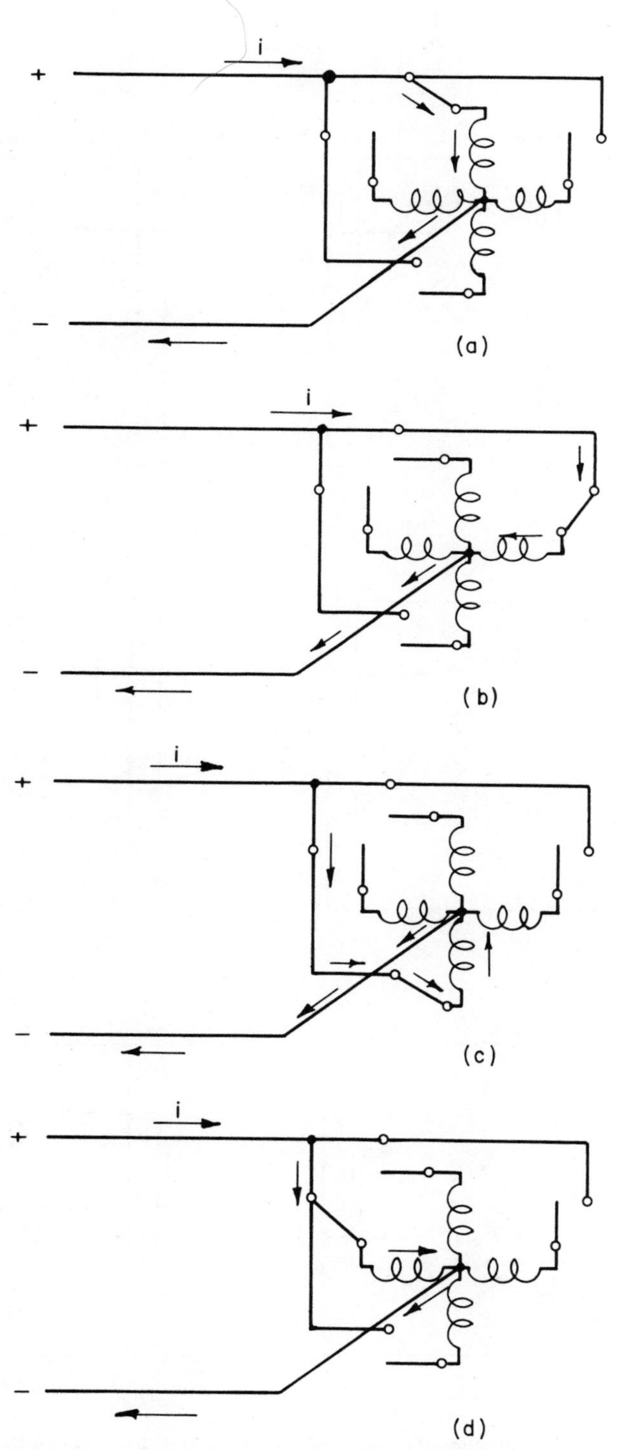

Fig. 5-12. Four switch positions showing the mode of operation of a four-phase, half-wave BLDC motor.

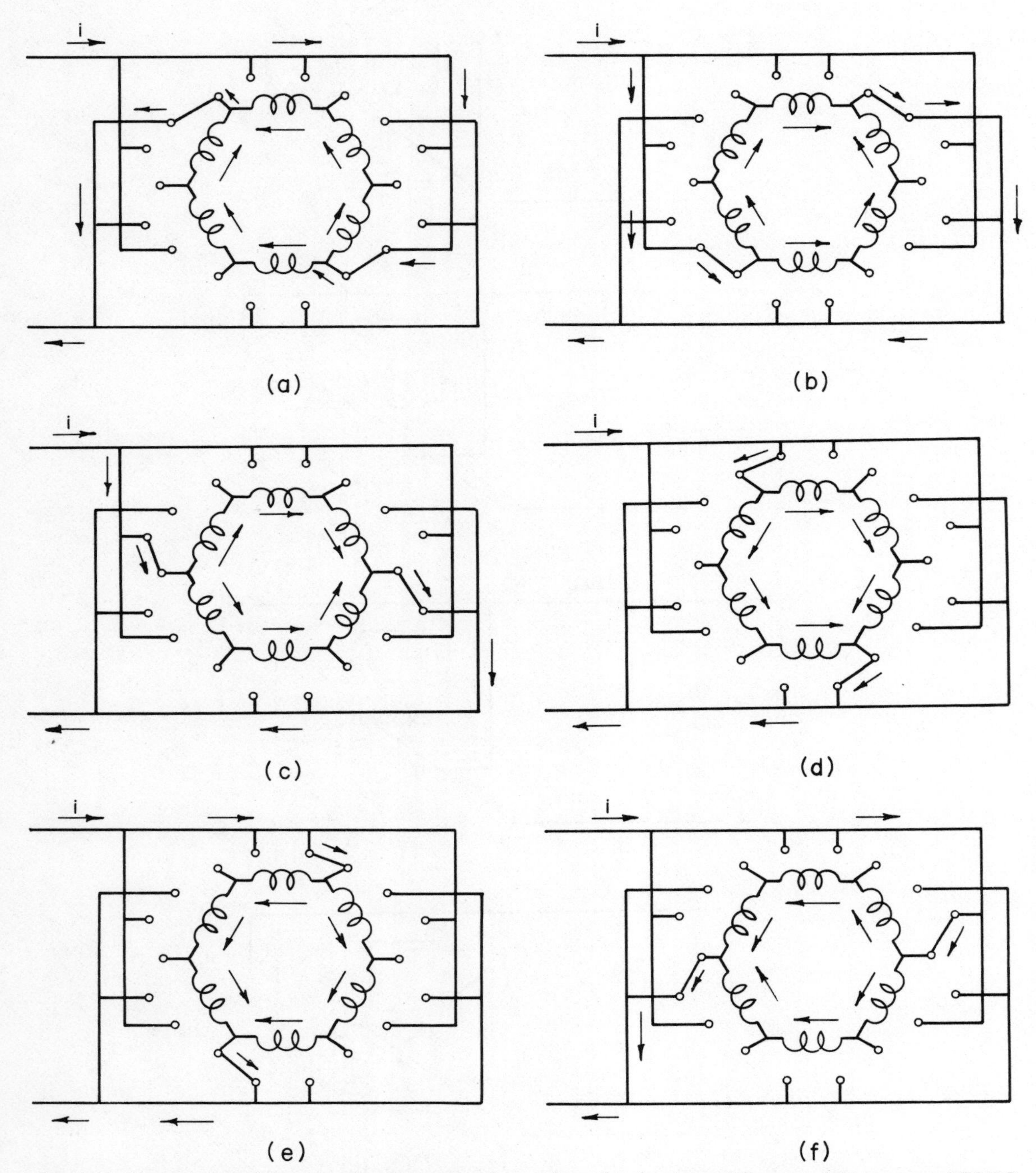

Fig. 5-13. Six switch positions showing the mode of operation of a six-phase, full-wave, delta-connected BLDC motor.

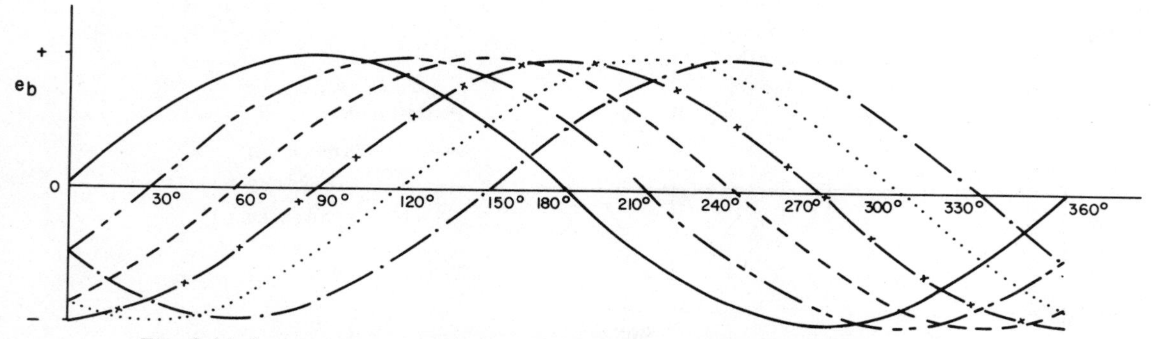

Fig. 5-14. Instantaneous e_b voltage distribution for six coils operating 30 degrees apart.

5.5. MOTOR CONSTANTS

5.5.1. Voltage and Torque Constants

The mode of operation of the BLDC motor was discussed in section 5.3. The back EMF and switching points of a full-wave, three-phase winding was illustrated in Fig. 5-4. The shape of the back EMF was the familiar sine wave. Different voltage shapes can be generated by proper design of the stator winding and by shaping the magnetic field by forming and magnetizing the magnets in special ways. One such shape is the trapezoidal wave form shown in Fig. 5-15 (a). If, as in Fig. 5-16 a constant dc voltage or current is applied to the terminal of the windings, the currents in each winding during the period of conduction is a square wave as shown in Fig. 5-15. If the effect of switching is neglected, the same motor constants K_E and K_T developed in chapter 1 can be applied. Therefore:

$$T = K_T I$$

and

$$K_T = K_E$$

This equation can be applied on a per-phase basis, making it a torque per phase. Constants might be applied to motor terminals, which shows that in the case of a full-wave operated, three-phase, wye-connected winding referred to in section 5.3, the relationship is:

$$K_T \text{ (motor)} = \sqrt{3}\, K_T \text{ (phase)}$$

On the other hand, in the three-phase, half-wave BLDC motor operation as in Fig. 5-7, which switches between line terminal and neutral:

$$K_T \text{ (motor)} = K_T \text{ (phase)}.$$

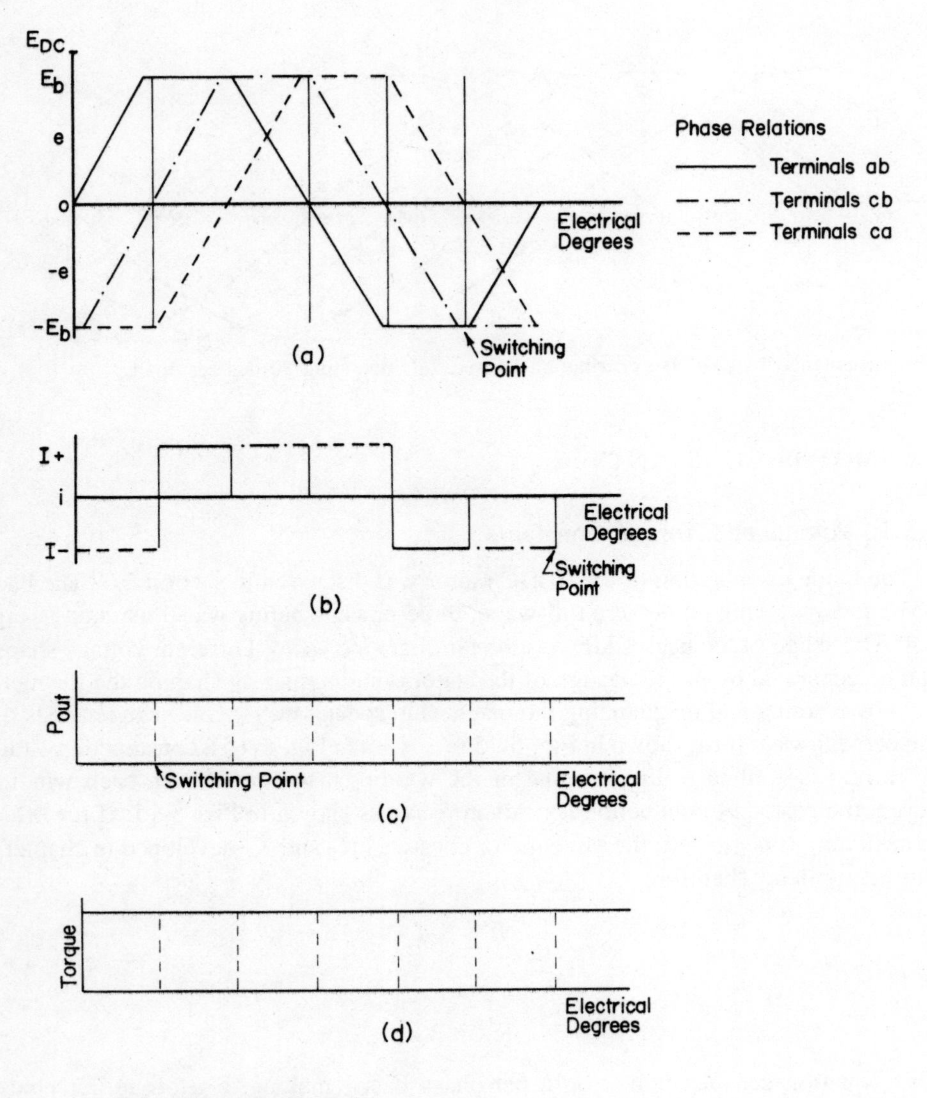

P_{out} = Gross power output

E_{DC} = Supply voltage

E_b = Back - emf between terminals

i = Current flowing between terminals

For switching sequence see Fig. 5-2

Fig. 5-15. Current, power and voltage relationships for trapezoidal back EMF.

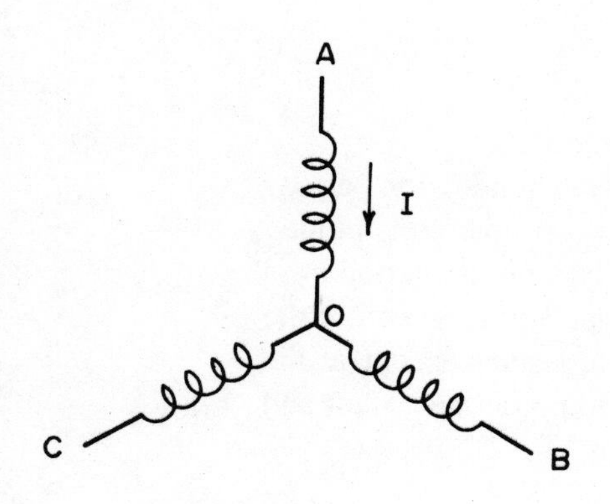

Line to Neutral

$K_E = K_T$ (In the international system)

$T_{(AO)} = K_{T(AO)}\,I$ for phase AO

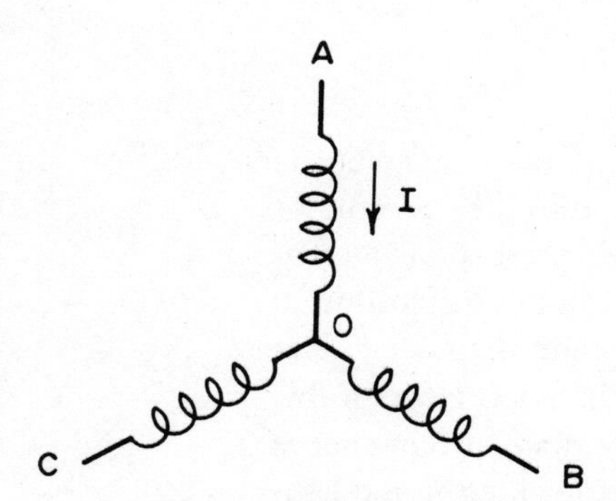

Line to Line

Two phases are always energized at a time for terminals A B

$T_{AB} = K_{T(AB)}\,I = \sqrt{3}\;K_{T(AO)}\,I$

$K_{E(AB)} = \sqrt{3}\;K_{E(AO)}$

Fig. 5-16. Torque constant for a three-phase wye-connection with line to neutral and line to line.

In the case of the three-phase, delta connection (see Fig. 5-6).

$$K_T \text{ (motor)} = K_T \text{ (phase)}$$

In conclusion, conventional dc motors constants K_T and K_E are applicable to the BLDC motor, but a given K_T value must be referenced properly to a given winding and switching pattern.

5.5.2. Power Output and Torque

Chapter 1 shows that gross motor output is:

$$E_b \times I_a \tag{1-6}$$

For the BLDC motor, the equation can be modified:

$$\text{Gross } p_{out} = e_b \times i \tag{5-1}$$

where p, e, and i are instantaneous values. In Fig. 5-15 if e during conduction periods is multiplied by i during the same periods, the corresponding power output is plotted in 5-15 (c). It will be noticed in Fig. 5-15 (a) that during the conduction period e_b is always a constant E_b. Furthermore, when E_b is negative, I is negative, therefore the product of the two is positive. Power in Fig. 5-15 (c) is a constant except at the switching point which might or might not be negligible depending on the circuit and motor constants.

If:

$$e_b \times i \approx S \times T_i \tag{5-2}$$

where S = Constant speed in RPM
T_i = Instantaneous torque

then it follows that as long as the speed does remain constant, the instantaneous torque is proportional to $e_b i$. Again, this is the gross torque produced by the motor and not the torque actually measured at the shaft, which is lower because of internal motor losses. Also the shape of the instantaneous torque curve will change due to inertia, which has a tendency to average out the torque, magnetic drag, etc., and might change considerably over the speed range of the motor. The importance of this relationship will become more apparent as less idealized voltage and current shapes than those in Fig. 5-15 are considered. The shapes in Fig. 5-15 resulted in the constant torque output shown in Fig. 5-15.

A common sinusoidal e_b shape is plotted in Fig. 5-17 (a). If the currents in the windings are manipulated so that they are in form of a square wave as in Fig. 5-17 (b), than the resulting torque has a ripple as indicated in Fig. 5-17 (c) where the minimum torque is 0.886 that of the peak torque and the average torque is 0.95 × peak torque. In this particular case, K_T would be 0.95 times peak torque/ampere, and the corresponding K_E is 0.95 E_{peak}/radian per second.

Referring back to Fig. 5-2, although the current in the winding is reversed by switching, the current into the motor system is always in the same direction from the positive power terminal to the negative terminal. The currents in the windings in Fig. 5-17 (a) are plotted in Fig. 5-18 to show the current flow to the power switching circuit of the motor from the power supply. This current is essentially a dc current, and it is the current that can be used for torque calculations and for determining the K_T. If the currents have a shape other than the dc current shown in Fig. 5-18, the average value of the current, which is the dc value of the current, must be used for calculating torque and torque constants. Frequently in lower-cost drives and in closed loop operation, the currents into the power transistors are anything but straight dc. A

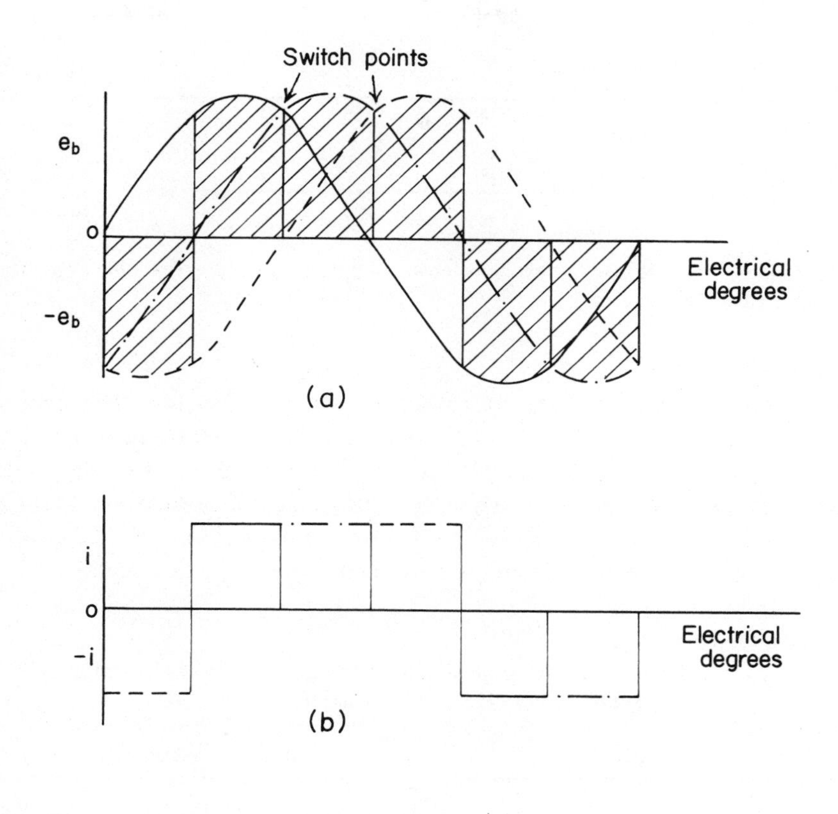

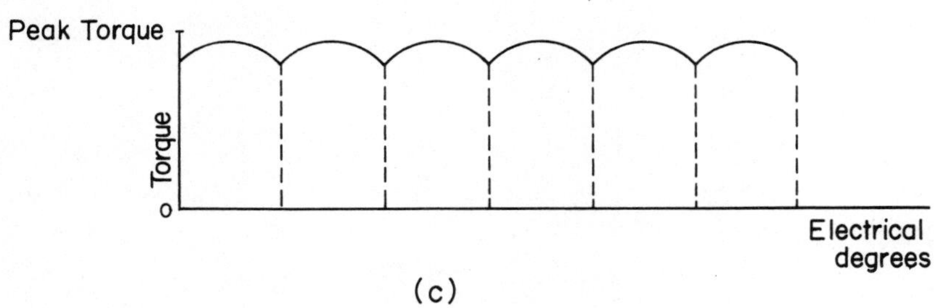

for further reference see 5-3-2
and 5-3-4

Fig. 5-17. Torque pulsations resulting from sinusoidal back EMF and square-wave currents for a three-phase, full-wave BLDC motor.

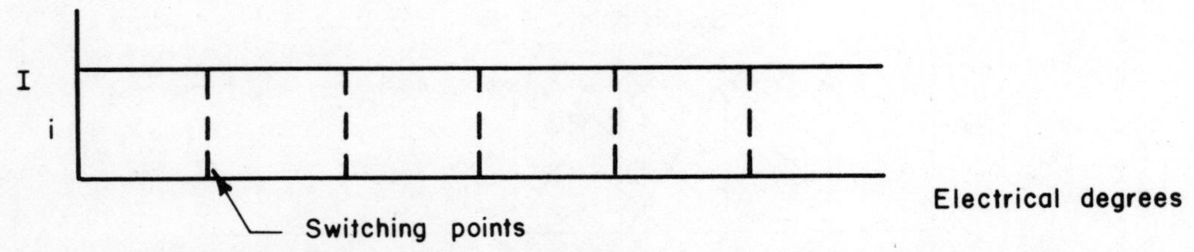

Fig. 5-18. Ideal shape of line current from power supply to the power switching circuit of full-wave; wye-connected BLDC motor.

situation prevails similar to that described in section 1.7.6 for permanent-magnet motors with rectified supplies. The RMS value of the current frequently exceeds the dc value by a considerable amount, creating considerable heat in the motor and lowering the overall efficiency of the system. Table 5-3 lists peak, average, and minimum torque values for sinusoidal voltages for windings other than the full-wave, three-phase wye-connection windings described in detail in this section.

Table 5-3. Torque Relationships for Different Modes of Operation of BLDC Motors Having Sinusoidal Counter EMF.

Mode of Operation	Relative Torque		
	peak	average	min.
3-phase wye, full-wave	1	0.95	0.866
3-phase delta, full-wave	1	0.95	0.866
4-phase delta, full-wave	1	0.91	0.707
6-phase delta, full-wave	1	0.95	0.866
3-phase wye, half-wave	1	0.83	0.5
4-phase wye, half-wave	1	0.91	0.707

5.5.3. Torque Distortion Caused by Stator Field Interaction

The currents flowing through the stator winding create their own field, which interacts with the main field from the magnet. This effect is similar to the armature reaction in a brush-type dc motor, and it is discussed in chapter 2. The amount of the distortion will depend on the magnitude of the current and the strength of the magnetic material. If saturation occurs, there can be a net loss of flux. The resulting torque envelope can be less than indicated by K_T. The effect is most pronounced on locked-rotor condition, resulting in smaller than expected minimum torque. This situation can be helped by advancing or retarding the phase switching against the rotation of the rotor, much like the shifting of brushes in a dc motor. In a more sophisticated motor, this shift is accomplished electronically with the help of a microprocessor that monitors the current and continuously determines the correct switching angle.

The armature reaction field might cause magnet demagnetization at a certain value of current. It is therefore imperative that the peak current of the motor as specified by the manufacturer not be exceeded.

5.6. EFFECT OF WINDING RESISTANCE AND INDUCTANCE

For the most effective electronic switching, keep the electrical time constant as well as the overall inductance of the windings to a minimum. The electrical time constant will determine how fast the current will reach its full value after a winding has been switched on. The energy stored up in the winding is a function of the inductance, the larger this stored up energy, the more likely it will produce larger transients in transistors during turn-off. As is discussed in chapter 6, measures can be taken in the electronic circuit to improve this situation, but it helps not to get into this situation in the first place. Because of the importance of the above factors on the overall cost and performance of the BLDC motor, it is worthwhile to have a closer look at these two motor parameters.

5.6.1. Electrical Time Constant

$$T_e = \frac{L_t}{R_t} \qquad (5\text{-}3)$$

where L_t = inductance of winding being powered
R_t = resistance of winding being powered

To illustrate the importance of this time constant assume the following example:

A three-phase, four-pole, full-wave BLDC motor, wye-connected, running at 12,000 RPM.

12,000 revolutions/minute = 200 revolutions/sec. or one revolution in 0.005 seconds or 5 milliseconds.

There are 360×2 electrical degrees per revolution.

It takes $[5 \times 10^{-3}]/720 = 6.9 \times 10^{-6}$ seconds to move one electrical degree.

Furthermore assume that terminal inductance is 0.0006 henries and the terminal resistance is 1.2 ohms:

$$\frac{L_t}{R_t} = \frac{0.0006}{1.2} = 0.0005 \text{ sec.} = 5 \times 10^{-4} \text{ seconds}$$

The on period for transistors is 60 electrical degrees. Time of *on* period is $60 \times 6.9 \times 10^{-6} = 4.14 \times 10^{-4}$ seconds.

Comparing the electrical time constant of 5×10^{-4} seconds and the time of the *on* period of 4.14×10^{-4} seconds reveals that the current would not reach full value in the time allowed. If a resistance of 10.8 ohms were externally connected in series with the winding, a time constant of 0.0006/12 or 5×10^{-5} seconds would result. The current would then reach the final value in a short time. Of course, the additional resistance would dissipate considerable energy, thus reducing the overall system efficiency.

If the motor speed had been 1500 RPM, the electrical time constant would not have been excessive for this speed. The value of inductance becomes a critical parameter as motor speed increases, and the designer must be aware of how this might affect motor performance and efficiency.

5.6.2. Effect of Inductance

It is important to distinguish between T_e and inductance alone. Two motors can have identical electrical time constants but very different inductances. The effect of inductance is to store up energy in a circuit.

$$W = 1/2 \frac{LI^2}{t} \text{ (joules)} \tag{5-4}$$

When the winding is switched off, the stored energy can result in very high peak voltages being developed across the drive transistor. In some cases, this inductive voltage can be diode clamped to the supply voltage. It is often necessary to use appropriate RC circuits at each transistor to control device dv/dt. Often called snubber elements, these circuits must be carefully designed to fully control voltage without being excessively dissipative. Insufficient attention in this area can lead to severe device derating requirements and in the worst case will cause device destruction by exceeding the transistor SOA. This subject is treated more fully in subsequent chapters.

The whole subject of winding inductance is of utmost importance to the designer of controllers. In practice, the motor designer can control to a large extent the self and mutual inductance of a winding. A motor with a toothless stator core construction is preferred where minimum winding inductance is deemed necessary. There the winding is located in the airgap of the motor (see section 5.7). In motors with a conventional laminated steel core stator with teeth, the permeability of steel plays a vital role in determining the inductance of the winding. It was pointed out in section 1.4 that for dc the permeability of steel varies with flux density, and different grades of steel have different permeabilities. The same holds true for ac where the ac permeability varies with flux density.

For typical steel laminations, the ac permeability also generally decreases with increases in frequency.

The motor inductance listed by manufacturers is usually measured with an inductance bridge or meter at a frequency of 1000 Hz.

In a polyphase winding, inductance can be broken down into self and mutual inductance as shown in Fig. 5-19 for a three-phase, full-wave, wye-connected winding. The typical value of the mutual inductance between phases in a conventional stator is 1/2 to 3/4 the value of a phase inductance. Mutual inductances as low as 10 percent as well as higher values than those mentioned formerly have been encountered, depending on the internal winding pattern of the motor.

The inductance of a given winding pattern will vary directly with the square of the number of the turns per coil and also varies with the stack length. The relationship is not linear because the winding inductance caused by the overhang remains the same. It might be advantageous to have the rotor and stator somewhat longer than required, which increases the total flux available and allows a reduction in the number of turns per coil and an overall reduction of winding inductance. The use of stronger magnetic materials requires fewer turns or shorter stack for a given K_T, which will again reduce the inductance.

If you design for a motor operating only in closed loop, you can design for different voltage constants (K_E) and still arrive at the same operating point. There are many offsetting factors involved here, and inductance is only one of them.

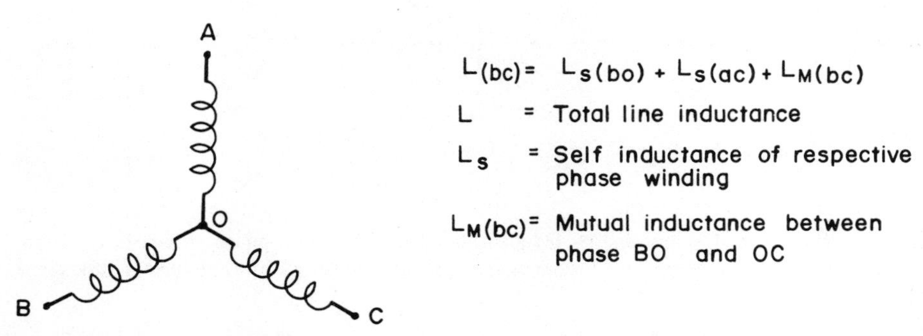

Fig. 5-19. Self and mutual inductance in a three-phase, wye-connected, full-wave BLDC motor.

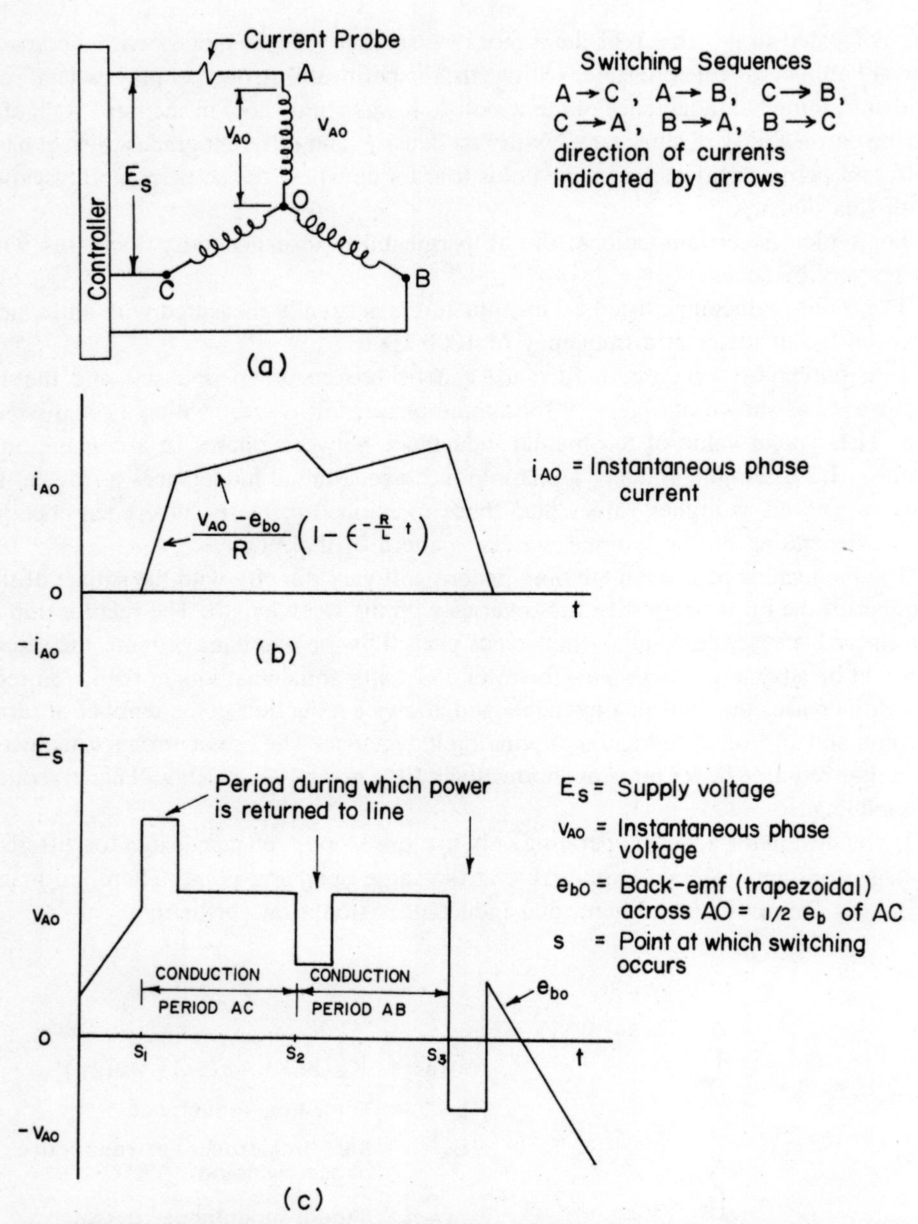

Fig. 5-20. Effect of stored energy feedback of the windings on phase voltage and current shapes: (a) star connection with switching sequence. (b) shape of face current. (c) shape of face voltage.

The authors have spent much time trying to reduce voltage transients that extra 10 percent to permit the use of certain transistors without which the cost of the bldc motor system would have been excessive.

Chapter 6 explains how the energy stored up in the winding is fed back into the line. Figure 5-20 shows the effect this process has on phase voltage and current shapes. When power is turned on across terminal A–C at time s_1, phase voltage A–0 rises a considerable amount above normal phase voltage during the period energy is being returned to the line from the previous conduction period (B C). This rise in voltage considerably increases $V_{A0}-e_{b0}$ and thereby speeds up the current build up. Similarly, at switching point s_2, the process stops the current from going to zero. At point s_3, the line voltage to leg A–0 is cut off. However, the current conduction period is extended beyond that point thereby returning the energy stored in leg A–0 to the line.

Figure 5-20 only illustrates the effect on voltages and currents from the energy transfer. It neglects other factors, such as the effect of mutual inductance, switching transients, etc.

In Fig. 5-20 a trapezoidal back EMF was assumed. In case of a sinusoidal back EMF, there would have been a noticeable current build up just before points s_2 and s_3 as the back EMF falls back from peak e_{b-peak} to 0.866 e_{b-peak}, causing a considerable increase in the term $V_{A0} - e_{b0}$. This occasionally proves detrimental to the BLDC system, particularly where commercial power line frequencies are not filtered out. Shapes will change with different loads on the motor as well as operating temperatures as the magnitude of back EMF is likely to change with temperature, particularly in case of ceramic magnets.

5.7. COGGING AND ROTOR CONSTRUCTION

It can be deduced from Table 5-3 that, for a given current, the magnitude of torque is a function of rotor position and this could be worsened by the field set up due to the stator current (see section 5.5.3). An additional source is a variation of torque due to the line-up of the rotor magnets and stator teeth in various positions of the rotor. These variations in torque could present a nuisance for start-up or low-speed conditions. One way to minimize these variations is to apply special techniques, largely proprietory, in magnetizing the rotor. Other designs use odd numbers of stator slots and special windings to accomplish the same effect. It is not practical to skew the stator slots because this would require, with present technology, the stator to be wound by hand making this option uneconomical. However, skewed magnet arcs are an option.

Another way to minimize cogging and at the same time reduce inductance is the toothless BLDC motor. Figure 5-21 shows the regular bldc stator core and rotor

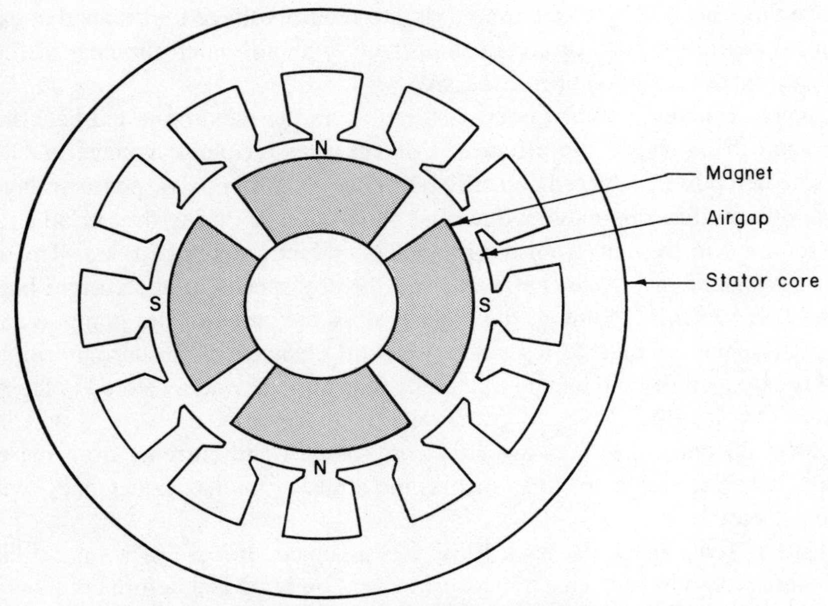

Fig. 5-21. Stator core and rotor configuration of a BLDC motor.

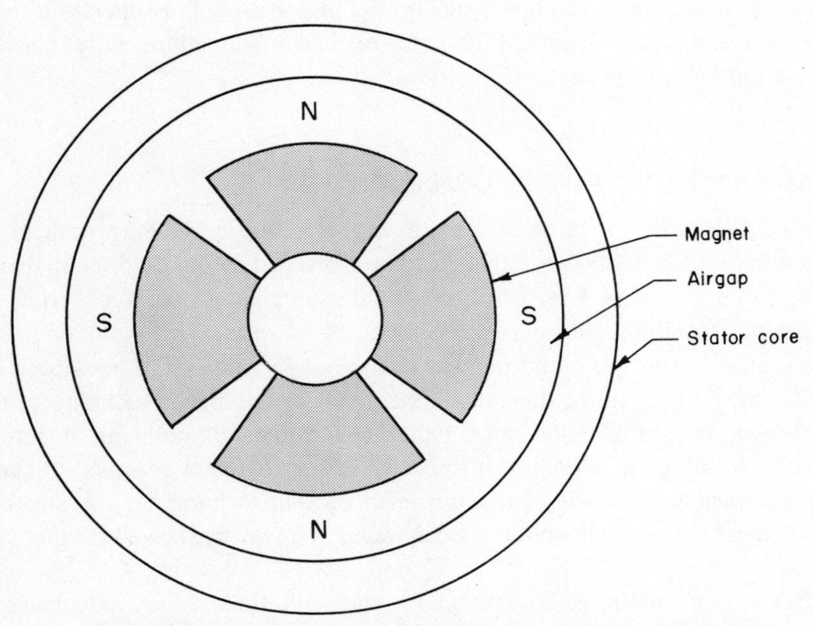

Fig. 5-22. Stator core and rotor configuration of a toothless BLDC motor.

configuration, and Fig. 5-22 illustrates the toothless stator core and rotor. The toothless construction has a very large air gap, which also accommodates the winding. A wound toothless stator is shown in Fig. 5-23. To compensate for a loss of flux and reduce leakage flux, the rotor diameter is usually larger in the toothless construction, which has the effect of increasing the inertia. However, an increased winding area due to the lack of teeth permits the outside diameter of the motor to remain the same except in the case of the very smallest motors.

The toothless configuration is very advantageous where high energy neodenium-iron-boron magnets are used and for very high speed BLDC motors because of low inductance and low core losses. It also is suitable for very low speed drives because of low magnetic cogging.

Fig. 5-23. Wound toothless stator. (Courtesy of ELECTRIC INDICATOR Company Inc., Norwalk, CT)

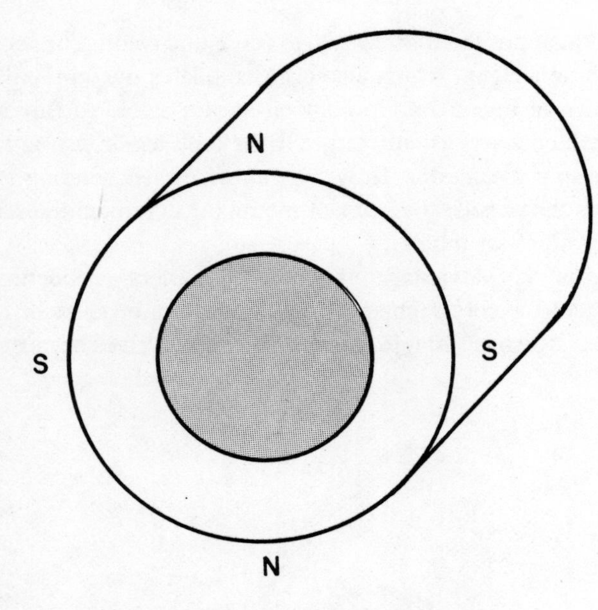

Fig. 5-24. Ring magnet.

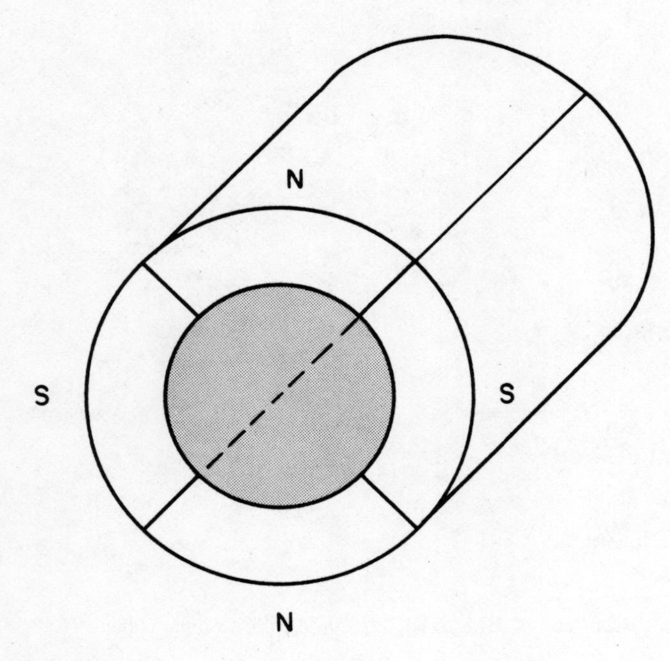

Fig. 5-25. Ring magnet built from four arcs joined together.

Rotor construction presents another major problem in the design and ultimately in the reliability of the BLDC motor. Typical rotor arrangements are shown in Figs. 5-24 through 5-26. The magnet rings illustrated in Fig. 5-24 are sturdier, and they are very practical where non-oriented material such as ceramic 1 are used or in a two-pole motor.

Rings are being made of unoriented rare-earth materials, but at a high cost in energy product. Also rings are being made by gluing four arcs together as in Fig. 5-25. This does make it possible to use oriented materials, but cost is relatively high. There is a widespread use of arcs as shown in Fig. 5-26.

A slightly different configuration is shown in Fig. 5-27, which consists of a bar magnet shaped in arc or semi-arc form on the side facing the air gap (see Fig. 5-27). The problem with these configurations is that the magnet materials commonly used not only have very low tensile strength, but many of the magnets have very small cracks not discernable by visual inspection. These cracks can cause the magnet to break on acceleration or even simply on turning. To protect the magnet assembly, many manufacturers put sleeves around the rotor made from stainless steel, brass, or other materials. Fig. 5-28 illustrates such a shrunk-on metal sleeve on a high-speed BLDC motor.

There are a number of molded-plastic magnets with high concentrations of ceramic or rare-earth magnet materials. Many of these magnets have very good mechanical characteristics but at the expense of magnetic and thermal characteristics. Because of the plastic rotor, temperatures must be kept relatively low. These molded magnets can also be manufactured to very close tolerances, reducing labor cost in the manufacture of BLDC rotors. As the number and reliability of molded plastic magnet

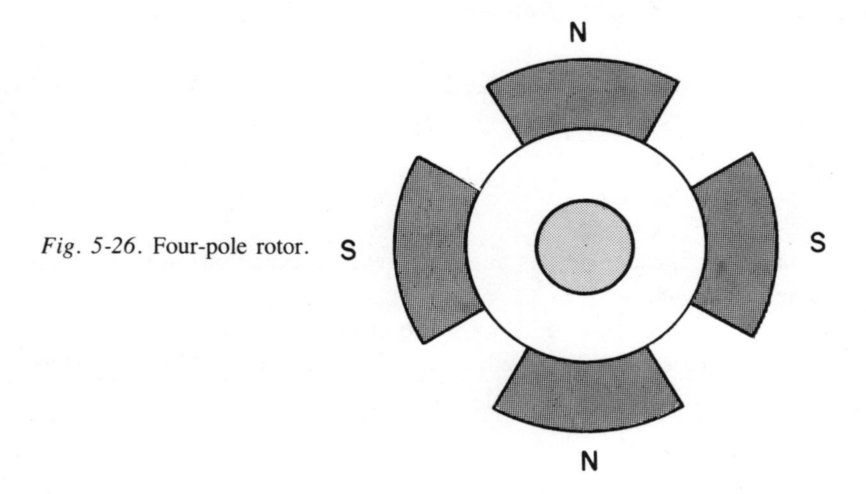

Fig. 5-26. Four-pole rotor.

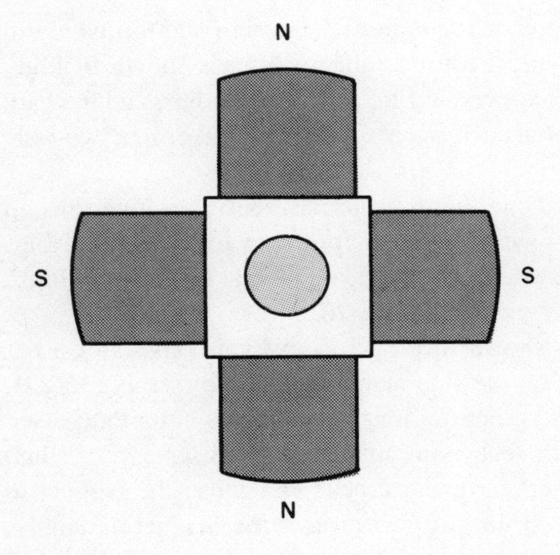

Fig. 5-27. Magnets mounted on square shaft. Magnet is basically a bar magnet with the outside diameter shaped to suit.

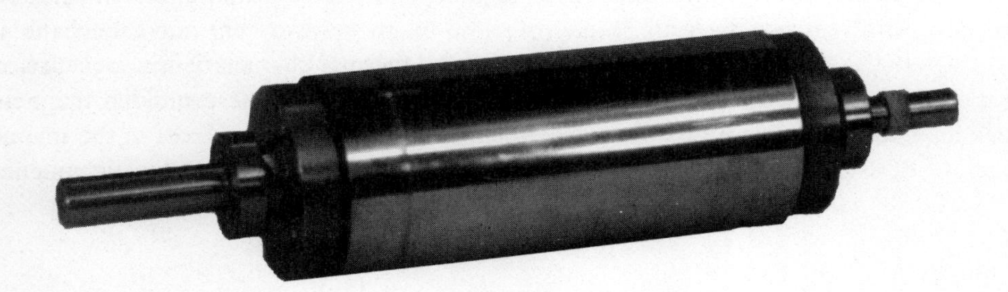

Fig. 5-28. BLDC rotor with shrunk-on metal sleeve. (Courtesy of ELECTRIC INDICATOR Company Inc., Norwalk, CT)

materials increases, these materials might find wide applications in BLDC motors for rotor and sensor magnets.

Many motor manufacturers specify a speed limit for their BLDC motors. It is very important to pay close attention and abide by that number. Magnet materials are discussed in chapter 1 in more detail.

5.8. THERMAL CONSIDERATIONS

The allowable temperature rise and continously rated current are indicated on the nameplate of the motor. But this data must be taken with a grain of salt.

As is the case with the brush-type, permanent-magnet dc motor (see chapter 1), the BLDC motor can develop a thermal runaway problem, particularly with a ceramic-magnet type rotor, unless the application is properly studied. Because of the mechanical complexity of the rotor (different expansion coefficients for magnets, shaft and sleeve material, temperature limitations of adhesives, and of course of plastic where applicable), even a short period of overheating could prove damaging to the motor.

A thermal-overload protection device is relatively easy to install where it can serve to interrupt the current in a common or neutral lead of the winding as is the case in half-wave BLDC motor windings (Fig. 5-7). For full-wave winding connections, other solutions are necessary. A thermal-overload device can operate a relay to interrupt the current in the power line.

5.9. UNEQUAL DISTRIBUTION OF CURRENTS IN MOTOR WINDINGS

BLDC motors are very sensitive to current unbalances because these motors are inherently polyphase machines. If the current in one part of the winding is larger than in another, local overheating in the winding may occur and the respective power transistors and snubbers also might overheat. Figure 5-29 shows curves for a three-phase, four-pole BLDC motor where the conduction period should be 60 electrical degrees for v–u in phase A and s–t′ in phase B. Instead it shows a 10 percent larger conduction period v–u in phase A and a 10 percent shorter conduction period s–t in phase B. Although 10 percent of 60 degrees is 6 degrees, in the four-pole motor there are 720 electrical degrees per revolution. A small 6-degree error (3-degree mechanical) could be caused by the position sensor.

Other electronic components can cause an unbalance, but it is also possible that the motor windings themselves are not fully balanced and the magnitude of the back EMF is larger in one phase than in another. Above factors must be considered when either designing or modifying a controller for a motor or replacing components such as Hall-effect switches.

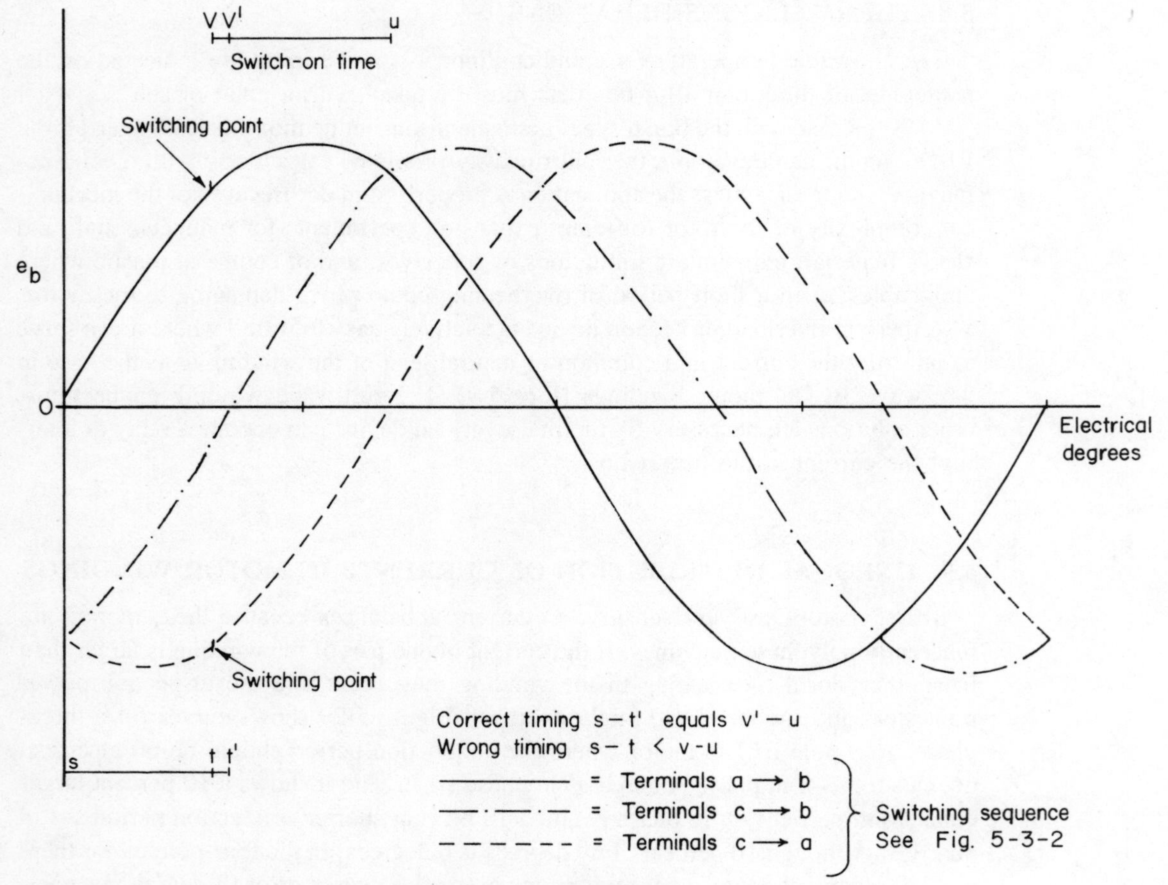

Fig. 5-29. Wrong timing by sensors.

5.10 SPECIALTY BLDC MOTORS

BLDC motors are so new, that practically every motor is a special motor adapted to a special application.

The physical differences between motors are numerous. There is the pancake- or disc-type motor very similar to the disk type motor described in chapter 1 for a brush-type motor. In this BLDC motor, the moving part is the magnet, which is magnetized axially. This motor is basically of toothless construction with negligible magnetic cogging and very low inductance. Among other advantages, it permits multipole construction of twelve and more poles, it is very adaptable to low speed applications. In view of its basic coil construction of limited number of turns, it basically carries a low voltage rating and a power transformer is required for a 115 or 220 V ac power source.

The inverted BLDC motor has the moving magnet on the outside, and the stator physically looks like a wound dc armature without a commutator. The winding techniques are similar to those of a wound armature, and the stator can be skewed. The rotor inertia is high. Rotor protection is the same as explained in chapter 5. Thermal characteristics of this motor are inferior because the heat developed in the stator is kept away from the outer surface of the motor by the rotating magnet.

A motor might have two seperate sensor systems where the speed control of the motor covers a combination of wide range with low speed, such as a speed ratio of 10 to 1 with a low speed of under 100 RPM. One sensor system is to sense absolute shaft position, which might consist of two or three Hall effect switches, depending on the number of phases. The other sensor system senses velocity and might consist of an encoder.

Among the early BLDC motors, two-phase versions were designed for low-cost control systems where ingenious ways had to be found to avoid dead spots during starting of the motors. The development of lower-cost electronic control circuits and low cost FETS make these schemes largely obsolete.

Chapter 3 section 3.4.2 describes the mode of operation of a polyphase synchronous motor. The rotor in Figs. 3-38 and 3-39 is of the reluctance type. With proper stator winding sequencing and position sensing, the rotor will follow a rotating electromagnetic field much like a permanent magnet rotor will. No dc field winding is required.

The cost of such a motor promises to be lower than the permanent magnet type. The rotor construction is rugged suitable for high-speed applications. However, the motor has a tendency to be noisy and is inferior to the permanent-magnet type in other performance characteristics.

For more on reluctance type motors refer to chapter 3 sections 3.4.4 and 3.5. Much more will be heard about reluctance motors in the future.

5.11 THE HALL EFFECT SENSOR

Sensing methods are discussed in chapter 6. Among the most commonly used devices are Hall effect sensors. These devices are very complex and it is important to understand how they function.

When passing a current through a block made of semiconductor material and applying a magnetic field perpendicular to the direction of this current, a voltage will be created across terminals located both perpendicular to the current and the magnetic field. This effect is illustrated in Fig. 5-30, and the voltage so generated is called the Hall voltage. When the magnetic field is withdrawn the Hall voltage is zero.

Although many materials show the same effects, they are particularly strong in semiconductors. Hall elements, also called Hall generators, are made of semiconductor materials such as indium antimony, gallium arsinide, and silicon. Their function is to detect magnetic fields, and the voltage generated is proportional to the flux which passes through the element.

The basic equation describing the Hall element is:

$$V_H = \frac{1}{d} \times I_c \times R_H \times B \sin \Theta \qquad (5\text{-}5)$$

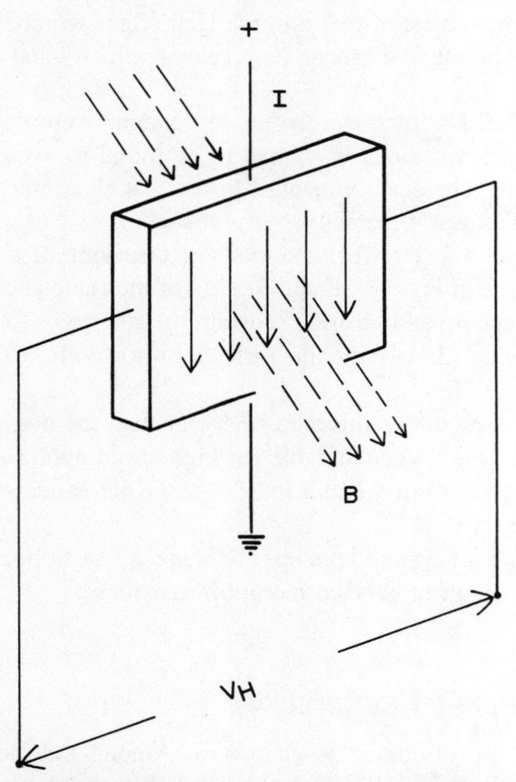

Fig. 5-30. Applying a magnetic field to block of current-carrying semiconductor material generating Hall voltage (V_H).

where $\quad I_c$ = Input current

$B \sin \Theta$ = The component of the magnetic field perpendicular to the surface of the Hall element

R_H = the Hall coefficient

d = the thickness of semiconducting material

V_H = Hall voltage

The above equation neglects some basic factors that affect the Hall element, such as the geometry of the device itself, the ambient temperture, and strain put on the element. As V_H is very small, an amplifier is added to make the signal more usable (see Fig. 5-31). Also in order to make the output voltage proportional to flux, I_c has to be a constant, and this requires a regulator unless the system using such a module already has a regulator.

The differential amplifier shown in Fig. 5-31 amplifies the potential difference, which is the Hall voltage. The voltage at each output terminal of the Hall element is the same with respect to ground and would read other than zero in absence of a magnetic field. Figure 5-32 shows a Hall integrated-circuit device, and Fig. 5-33

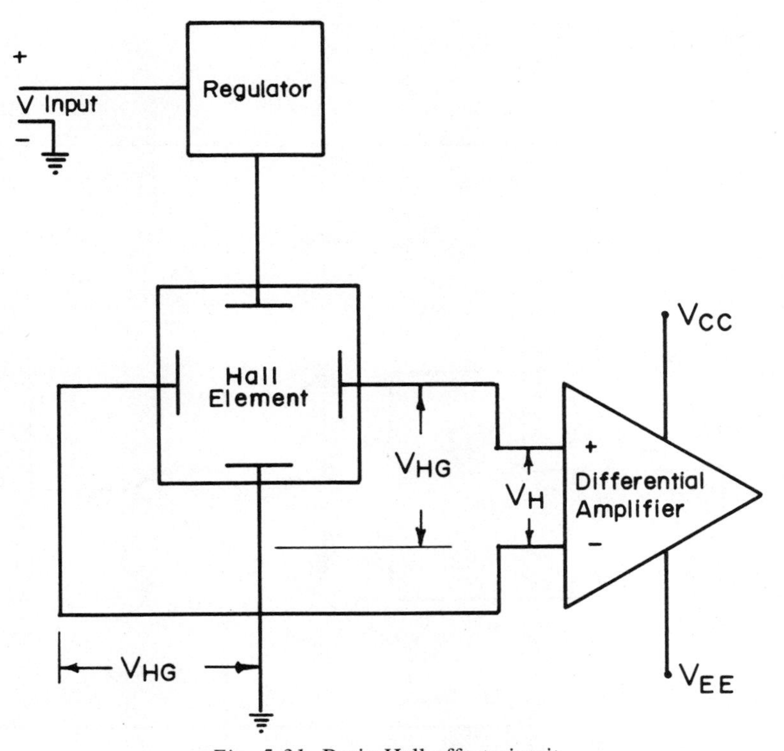

Fig. 5-31. Basic Hall effect circuit.

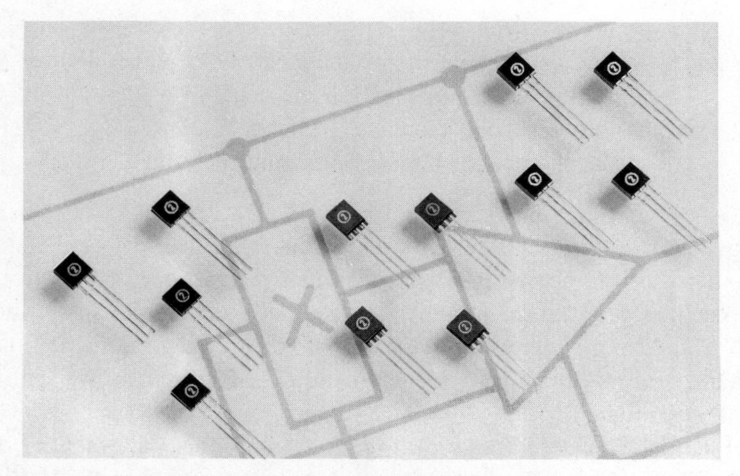

Fig. 5-32. Hall IC device. (Courtesy of SPRAGUE ELECTRIC COMPANY, Concord, NH)

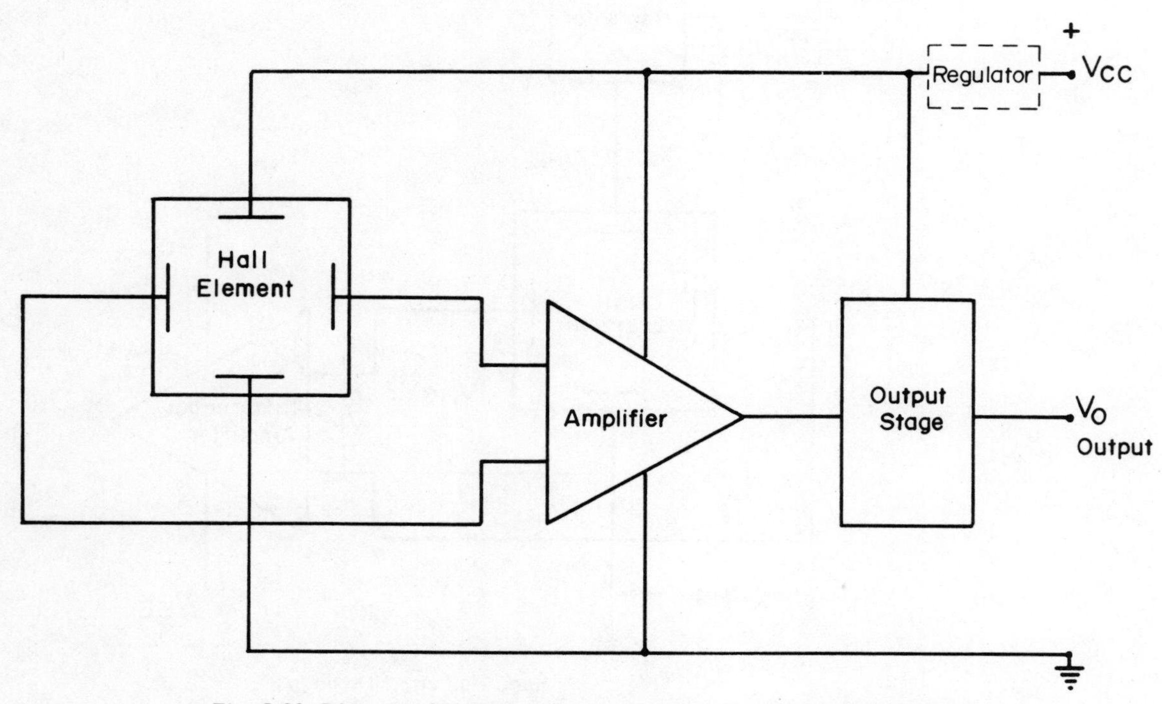

Fig. 5-33. Diagram of Hall IC with linear output. The regulator is optional.

shows a typical diagram of a linear device. The output stage usually consists of an output transistor. Depending on the polarity of the magnet, the output voltage (V_o) can be either positive or negative and the relationship between flux density and voltage is linear until the amplifier saturates (see Fig. 5-34). Frequently it is not desirable to have a negative output voltage because it requires two power supplies. By introducing a bias into the amplifier, a linear flux density to V_o relationship can be obtained while the voltage always remains positive as in Fig. 5-35. A digital switch is

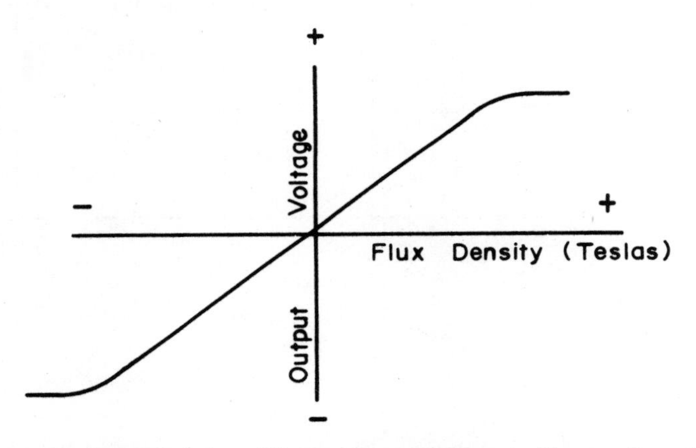

Fig. 5-34. Characteristics of linear-output transducer without voltage bias.

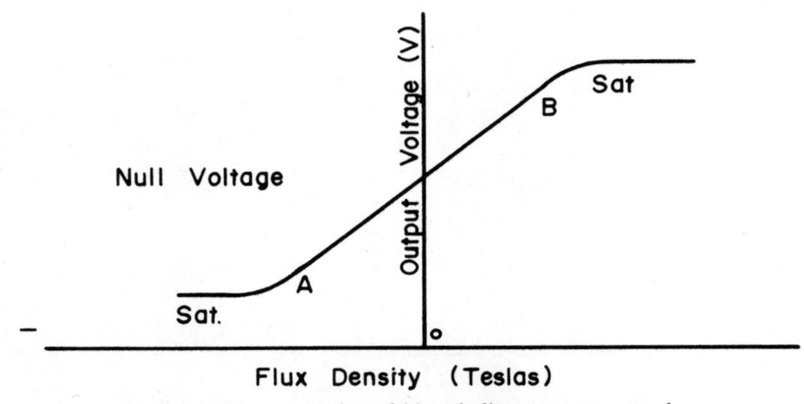

Fig. 5-35. Characteristics of biased, linear-output transducer.

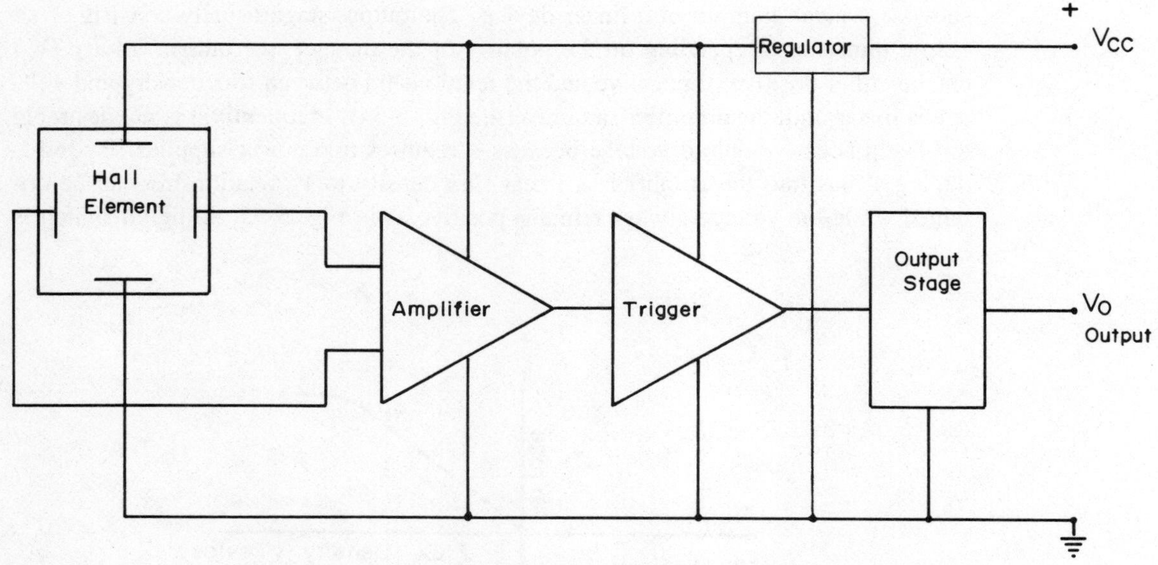

Fig. 5-36. Diagram for digital Hall switch.

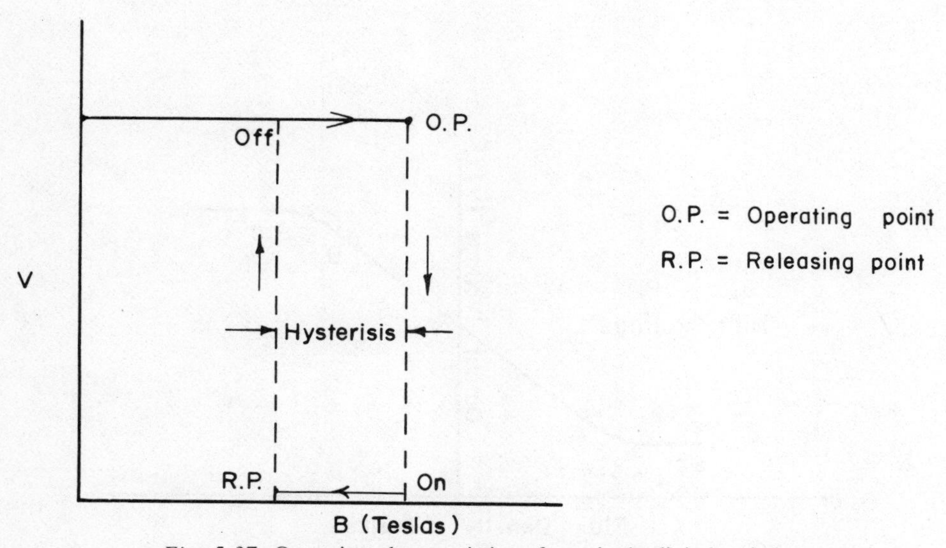

Fig. 5-37. Operating characteristics of a unipole digital switch.

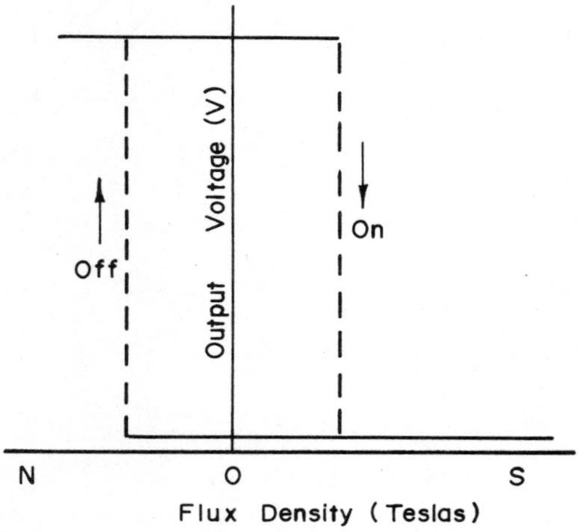

Fig. 5-38. Operating characteristics of a latching bipolar digital switch.

the result of adding a trigger circuit to the Hall effect circuit as in Fig. 5-36. The operating point occurs at a higher flux density than the release. The difference between these two levels is called hysterisis (see Fig. 5-37).

In common use for BLDC motors are latching bipolar switches, which operate on one polarity and release only on opposite polarity. An example of this is shown in Fig. 5-38, where the switch turns on when the south pole of a magnet faces the switch, and it turns off only when the north pole faces the switch.

The operating and release points of most Hall switches will undergo reversible changes with temperature within their temperature operating range.

Bibliography

"Hall Effect Transducers" Micro Switch Co., 1982, Chapter 2.

6

Brushless Motor Drives and Systems

6.1. INTRODUCTION

The preceding chapters have dealt with the physical and magnetic aspects of ac and dc machines of more conventional design. This chapter describes the various electronic drive methods now in general use. Various methods of commutation and feedback are reviewed with emphasis on practical considerations. Although this chapter is not intended to be a step-by-step design guide to brushless drives, the more practical side of this subject is covered in detail. This approach arises partly from the proprietary nature of most commercial systems and, of course, partly from the limited space available. However, you should gain valuable insight into the design constraints and potential uses of todays brushless motor systems.

6.2. ELEMENTS OF A TYPICAL BRUSHLESS DRIVE

In most industrial applications, the three-phase, full-wave brushless drive has attained wide acceptance for a mixture of reasons. One reason is that the three-phase design offers the best performance/cost/complexity trade-off. However, in a great many product-specific applications, the two-, three- and four-phase, half-wave approach might have considerable merit. These specific designs are considered in this chapter.

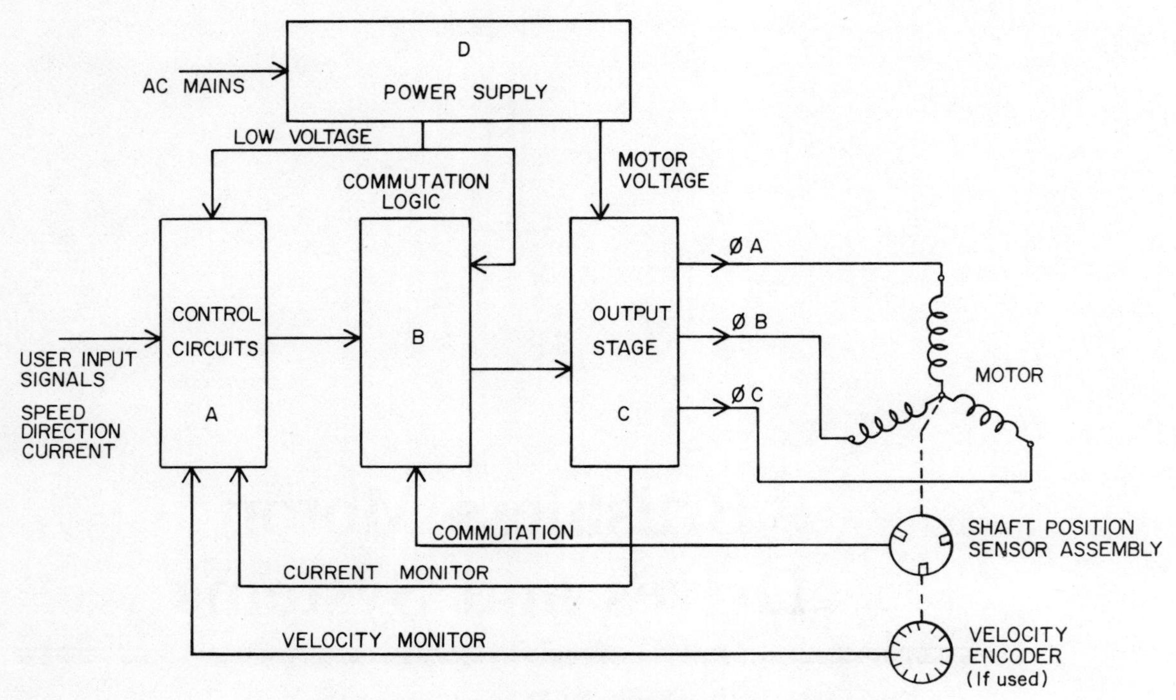

Fig. 6-1. Elements of a three-phase BLDC motor system.

Figure 6-1 shows the outline of a typical three-phase, full-wave drive feeding a wye-connected motor. For the sake of discussion, the major portions of the system are labeled A through D. In practice, the sectional lines often blur because novel circuit design concepts can combine various functions into one circuit grouping. However, the usual drive system consists of the following:

6.2.1. Control Circuits—Speed Control (A)

This section comprises the user interface and housekeeping circuits. In some cases, control of speed is the most important user parameter, closely followed by direction and torque. In servo applications, a four-quadrant design is specified that is a combination of both speed and direction if viewed against conventional servo systems. In some cases, the user signal is analog with speed represented by the input signal amplitude and direction a function of polarity. In this case, zero volts would correspond to zero RPM. The input could just as well be digital using an input of n bits to provide speed data and one or two additional bits for direction and stop/start. Regardless of the input configuration, the input section must convert user information to values that can be used to control the key system parameters of velocity, direction, and current.

6.2.1. Commutation (B)

This section must convert the signals generated by the commutation sensor into a form suitable for controlling the motor coil-switching sequences. In Fig. 6-1, the sensor system is three Hall effect devices. This is a very common approach in many designs. However, it is also found that optical shaft encoders and syncro resolvers are commonly used for this function. Regardless of the method used, the commutation circuits must decode the sensor signals and provide a suitable switching pattern which permit efficient operation of the motor.

6.2.3. Output Stages (C)

This section must switch the motor phases in the proper sequence as dictated by the commutation circuits of section B. To this end, the output stages must carry the necessary current to provide the required torque and must operate at a voltage compatable with the speed requirements. Obviously, this section usually operates at a high power level. In almost all cases, it operates as a saturated switch.

6.2.4. Power Supply (D)

This section provides the necessary circuit operating voltages at the proper current and is usually fed from the ac power source. In some systems, this section is part of the external circuitry of the device in which the motor operates. In conventional applications, the power supply can be totally transformer operated and thus isolated from the ac mains. In other designs, only the low-level (logic, linear, etc.) circuits are line isolated with the motor output stages often fed from the ac mains via a rectifier-filter combination.

Each section described above is discussed starting with the output stages (section C in Fig. 6-1) and working back towards the control and low-level portions.

6.3. OUTPUT STAGES FOR THREE-PHASE DRIVES

The three-phase system outlined in Fig. 6-1 would typically use three half-bridge output circuits as in Fig. 6-2. This figure shows two NPN transistors arranged in *totem-pole* fashion. This is a very common configuration in many power applications, including linear servo amplifiers and switch-mode power supplies. The circuit function is self-explanatory and can be viewed as a *SPDT* (single-pole, double-throw)

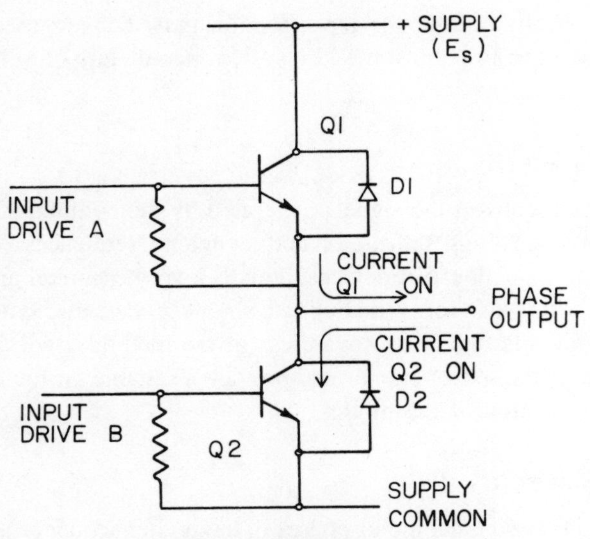

Fig. 6-2. NPN half-bridge output section.

switch. The diodes D1 and D2 serve to commutate voltage to the supply and ground rails during turn on and turn off into an inductive load. These diodes are aptly called *free-wheeling* or commutation diodes. The diodes are inherent in certain semiconductors such as FET devices and are built into other types, notably power Darlington structures.

Figure 6-3 (a) shows three half-bridge circuits as they would be connected to a typical three-phase stator.

Figure 6-3 (b) is the timing sequence required to produce proper operation in a two-pole motor. The three phases are switched at a 120-degree electrical phase angle in order to produce the necessary rotating magnetic field. Note that Q1 through Q3 conduct only in their proper time interval in serial fashion, and Q4 through Q6 allow for overlap referenced to Q1 through Q3. This follows the switching sequence in chapter 5 (Fig. 5-4). The proper commutating sequence is provided by the commutating circuits of section B in Fig. 6-1. The semiconductors in the output stages must be rated to supply the current and voltage necessary to provide desired motor performance. In drives with fairly low power output, operating at 50 V or less, the use of relatively common power transistors is usually practicable. At higher power levels, the choice of device becomes more critical. Keep in mind that the motor windings

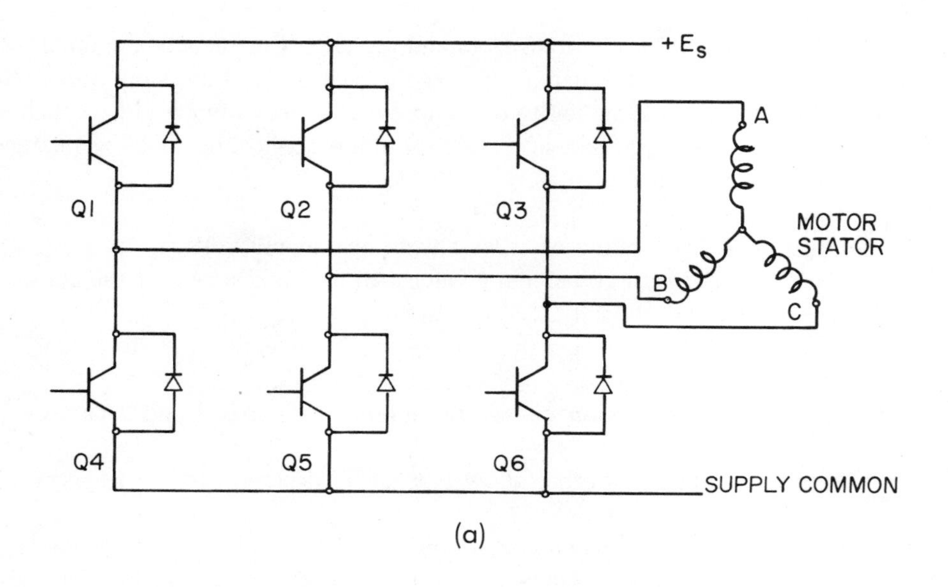

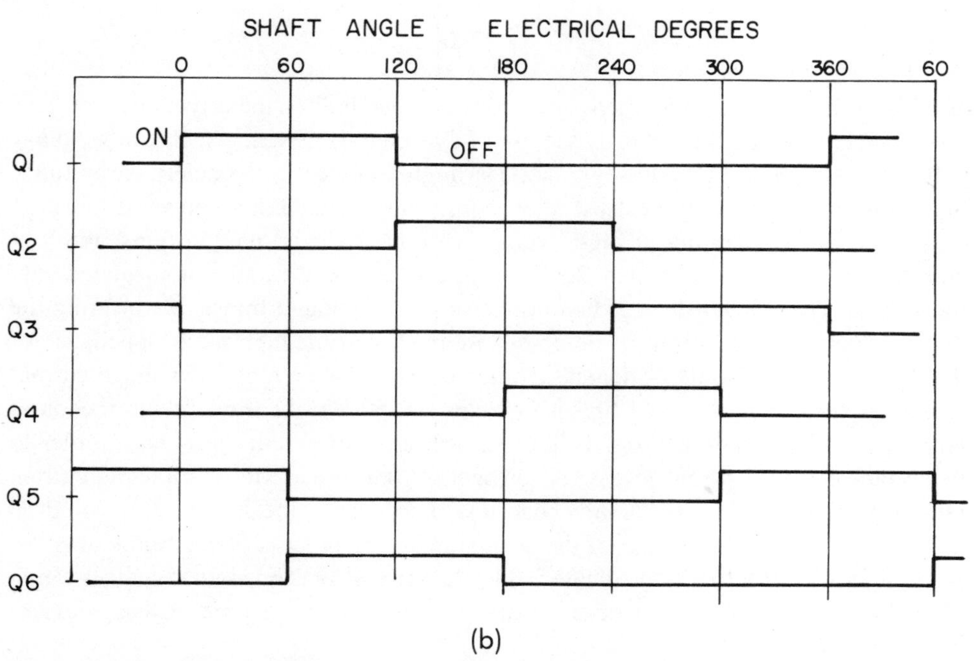

Fig. 6-3. Three half-bridge circuits for three-phase drive (a) and three-phase power-switch timing (b).

present an inductive load to the transistors and the effects of inductive spiking and load-line control must be considered. Of course, because the transistors operate in saturation, the power-handling ability of a particular device is much greater than in linear service. The basic requirement for service in this application could be summed up in the following manner:

- Voltage breakdown rating of at least twice the supply voltage
- Current rating at least 50 percent greater than the highest peak phase current expected under worst case conditions
- Switching times fast enough in comparison to conduction time to assure efficient, cool operation
- Reasonably low saturation voltage to minimize power loss and heat rise when in conduction
- Current gain high enough to allow reasonable drive circuits to be used

At voltages below 100 V, the choice of power devices is fairly broad even at high currents. Note that as voltage ratings increase, the current gain, h_{FC}, for single devices falls to values on the order of 5 to 10. This results in higher base drive requirements because:

$$\frac{I_c}{h_{FE}} = I_b$$

The higher base drive requirement often adds cost and bulk to the driver circuits. This constraint can be circumvented by the use of Darlington devices, which can yield h_{FE} values to as high as 250. However, the Darlington device is characterized by fairly high saturation voltage, typically 2 V or more. This results in high power dissipation especially when operating at high average current. In most new designs, the best choice is the FET or a related device, such as the new family of insulated-gate transistors. These latter devices can be viewed as compound transistors offering the low conduction drop of bipolar devices combined with the high input impedance of the FET. The FET family of devices available cover a wide range of voltage-current ratings at reasonable cost. At higher voltages (>250 V), the die structure becomes large, and current ratings drop. It is often necessary to parallel devices in order to reach the required current levels. At present, 500 V units with continuous current ratings of 13 A are available at high cost. It is expected that the cost of FETs will drop as the ratings improve because of the normal maturing process of electronic devices. At present the *IGFET* (insulated gate field-effect transistor) and similar devices might offer the best price-performance trade off if the slow turn-off time of these devices can be tolerated.

The general trend in the future will probably be towards various smart power devices containing built-in logic circuits to monitor current, voltage, and perform the necessary driving functions such as level shifting and isolation. The latter requirement of level shifting and isolation become apparent when the circuit of Fig. 6-2 is analysed in detail. Component Q2 of this circuit is emitter referenced to supply common, and the base or gate drive can be applied between common and Q2. For Q1, the emitter or source (for a FET) is the active output node. This is not at a convenient reference point for ease of driving the device. In the circuit of Fig. 6-3 (a), the problem of transistor isolation can readily be seen because there is no convenient reference common to Q1 through Q3, except for the positive supply rail. The circuit of Fig. 6-4 takes advantage of this by using a PNP or P-channel device in the Q1 position. Base drive is thus provided by R_b and Q_b. Component Q_b is driven in a conventional manner. This method is in widespread use at low to medium power levels (<250 W). The method has some severe drawbacks, however, which limit its total usefulness. The use of certain bipolar devices often requires that operation be in the *RBSOA* (reverse biased safe operating area) mode. It is often difficult and expensive to design the necessary circuits to insure base reverse bias at turn off as is required by RBSOA. When P-channel FETS are used the range of devices available to the designer is restricted, and cost is high. Another drawback to the circuit of Fig. 6-4, is that the resistor R_b must dissipate the voltage drop from the base of Q1 to the

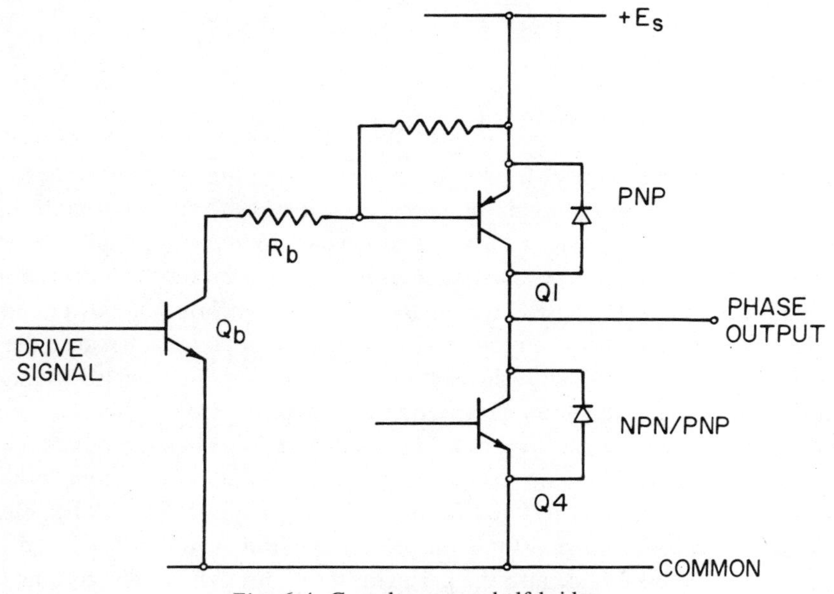

Fig. 6-4. Complementary half bridge.

supply common. For single bipolar devices having low h_{FE}, this circuit is not very practical. Darlington devices are a must in this configuration. As an example, assume a supply voltage of 168 V, common enough in line operated drives. Let the following apply:

$$
\begin{aligned}
E_s &= 168 \text{ volts} \\
I_m &= \text{motor current, } 10 \text{ A } (I_c) \\
h_{FE} &= 100 \\
V_{ce}\ Q_b &= 1\text{V} \\
V_{be}\ Q1 &= 1\text{V}
\end{aligned}
\tag{6-1}
$$

Find base current:

$$\frac{I_c}{h_{FE}} \text{ or } \frac{10}{100} = 0.1 \text{ A}$$

Find available voltage:

$$E_s - (V_{ce} + V_{be}) \text{ or } 168 - (1 + 1) = 166 \text{ volts}$$

Find R_s to allow 0.1 A I_b

$$\frac{166}{0.1} = 1660 \text{ ohms}$$

Power dissipation in R_s:

$$I^2R = 0.1^2 \times 1660 \text{ or } 16.6 \text{ W}$$

Note that if h_{FE} had been only 10, then the power dissipation would have been on the order of 166 W. Clearly high-gain devices are required in this configuration.

The circuit of Fig. 6-5 requires a separate isolated low voltage supply to provide drive to Q1. If a bipolar supply is used, the driver can permit RBSOA operation and, by using optocoupling, the base drive input can be isolated from the power common. Three such isolated supplies are required for three-phase operation because the upper three transistors Q1 through Q3 in Fig. 6-3 (a) must remain electrically isolated inasmuch as their individual outputs are the three-phase motor outputs and cannot be electrically connected together. In motor drives that are operated directly from the ac mains and no mains isolation transformer is used, the drive to transistors Q4 through Q6 must also be electrically isolated from the driving logic if the user has electrical connection to the control signal functions. A circuit similar to that used to drive Q1 through Q3 can be used. Because the emitters of Q4 through Q6 are common, only one extra isolated power supply is needed to furnish low-level power to the three additional driver circuits.

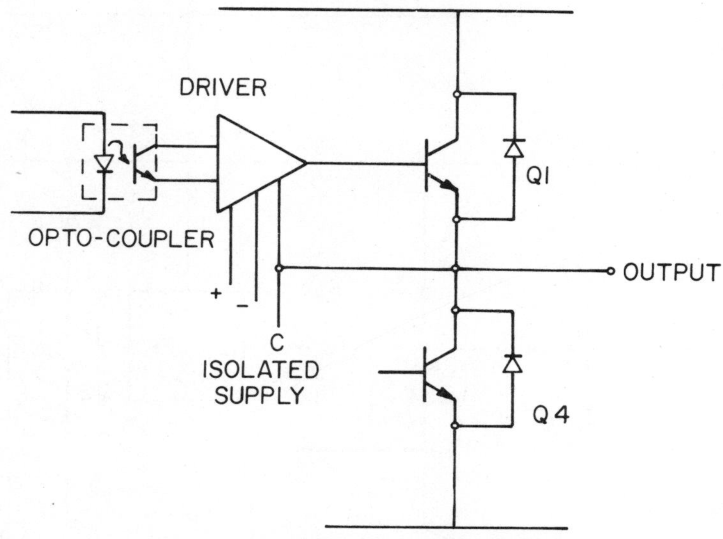

Fig. 6-5. Isolated drive in half bridge.

An alternate driving scheme is shown in Fig. 6-6. The bias supply can be single ended and referenced to the main supply. Of course if the bias supply be ground referenced, its voltage must then be E_s higher. This method is very useful with FET devices because the current requirements of FET drive are low except at turn on when the gate-source charging current is at maximum.

Figure 6-7 shows a method that allows driving power FET devices using ground referenced logic. Component Qd is a PNP device that supplies gate drive when its base is pulled low. There are a few practical considerations to the use of this configuration:

- Qd and Qd^1 must have a withstand voltage greater than $+E_s$.
- The circuit impedance values should be kept low to ensure fast device turn on. Often speed-up techniques are required.
- Diodes d1 and d2 must be used to keep the maximum gate-source voltage within safe values. These diodes, in practice, range from 10 to 15 volts.
- The value of R_g is usually kept low to provide the needed device turn-off time. Note that R_g is the only return path for discharge of the gate-source capacity. It is possible to control turn-off time by means of the value of R_g, and in some designs this may be an advantage.

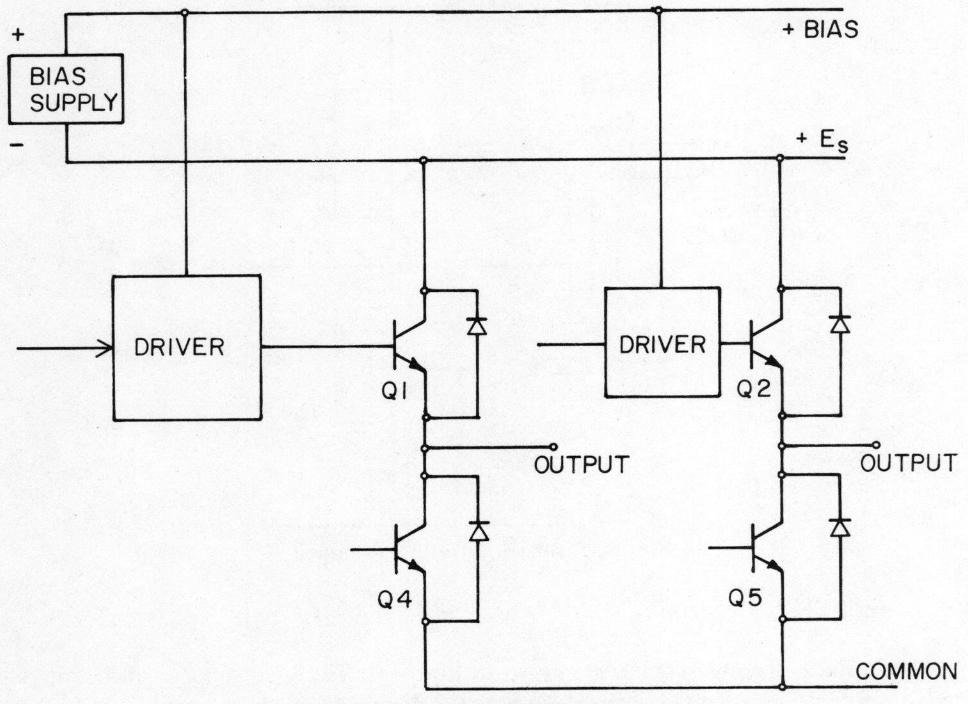

Fig. 6-6. Boosted bias supply drive circuit.

- This circuit cannot provide reverse turn-off bias as required by bipolar switching devices. Additional transistors and energy-storage means must be added to gain a driver capable of providing RBSOA drive characteristics.

When this circuit is used it is best to reference the bias supply to E_s. This makes gate or base drive values less dependent on the absolute value of E_s.

This fact is important if E_s is variable as is often the case in practical designs. The circuit of Fig. 6-4 is extremely vulnerable to variations in the value of E_s, as it is this voltage which provides base drive by means of R_b. Consequently this circuit is best for small, low-power, fixed voltage drives.

There are a great many more drive circuits which can be applied to bipolar or FET devices, most of which are proprietary to the particular drive manufacturer. The output driver section is one that can run up the cost of a three-phase drive especially if

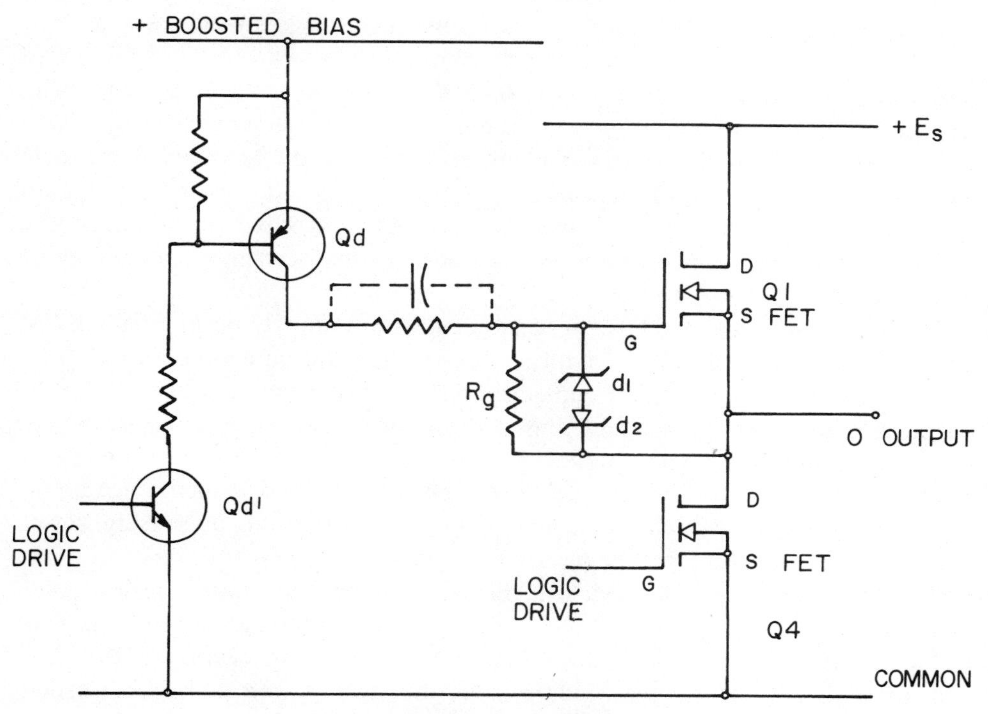

Fig. 6-7. Boosted-bias FET driver.

direct line operation is required. Line operation requires consideration of logic isolation methods which leads to more complicated driver designs.

No discussion of output circuits would be complete without a discussion of switching speed considerations. As mentioned earlier, the purpose of the output transistors is to perform phase switching at the voltage and current levels required by the motor. It is easy to visualize low speed commutation sequences and fall into a false sense of security. For open-loop motor drives, the commutation frequencies can approach steady state. The commutation frequency of a four-pole, three-phase motor operating at 1800 RPM is 60 Hz. This is given by the following expression:

$$\frac{\text{Speed (RPM)} \times 2}{60} = \text{frequency of one sensor}$$

Even at shaft speeds of 25,000 RPM the resulting frequency of 833.3 Hz is slow compared to modern transistor capability. This scenario changes, however, when you consider *PWM* (pulse width modulation) systems. A typical high-performance PWM brushless speed control might operate at chopper rates in excess of 25 kHz. This results in a 40 microsecond period (at 25 kHz), which at 80 percent duty cycle, results in an 8 microsecond off time. This requires that the output devices have very fast turn-on and turn-off times. A 1 microsecond on and off time would represent almost 10 percent power loss under the above conditions. The driver circuits must also be fast enough so as not to impair the switching time of the output stages. The output and output driver delay time must also be taken into account when considering design and device selection.

Needless to say, the fastest circuits and devices are initially desirable for PWM operation, provided cost and reliability are considered. If you choose a good, low-impedance drive circuit and FET output stages, the turn-on and turn-off times can be on the order of <250 nanoseconds. This is ideal from an efficiency viewpoint but can raise many problems within the system. First is the problem of EMI, which becomes a major concern at fast rise and fall times. Second, the wiring inductance of the circuits can produce sufficient voltage spiking due to rapid di/dt, causing device failure or at least reduce logic and output device noise immunity. In some cases, if the FET dv/dt is too great, the device might latch due to the parasitic device action inherent in the substructure of the device. In bipolar transistors, the inherent speed of the device may be exceeded causing difficulty in maintaining saturation. Of course you might say that the motor winding inductance would limit di/dt to reasonable levels, but in most stators there is sufficient leakage inductance and stray capacity to allow very large currents especially at turn on.

The last item to consider is the effect of fast on-off times on the current sharing of parallel devices. There is a popular view that FETs are easily paralleled. This is true only to a point; the problem of operating FETs in parallel involves more than just static power sharing. The gate capacity of each FET might be mismatched to the extent that it might be very difficult to ensure proper dynamic load sharing. As the switching speed increases, so does the problem of equal load sharing. An additional concern is that FET devices in parallel are more prone to parasitic oscillation. Paralleling devices entails much careful design work, and unless all the problems are worked out, it is best to avoid parallel devices running at high speed.

If this commentary seems somewhat contradictory, keep in mind that the problems in designing a good output stage are myriad and require trade offs in terms of maximum switching speed, cost, reliability, heat rise, circuit complexity, and EMI. With all this in mind, consider that the motor is an inductive load with a series generator (back EMF) that often has nonlinear characteristics. There exists no simple step-by-step design process that brings all the elements together to form one elegant design. Cost and common sense seem to be the driving forces in modern drives at this time.

6.4. OTHER OUTPUT CONFIGURATIONS

Although the three-phase connection is the most popular, the two-, four-, and six-phase, full-wave configurations are sometimes encountered. The choice of the latter configurations for a specific application depend entirely on the cost-performance trade off. For very smooth torque at low speeds, a six-phase design might be the ideal choice if the higher cost can be tolerated. A four-phase, full-wave design might be considered as an improvement over the three-phase system if the design parameters cannot be met by the latter. A two-phase, full-wave design might offer an attractive trade off as a replacement for traditional synchronous motors at moderate power levels. The important thing to remember is that each full-wave phase requires two semiconductors and associated driver circuit. The advent of low-cost FETs has blurred the need for distributing the load among a large number of output devices as is found in four- and six-phase drives.

The half-wave configuration can offer some cost savings, particularly in application-specific designs. The half-wave connection operates with unidirectional current in the motor windings and thus makes less efficient use of motor winding space. This selection can result in a motor of larger size for the same power compared to a full-wave design.

Figure 6-8 shows connections for two- and four-phase windings. The first apparent advantage is the fewer number of transistors. The second advantage is that the transistors are ground or common referenced. This arrangement allows easier transistor driving circuits, whether they are bipolar or FET. In terms of device rating however, the two- and four-phase configurations demand more from the transistors than an

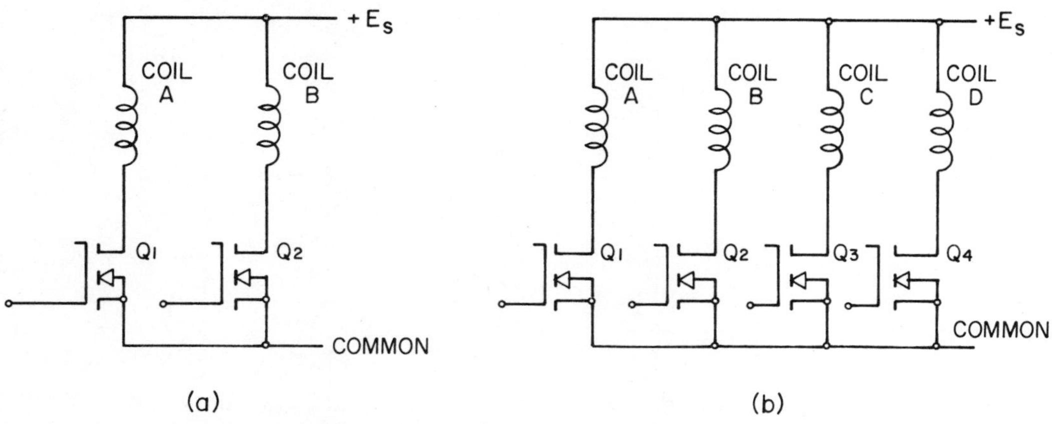

Fig. 6-8. Typical half-wave circuits: (a) two-phase. (b) four-phase.

equivalent three-phase design of equal power output. The three-phase design only requires that Q1 through Q3 be in conduction for 33 percent of the time. In Fig. 6-8 (a) the two-phase transistors operate at a greater duty cycle (0.5); the four-phase design is better since each transistor conducts for 25 percent of the time. The disadvantage is that the coil current is unidirectional, which results in poor coil usage and high average-to-peak current values. While the efficiency is not as good, the simpler circuitry can be used to advantage in certain fixed-speed, single-direction applications where the motor design can be tailored to the operating requirements. A three-phase, half-wave design could also be used, but in some instances the commutating circuit cost can be greater. Only two Hall or optical sensors are required for two- and four-phase systems, as opposed to three sensors for three- and six-phase designs. The commutation logic is also simplified in the two-phase approach, often permitting compact circuit layout. Most of the practical two- and four-phase applications are those in which the mechanical load is fairly constant, such as in fans, centrifuges, and certain pumps. Because these designs are usually single quadrant, their use as servos is limited.

There is only one major drawback to the use of two- and four-phase, half-wave systems and that is the problem of what to do with the energy stored in the motor coils at the end of conduction. Fig. 6-9 shows timing for the respective transistors. In the two-phase design, consider the instant of turn off of Q1. The instantaneous voltage

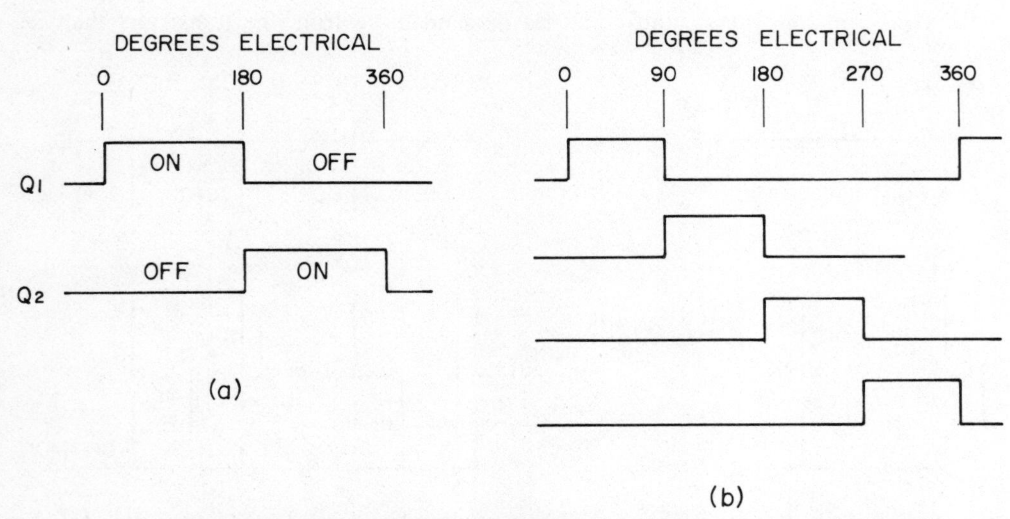

Fig. 6-9. Timing for two and four-phase half-wave circuits: (a) two-phase. (b) four-phase.

across the winding A can be expressed as:

$$V = L \frac{di}{dt}$$

where L = inductance
i = current flowing at turn off

Because the turn-off time is usually fast, the stored energy can result in infinitely high voltages being developed, which can destroy the transistor unless the voltage is properly managed. It is necessary to clamp the induced voltage to a safe value without introducing adverse effects. A simple diode clamp as shown in Fig. 6-10 (a) would limit peak voltage, but it would also keep current circulating well into the conduction time of Q2. This current circulation would result in the generation of a counter torque of large value. The circuit of Fig. 6-10 (b) will serve to clamp the voltage to twice the supply voltage, resulting in fast reset of coil flux but at the expense of an auxiliary supply voltage. A clamp of the dissipative type as in Fig. 6-10 (c) can be designed to limit the voltage to a range of 1.5 to 2.0 times the value of E_s. This circuit will dissipate power but, if properly designed, will only represent 4 to 7 percent of the system throughput power. In many cases, the low cost and flexibility of this clamp make it the best alternative. In low-power systems, operating at low voltage, a zener clamp can be used to advantage. The three- and four-phase, half-wave circuits of Fig.

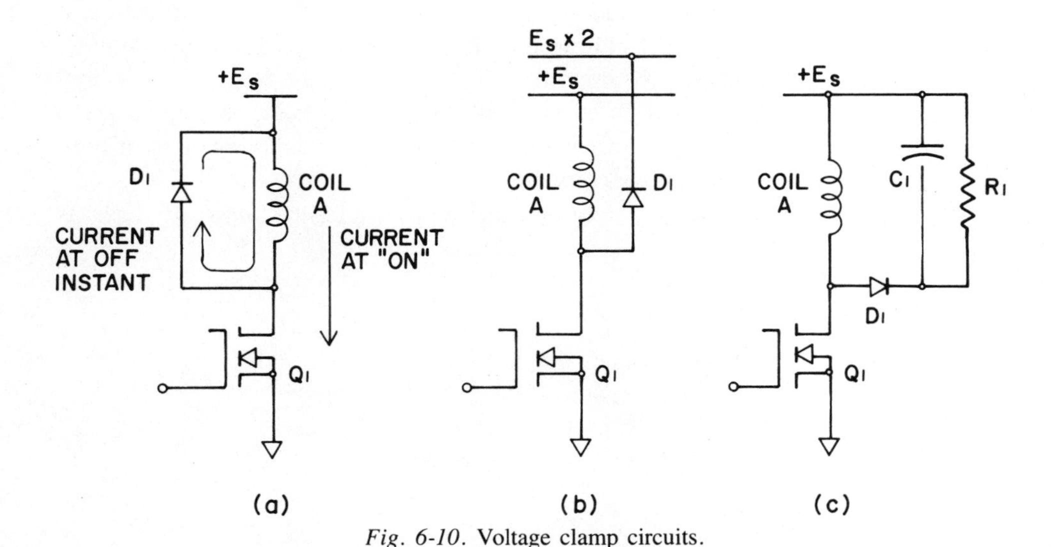

Fig. 6-10. Voltage clamp circuits.

6-8 are also used with stepper motors and will have the same need for inductive energy control. In full-wave designs, the stored inductive energy is conducted back to the power supply by means of the commutating diodes.

If you are familiar with stepper motors, the circuits of Fig. 6-8 (a and b) will seem familiar. In many respects, two- and four-phase, half-wave BLDC drives are very similar to the stepper counterpart. All the problems of L/R (inductance/resistance) ratio, clamping and driving the transistors are shared in both technologies.

6.5. OUTPUT CURRENT CONSIDERATIONS

The voltage into two terminals of a three-phase BLDC motor will see a circuit as in Fig. 6-11. At the instant of Q1 and Q2 switching on, the current will begin to rise as a function of the L/R ratio. If the rotor is not in motion, as during startup, then the final current will be that which is determined by R, the winding resistance. If the rotor is turning, then the instantaneous value of the back EMF will subtract from E_s and the resulting current, as allowed by R, will produce torque. The usable torque is that produced by the average current as explained in previous chapters. In a situation as described above, the current often might be large enough at stall to damage the driver transistors, yet at run it might only reach one-tenth or less of this value. Of course, current limiting of some type is obviously required and is covered in this chapter. The main point is that the output transistors be rated to handle the worst-case peak current expected in the system. An ideal drive system would use transistors rated for orders of magnitude greater than any expected peak. This is, of course, highly impractical if not impossible. The task is to select power devices in as practical a manner possible, consistent with the expected performance and cost.

In a full-wave, three-phase BLDC system intended for constant-speed operation in nonreversing mode and having a reasonable acceleration time, the selection of transistor current rating can be straightforward.

In this case, the required shaft output in watts can be used if the motor efficiency is known:

let

P_o = shaft output in watts
n = motor efficiency
E_s = supply dc voltage
E_d = voltage drops in circuit

then

$$I_s = \frac{P_o \times n}{E_s - E_d} \tag{6-2}$$

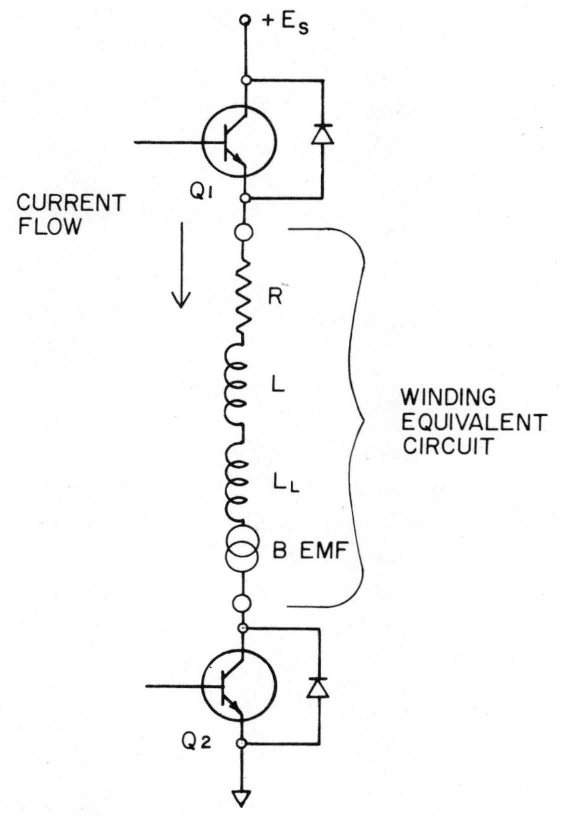

Fig. 6-11. Equivalent circuit of a phase.

In most practical instances, E_s is known or at least predicted. The resulting current, I_s, will flow through the transistors on each conduction period. Because devices Q1 through Q3 must carry the same current but at different times, the transistor dissipation can be viewed as:

$$W_d = \frac{I_s}{3} \times V_{ce} \tag{6-3}$$

Where W_d = watts dissipation
V_{ce} = saturation voltage or $R_{ds} \times I_s$ for FET devices

The I_s value above assumes a steady state condition with a current form factor of unity. In most cases, the form factor is more on the order of 1.2 to 1.5 so that this additional current must be carried by each transistor. Allowing for a 2:1 starting current, the net result for a 100 W output in a 77 percent efficient motor operating with a 90 Vdc source using a Darlington device having a V_{ce} of 2 V would be:

$$\frac{100 \times 1.3}{90 - 4} = 1.52 \text{ amps.}$$

Allowing for form factor of 1.2, 1.52 × 1.2 = 1.82 A. For starting, the current would be 2 × 1.82 = 3.64 A. The power dissipation per device would be:

$$\frac{2 \times 3.64}{3} = 2.42 \text{ W}$$

Additional power dissipation can be realized by switching losses and, for FETs, by current flow in the body diode during commutation of current decay through the body diode. In higher power bipolar Darlington devices, the base drive current can add an appreciable amount of dissipative power.

If FETs were chosen for the above design, it would be necessary to approximate the current to get the equivalent drop.

Thus:

$$\frac{P_o \times n}{E_s}$$

then, $I_s \times R_{ds}$ will yield the approximate voltage drop. Dissipation is determined by I^2R_{ds}. Corrections for form factor can then be added in along with starting current. In higher-power output stages using FETs, the rating of the body diode and its recovery time should be closely examined. The body diode is far from a perfect model, especially at high speeds. Furthermore, the current through the diode in FETs and Darlington devices during the flywheel period will contribute to the heat rise of the device. This rise can usually be assumed to be no greater than 10 percent of the power transferred per device.

In the above example, the motor operated in rather benign fashion, running in one direction, starting rather slowly, and using current limiting to keep start current to twice run. In servo and in PWM modes of operation, the operating situation becomes more complex. In servo systems requiring rapid reversing, it is the peak current that must be considered. At the instant of reversing, the voltage across the phase windings can rise to over twice the normal voltage. In this case, the winding resistance will determine the current and this over-current condition will last for as long as there is system inertia. The load kinetic energy must be dissipated during the deceleration period, which translates to additional current. The peak currents during fast reversing can often exceed normal run current by a large factor. This mode of operation requires active current limiting techniques and considerable overrating of transistors.

The use of PWM speed control can require overrating of the transistors since, in some instances, the current form factor will increase. In order to select proper transistors, you must know all operating parameters.

It is for this reason that commercial drive packages are usually rated for a peak output current. The peak current is typically the current limit value and is not intended for continuous operation. A drive package having a 10 A peak current rating is probably best operated at 7.5 A if good motor performance is to be obtained. This implies a 25-percent derating factor, which for most applications is adequate. It is always wise to check with the manufacturer when in doubt, because poor system performance can often be traced to incorrect driver choice.

6.6. POWER SUPPLY CONSIDERATIONS

The power supply section D in Fig. 6-1 might be a simple transformer-isolated, low-voltage regulator supplying logic power only. In this case, the motor dc is provided by the user. In other situations, the motor dc is derived by full-wave rectification of the ac mains with or without an isolation transformer. Although this section of the drive would appear mundane, it can be a very important part of the overall system and, if poorly designed, can adversely affect performance. Reviewing the basic BLDC operating principles as outlined in chapter 5, you can see that the motor output torque results from the current which flows due to the difference in potential between the supply and back EMF voltages. The power supply must therefore be able to supply this current to develop the necessary output torque. Furthermore, the voltage must be high enough to permit the current to flow at a given maximum speed. The motor dc source must have good regulation and low ripple if full system potential is to be realized. For power ratings of up to one horsepower, it is common to find single-phase ac used. This is usually full-wave rectified and filtered. For larger sizes, three-phase rectifiers are used, which result in greater conversion efficiency and lower percentage ripple. The improved efficiency reduces capacitor cost and size.

Because the rectifier system must also handle the motor starting current, it must be sized to prevent excessive voltage droop during this critical mode. This is particularly important in multiquadrant operation where large peak currents are experienced during reversal periods. In such cases, large amounts of energy storage are required at the filter capacitors.

The importance of low ac ripple on the dc supply can be appreciated by the fact that if the negative-going crest of the ripple component falls below the back EMF value for any part of a phase conduction period, the instantaneous torque will drop. This will result in torque cogging at the least and, in high-gain, closed-loop servos, can lead to severe instability and possible driver transistor failure. Most practical drives will allow a fair amount of head room to allow for ripple, ac mains voltage droop, transformer regulation, and some allowed percentage of torque overload. It is not unusual to find a 25 to 50 percent overvoltage applied to a driver so that all adverse conditions can be met.

For power isolation transformers, note that a well-designed transformer should be used. The authors have observed that in many instances this is not the case, because the transformer can represent a large percentage of total system cost. It is natural to try and save money with this component. Poor system performance is often the result of this saving, with excessive heating and early failure as the dividend.

In some BLDC systems, it is possible to use voltage regulation at the dc source. This is especially true at low power levels, below 200 W. At this level, the cost of preregulating can often be low enough to make an attractive trade off. The advent of switch-mode power supplies might offer an alternative especially if standard voltages are used (for example, 12, 24, or 48 V, which are common today. Even linear regulators offer a low cost alternative for voltage levels of 24 to 48 V at up to 10 A. Of course, bulk is a problem with linears due to transformer, heat-sink, and capacitor size but offer lower EMI possibilities than switchers. Note that preregulation allows for a simple means of speed control by playing with the regulator reference voltage. This method is discussed in this chapter.

At higher power levels, especially at line voltage, the cost of preregulation often becomes prohibitive. With large motor ratings, it might be practical to preregulate using three-phase SCR regulators, where the regulator cost is offset by the expensive drive and motor.

A common power supply phenomenon in four-quadrant drives is *pump up*, where the motor feeds voltage back to the supply during regeneration. Pump up will occur when the motor is overdriven by an external load. In most low-power applications, it is not seen as a problem; in large motors or in traction applications, pump up can occur. The supply voltage can often rise to unsafe values, and means to protect both supply and drive must be incorporated in the design.

In systems using PWM speed contol, the power supply internal impedance is important because in some cases the current into the drive is discontinuous. The discontinuities result from short periods of time when the output drive devices are not in conduction (see section 6.9). During periods of no conduction it is possible for inductive energy to cause spikes to appear on the dc supply line. Therefore the filter capacitors must serve as off time snubbers to limit this dv/dt. Separate capacitors of lower value can also be placed close to the output devices to provide snubbing. Furthermore, during the on time, energy is transferred to the output devices and the initial energy is that supplied by the filter capacitor. This produces a ripple current in the filter capacitors, which can lead to excessive capacitor heat rise. This is the result of the finite ESR/ESL component found in all electrolytic capacitors. In most high-quality capacitors, the *ESL* (equivalent series inductance) derived impedance is at minimum near 50 kHz and rises linearly with frequency above this point. The ac value of current at higher frequencies thus contributes a loss factor that is dissipative in nature. The ESR will be the limiting factor at line frequencies. The presence of excessive 120 Hz ripple on the supply in a PWM system will be seen as an additional error signal and will reduce the control loop dynamic range.

The role of the low-level power supply used to operate logic and linear control functions is an important one. The stability of the control functions is directly related to the quality of this part of the system. Good regulation and low drift with time and temperature are required. Isolation from the high-level portions of the system is required to prevent noise from the high current drivers from introducing control errors. In all quality designs, well-constructed, low-level transformers along with large capacity filters and stable regulators are the norm.

6.7. COMMUTATION LOGIC

In Fig. 6-1, the section C provides decoding of the Hall devices into the proper sequences for driving the motor windings via the power stage. Figure 6-12 shows the various timing states for a four-pole, three-phase, full-wave BLDC motor over 360 degrees of shaft rotation. Note that the logic must provide six discrete outputs, which ultimately drive transistors Q1 through Q6 in Fig. 6-3 (a). The logic function shown in Fig. 6-13 will decode the three sensor outputs Sa, Sb, and Sc into the six outputs required for the driver stage.

In Boolean terms, output Q1 can assume the function A. Therefore $A = ab\bar{c} + \bar{a}b\bar{c} = b\bar{c}(\bar{a} + a) = b\bar{c}$. This form applies for the remaining five output functions. The direction of rotation can be reversed by negation of the input signals Sa, Sb, Sc. Note that in the figure shown, three logic ICs are required to make up the decode function. If direction change means are added, the chip count can reach six or more. This is a fairly large number of parts to dedicate to a single, although important, system function. Other methods might be used to reduce the chip count; one simple method shown in Fig. 6-14. This approach uses a *ROM* (read only memory) to implement the logic operations of Fig. 6-13. The ROM can be programed to provide clockwise and counterclockwise enable inputs as shown in the figure. In this particular instance, two control lines are used, one for each direction. Only one can be high at a time and if both go high, the result is OFF. OFF is also the result if both control lines are low or if the Hall devices fail or otherwise produce missing codes, which could cause simultaneous conduction of the output devices. This logic configuration

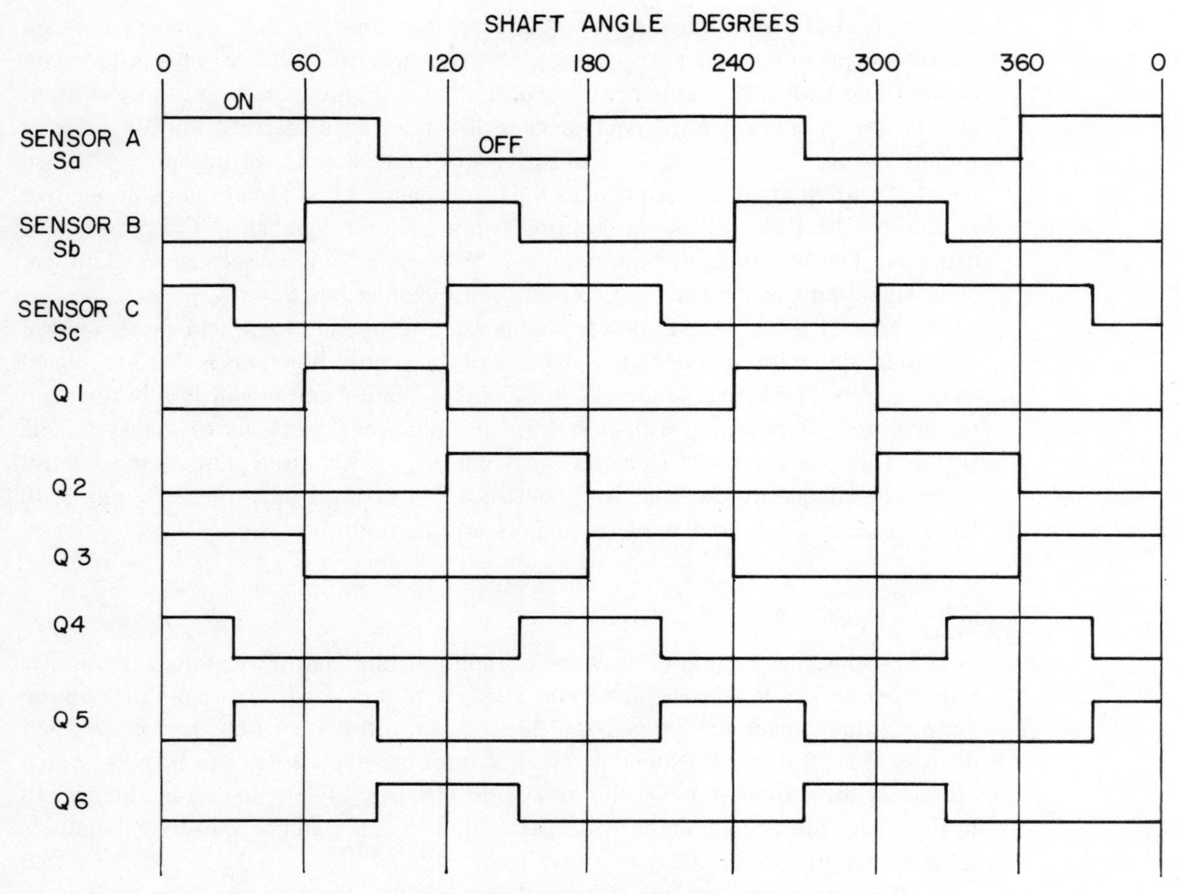

Fig. 6-12. Sensor and output timing chart.

is useful in four-quadrant operation as well as in simple reversing or single direction decoding.

There are a great many other methods available to decode the position-sensing signals, but the ROM offers a single-package approach.

In some cases, it would be advantageous to use a microprocessor to generate the commutation logic function as a direct process using the position sensors as input devices. This method works very well at moderate speed, but at very high shaft speeds, the *CPU* (central prossing unit) instruction and process time might become a limiting factor, particularly if the CPU is also monitoring current and velocity loops. The ROM approach is very cost effective in small systems requiring analog speed and current control. The commutation timing is, of course, fixed and cannot be varied to permit optimal performance over wide speed and torque ranges. It is known that

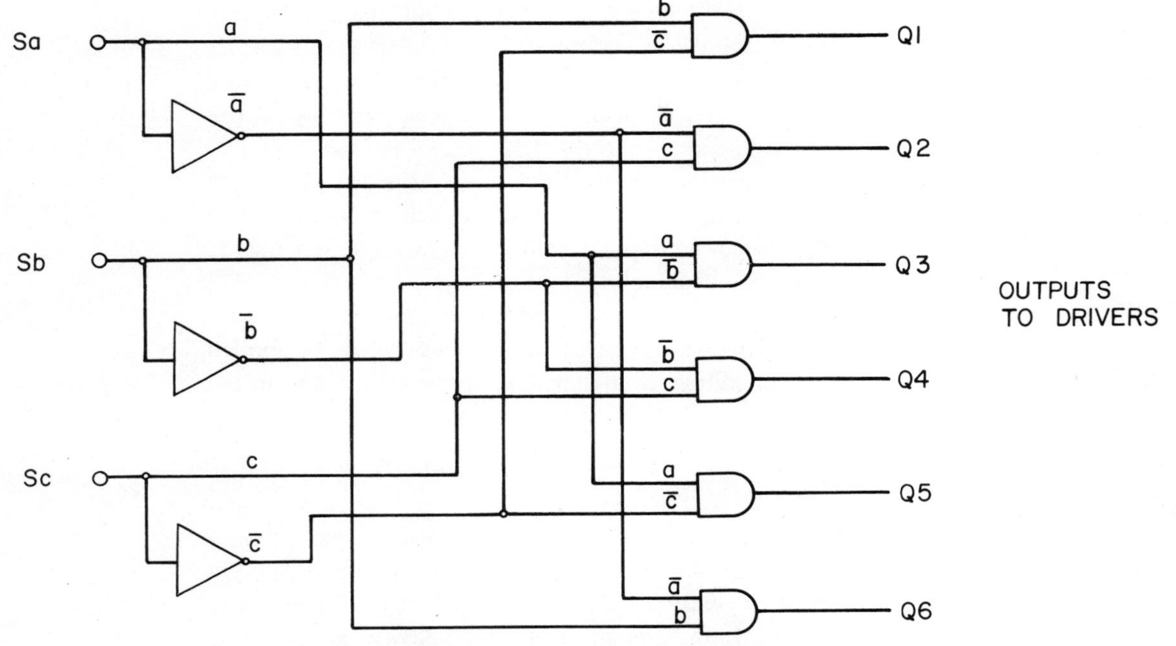

Fig. 6-13. Basic commutation logic for three phase.

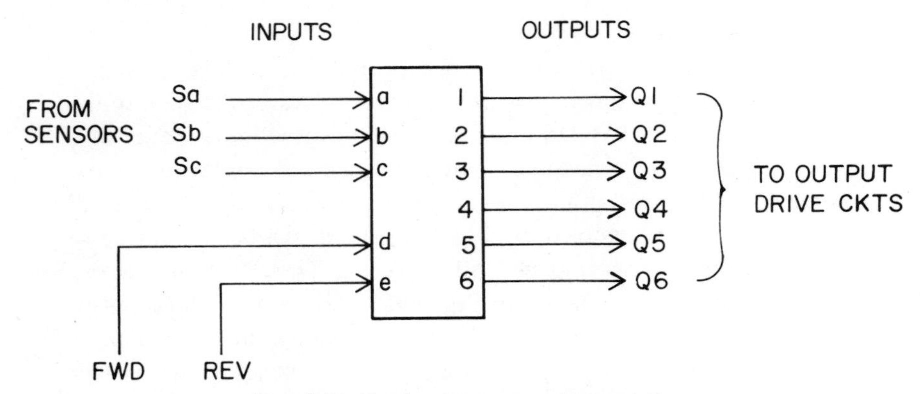

Fig. 6-14. Read-only memory commutation.

lagging or leading the commutation point with respect to the dynamic magnetic axis is often desirable in order to achieve maximum system efficiency. The use of a CPU along with one of the new integrated system controllers (such as the Hewlett Packard HCTL-1000) will work well if the system specifications demand such optimized performance.

Three- and four-phase, half-wave designs can use simple 2-to-4 line decoder ICs to great advantage and at low cost. Steering logic can be added to achieve bidirectional operation. PWM speed control also can be implemented in most decode schemes as will be outlined in section 6.9 of this chapter.

The important thing to remember concerning the commutation logic circuit is that it must be able to lock out error codes that would cause simultaneous drive to be applied to the half-bridge sections. Such condition would, of course, be destructive to the output transistors.

6.8. COMMUTATION SENSORS

In all of the discussion of BLDC motors so far, the shaft-position sensors were assumed to be Hall effect devices. This sensor is by far, the most common method in use. The Hall integrated devices currently available offer the most cost effective sensor for moderate temperature use. In fact, integrated latching devices are available to operate at temperature ranges of −55°C to +150°C. In most cases, the maximum operating frequency is on the order of 100 kHz, which in a four-pole motor is equivalent to 3×10^6 RPM. It is anticipated that as the Hall device technology matures, price and performance will improve.

Three Hall-effect devices are required for generating commutation data in a three-phase system. These are usually mounted on a circuit board structure at the rear of the motor. The devices are typically mounted on a 120- or 60-degree radial pattern. A small magnet disc is normally used to actuate the Hall devices and is mounted on the motor shaft. In some cases, the Hall-effect sensors are embedded in the stator structure. This is useful only when the stator operating temperature can be guaranteed to stay below a safe temperature, of approximately 50°C to 60°C. The electrical relationship in a four-pole configuration is shown in Fig. 6-15. The typical three-sensor approach is capable of providing only limited position and velocity information to the control system. This approach is sufficient for commutation purposes and, if proper steps are taken, can be used for limited speed control. In moderate performance, closed-loop systems operating above 1000 RPM, the three Hall device outputs can be logically summed and fed to a speed control circuit as in Fig. 6-16. The circuit will yield 12 pulses per revolution which, at 1000 RPM, would be equivalent to 100 Hz output of the combiner logic. This is a low but usable sample data rate for most

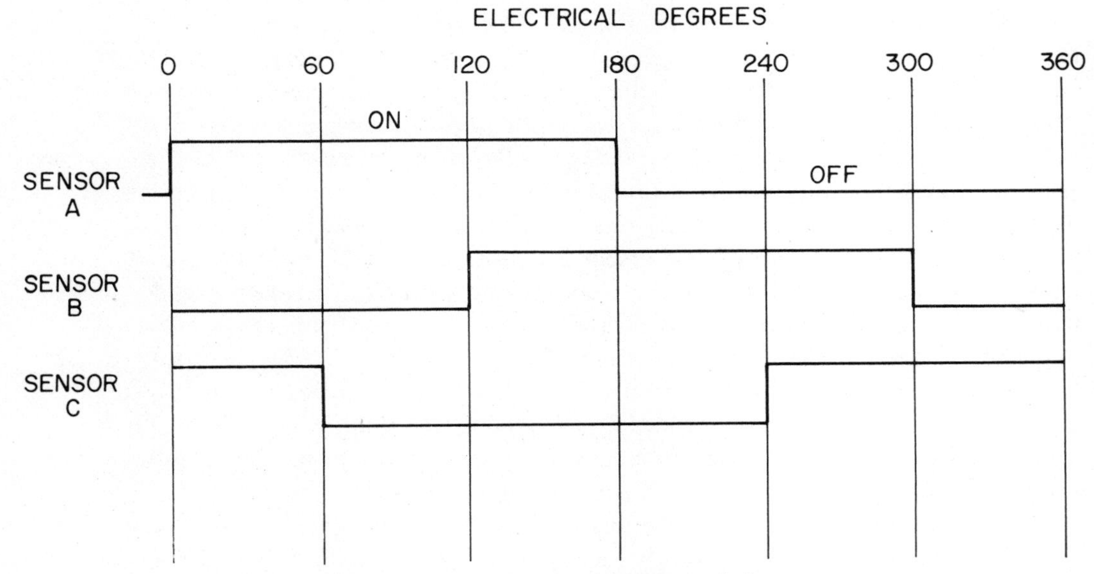

Fig. 6-15. Typical three-phase sensor timing.

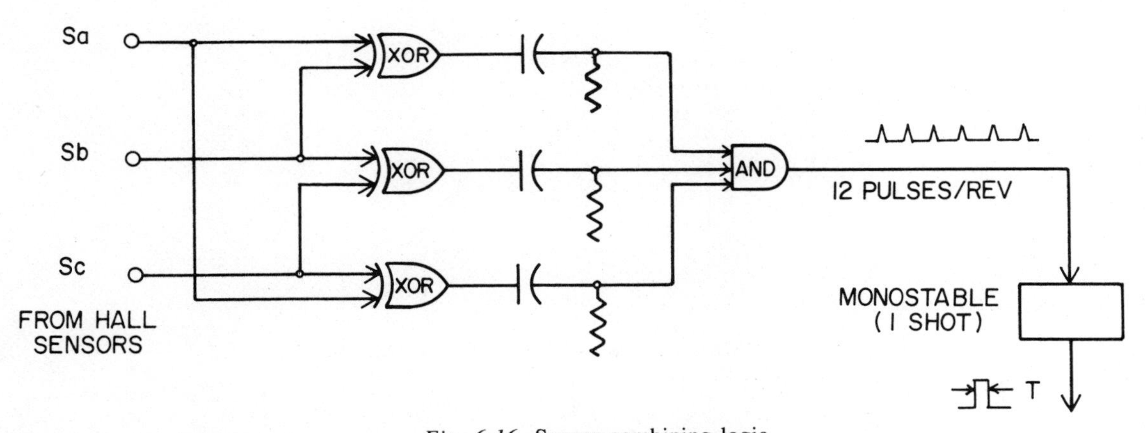

Fig. 6-16. Sensor combining logic.

constant speed applications. This low sample data rate limits the low-speed performance because of the high output ripple component of a synthesized electronic tach.

Where operation to near zero speed is required over a wide overall speed range, it is necessary to increase the resolution of the shaft sensor system. Of course, a dc, brush-type tachometer generator could be used. This would be a contradiction in terms but, in some cases, a dc generator is not so odd on a BLDC motor as it seems. Most high-quality dc tachometer generators can offer long life because the brushes are not required to handle any appreciable current. However, the high-tech approach is to use an optical shaft encoder to improve resolution. Encoders are normally available with quadrature-related two-phase outputs, which makes it easy to derive directional information as well as speed data. Figure 6-17 is the schematic of a simple, but usable velocity- and direction-sensing circuit for use in four-quadrant servo operation. Note that the two phases of the optach are combined in an *XOR* (exclusive or) circuit to give an output of twice the frequency. This permits use of an encoder, having fewer lines or allows use of a higher low-pass filter cutoff frequency, which might be of value in improving response time. The circuit of Fig. 6-17 is, in effect, a brushless tachometer. Fig. 6-18 is the transfer function for the analog output of this circuit. Similar results could be obtained by substituting two of the Hall-effect outputs for the encoder channels A and B. Of course, the resolution would now be 12 pulses per revolution, which is not a suitable value for servo work.

It is also possible to multiply the two-phase optach output by four. A circuit similar to that in Fig. 6-16 could be used. This would allow a faster analog loop response time or permit improved ripple output for a filter of fixed response.

If a two-channel optical encoder is fitted with a third output which indicates a specific or zero position, it is possible to provide commutation signals by using

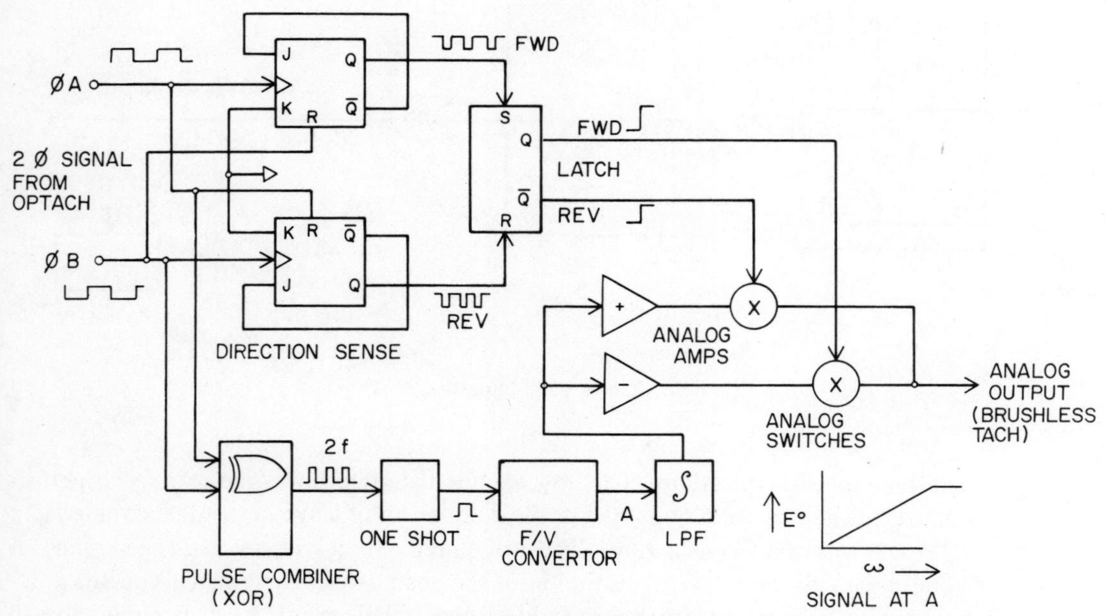

Fig. 6-17. Block diagram of electronic tachometer.

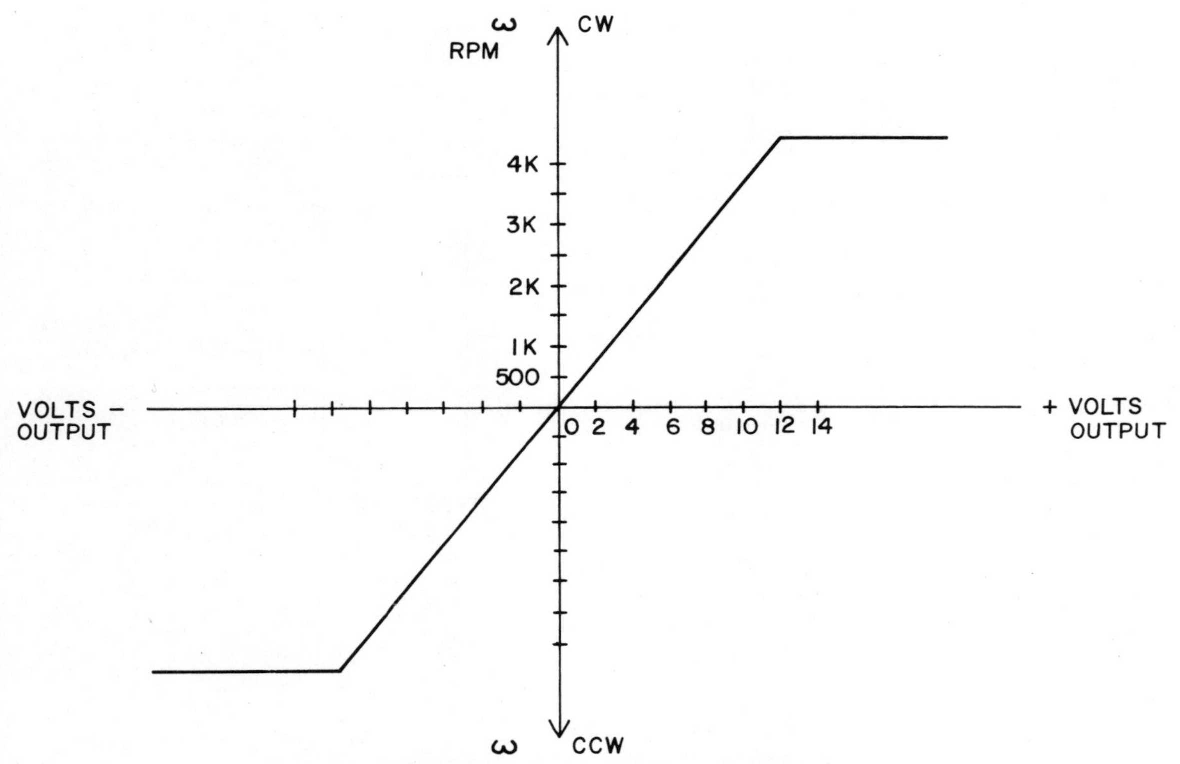

Fig. 6-18. Transfer function of electronic tachometer.

proper logic. Figure 6-19 shows such a method in block form. The three blocks A, B, C are counter/logic functions that provide outputs at a′ through c′ in accordance with the timing of Fig. 6-13. The zero input clears or sets up the counter values, which are used to divide the pulses at the phase inputs A and B. This zero pulse is aligned with the magnetic axis of the stator, thus providing a positive magnetic alignment to ensure proper start up. The counting ratios of A, B, and C can be varied during operation to provide dynamic advance-retard of the commutation phase angle. This circuit is probably too complex to implement in discrete logic, and variations in integrated form are currently available. The Hewlett-Packard HCTL-1000 is an integrated subsystem that operates much on the order of the system just described. The use of advanced commutation methods implies the use of microprocessor control over the major system parameters, including commutation. This will no doubt become the way of the future, particularly in high-performance servo systems.

Syncro resolvers offer another alternative for obtaining the required positional and velocity data. Resolvers are externally excited wound rotor generators that produce ac sinousidal outputs as a function of the shaft angle. Resolvers usually do not use slip

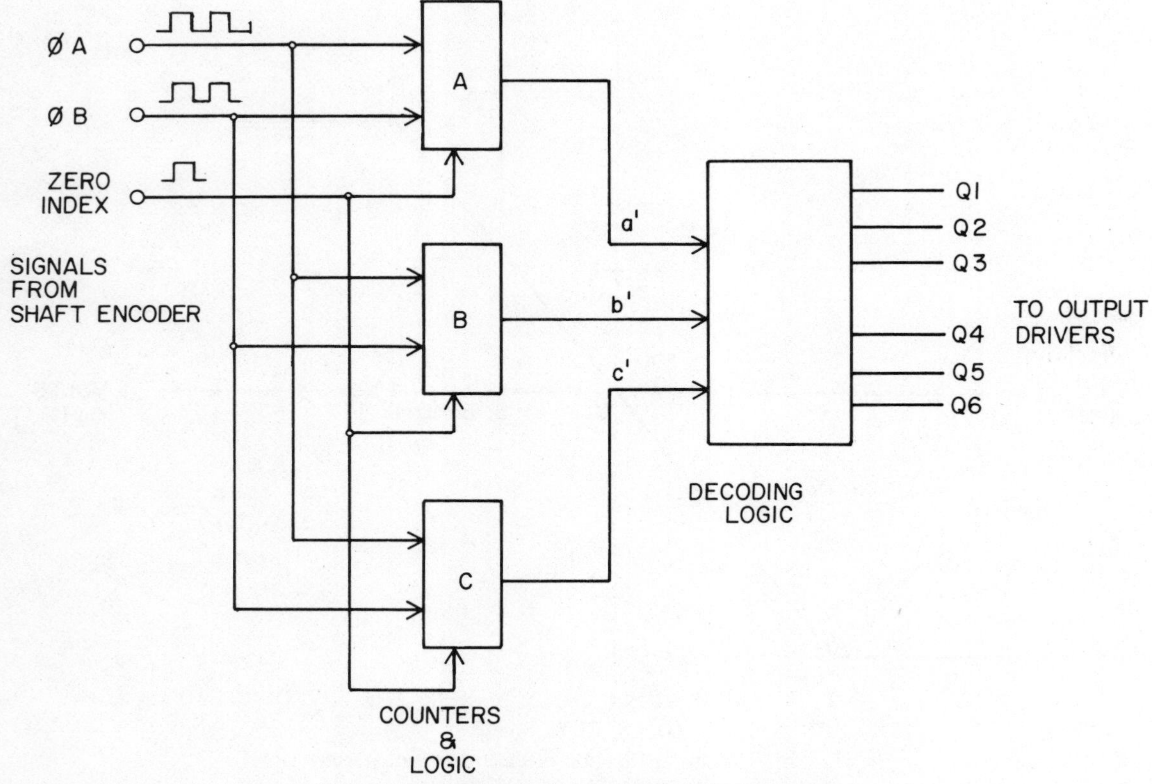

Fig. 6-19. Synthesized commutation block diagram.

rings and brushes; instead the ac excitation voltage to the rotor is coupled by means of an integral rotary transformer. Thus, they are ideal for BLDC use. However, the output signals must be extensively processed to obtain the necessary outputs. Synchronous demodulation methods are normally used to permit the generation of commutation and tachometer signals as shown in the block diagram of Fig. 6-20. The demodulation circuitry can be designed to produce three commutation signals, which can be processed in the same manner as Hall device outputs. Additional outputs can be generated to provide sinousiodal three-phase where needed, and a bidirectional tach signal similar to that of Fig. 6-18. The excitation frequency is usually in the range of 1 to 30 kHz with the higher frequencies preferred because the low pass filters normally used in signal processing can be designed for greater ripple attenuation at these higher frequencies. Additional signal processing employing A/D conversion can permit the resolver outputs to be used in digital position control. This latter application requires resolvers having a high degree of electrical/mechanical accuracy. Commercial resolvers are available in accuracies of from 1 to 30 minutes and are now

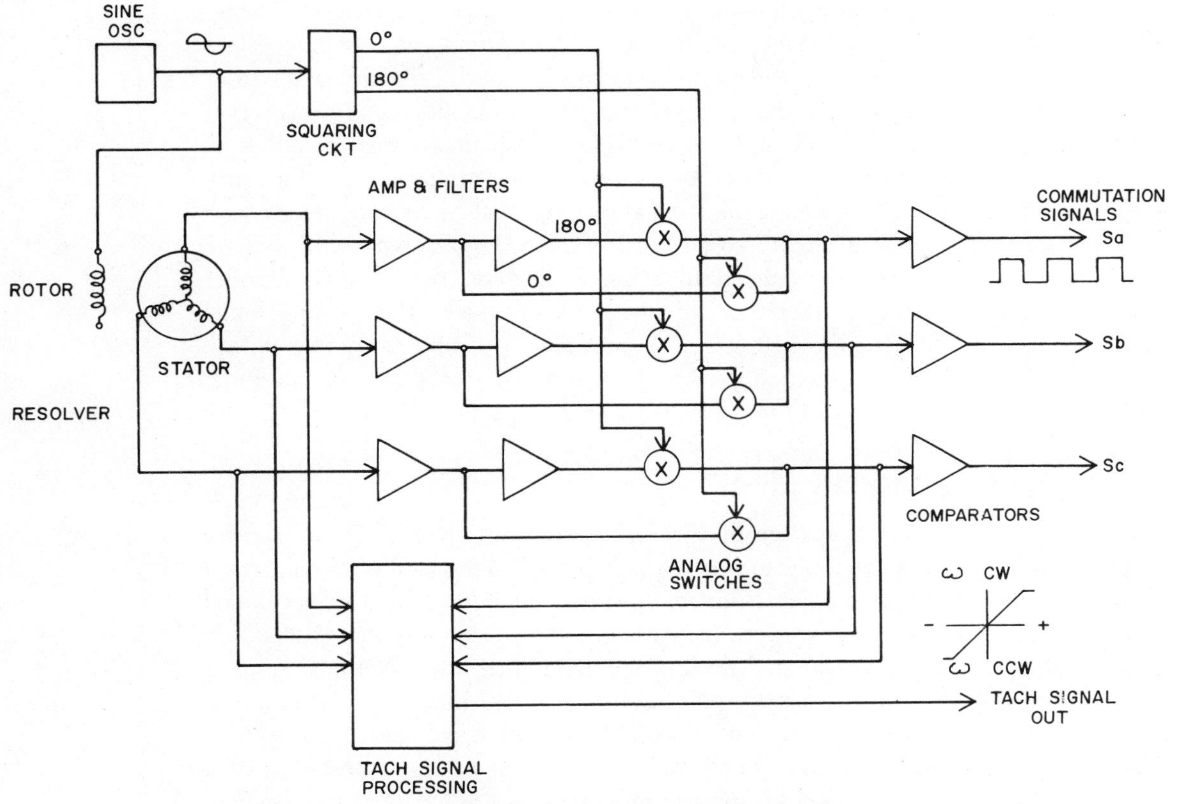

Fig. 6-20. Resolver system block diagram.

available as pancake units, that are designed without bearings, for integral mounting on a BLDC frame. Cost in the present market can run from sixty to several hundred dollars per unit, depending on accuracy and options. Most resolvers are limited to a maximum speed of 10,000 RPM. The limit is primarily electrical, arising from increased eddy current and phase shift at higher speeds. Improvements in resolver design and materials will, no doubt, extend the speed range in future. Demodulating electronics is available in IC form from several manufacturers but at high cost.

There are many novel commutation sensor techniques in the literature, ranging from imbedded Hall devices in the stator to fiber optic pickup methods. All have their uses and should not be discounted no matter how bizarre they might seem. On the subject of commutation, there have been attempts to use the back EMF as a source of commutation signal. This method has some merit, but being volatile to the extent that true position data does not exist at rest, these methods require special circuit designs to aid in starting up in the right direction and switching sequence.

In all of the conventional methods just described, the commutation and velocity pick-ups are usually mounted external to the motor, typically at the rear in a protective housing. This adds length to the motor package and requires sealing out environmentally borne dust, debris, and fluids. In harsh environments, the use of a resolver is sometimes recommended, particularly when high temperatures are involved. Cost and performance will dictate which of the methods are best. In terms of circuit simplicity and cost, the Hall method is the most attractive. Optical encoders along with the Hall commutation is the most cost effective method for servo application in moderate environments. This is the result of new, low-cost optical shaft encoder packages presently being marketed. A number of companies offer modular units ranging in cost from $70.00 to $100.00. This makes for a simple, easy-to-interface sensor at reasonable cost. When coupled with existing Hall packages, it is a tough combination to beat.

6.9. CONTROL CIRCUITS

Section A of the system outline of Fig. 6-1 is the portion of a BLDC control responsible for the user input signal process. Additionally, the control circuits must monitor the motor current in order to protect the motor and transistors from accidental damage. In a great many applications, the current is the primary controlled function. In the basic BLDC drive, the control block is required to perform operations on speed and current only. Position is usually processed externally. From the discussion in chapter 4, there are two basic methods available by which the speed can be controlled: linear and nonlinear (switching). Figure 6-21 shows implementation of a linear speed control on a three-phase motor. Here Q1 is used as a pass element to vary the voltage, hence current, into the output drive section. Obviously Q1 must be rated to supply the worst-case current, and at most operation points will exhibit high power dissipation. Thus, this approach is used only at very low power levels. Another potential problem exists, which manifests itself as a potential reverse-bias of Q1 should E_s fall to zero while the motor is still in motion, as would result from kinetic energy in the motor rotor and load. This is because a BLDC motor is a very efficient generator and the generated voltage (back EMF) is rectified by the commutation diodes and fed into the emitter of Q1. The diode CR shown in dotted lines will protect Q1 from the back EMF. If a FET is used for Q1, the diode is automatically in place.

Q1 could also be operated in switch mode if desired. A further modification could be made as in Fig. 6-22. The circuit is a buck (step-down) PWM regulator. This circuit is useful for small, high-performance, closed-loop systems where the power level is fairly low, usually not greater than 500 W. Of course, Q1, CR1, L1, and C1 must be sized for the power levels expected in operation. Other variations of this

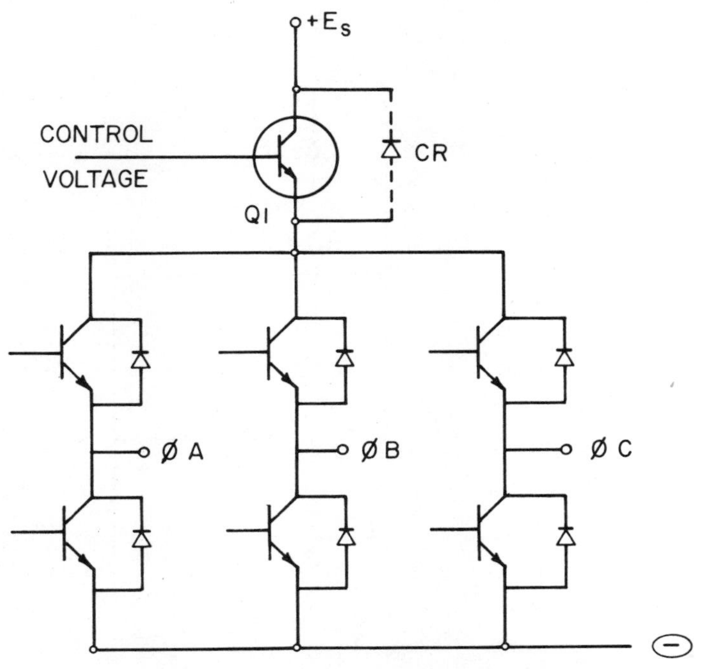

Fig. 6-21. Voltage control of speed using pass element.

approach use an externally programmable power supply of either linear or switch mode design to provide the variable E_s voltage to control speed.

In most commercial BLDC drives available today, speed control is by PWM, with switching being performed by the output transistors. This is an approach that offers the most economic measure to speed control as the switching devices are already in place, namely the output transistors. The switching logic can be implemented in the low-level commutation circuitry, and the savings in cost and bulk are readily apparent. When using the output devices in chopped or PWM mode, it becomes necessary to review the basic mode of operation. Two approaches are possible: the continuous and discontinuous current modes.

The simplified action of the continuous current mode is shown in Fig. 6-23. For simplicity, only two phases are shown in Fig. 6-23. T1 corresponds to the time Q1 is conducting, T2 to the off period. Current flow during T1 is shown in heavy lines. Note that during T1, current flows through the motor windings A-B and to return via Q5. Current will rise in the motor winding as a function of winding *L/R* ratio, applied voltage, and duration of T1. Note that Q2 and Q4 are off at this time. At the end of

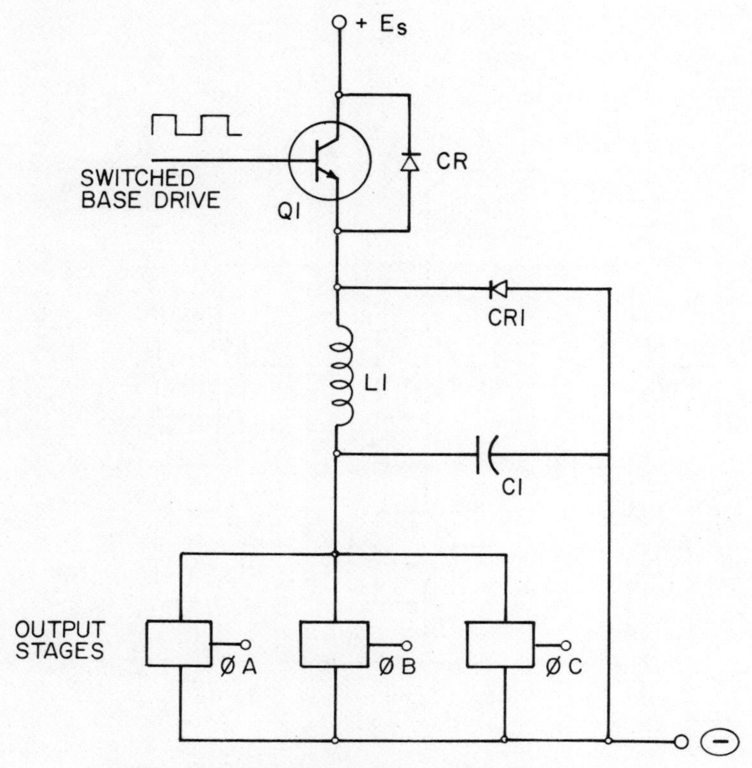

Fig. 6-22. Switched regulator for speed control.

period T1, Q1 is switched off (T2 period). Note that Q5 is allowed to remain in conduction. Current in the winding now falls, however it is kept flowing via the path (light lines) formed by CR4 and Q5. Thus the current in the winding is continuous for both T1 and T2 periods. Because the current is integrated in this manner, a continuous torque is maintained and the effects of the PWM clock ripple is minimized. The clock frequency must be chosen to be high enough so that the average current variation over T1 and T2 is 10 percent or less of the average torque current requirement. This parameter will result in the best current form factor.

At the end of T2, diode CR4 is still in conduction. When T1 occurs for the next cycle, the applied voltage will force CR4 off. The time required is a function of the recovery time of CR4. During the recovery time of CR4, very large currents can flow through Q1 and CR4. These currents are limited solely by stray circuit inductance or, more properly, a surge inductor placed in the $+E_s$ lead. Attention must be given to this action because there is a potential for device stress. In low-voltage, high-current designs, it is often advantageous to place a Schottky diode across CR4 (Q4) to provide a lower forward drop (less power dissipation) and a faster recovery time. In the

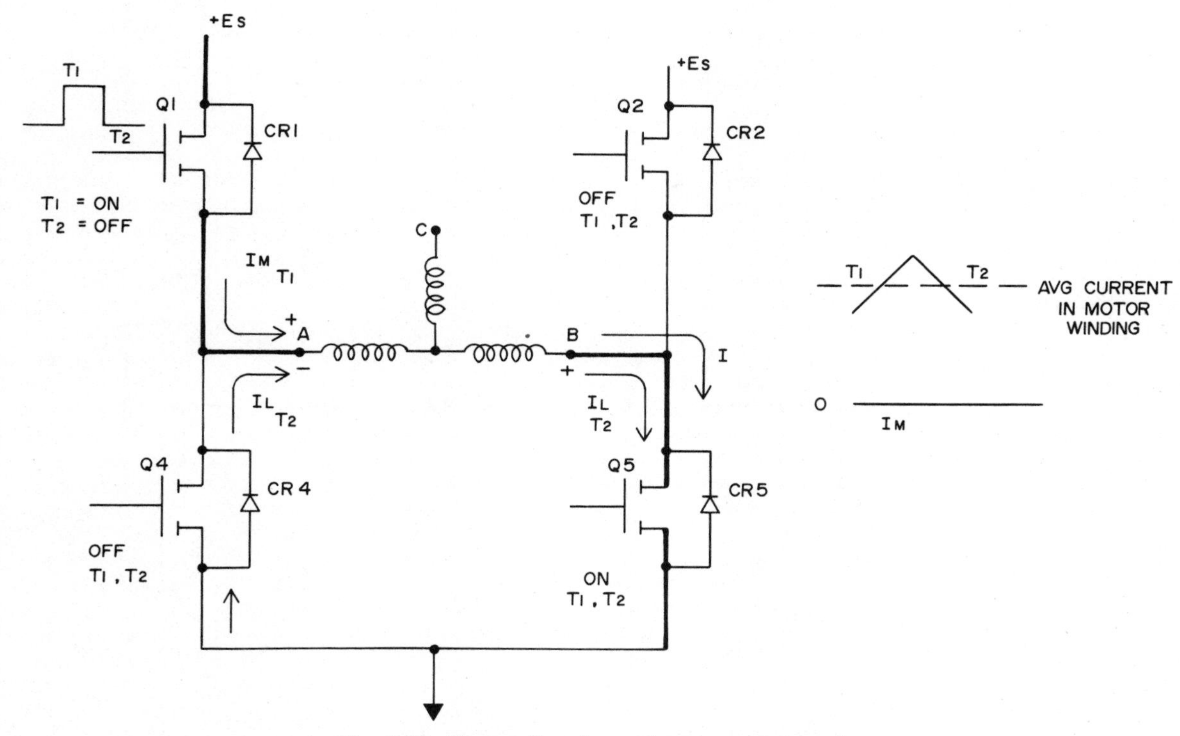

Fig. 6-23. Current flow in continuous current mode.

discontinuous mode as shown in Fig. 6-24, all devices are switched off at T2. In this case, the stored energy in the motor winding takes the path through CR4 and CR2. Thus, at the next T1 period, two recovery currents can flow because Q1 and Q5 will then be in conduction. This results in double trouble if the respective diodes have a long recovery time. In addition, the motor winding current can fall to a low value during T2, thus requiring a higher peak current at the next T1 cycle. This effect is most noticeable at low-speed operation. Indeed, in motors possessing high tooth cog, it will be seen that low-speed operation is difficult because of the low average current at low duty cycle. Another serious drawback of discontinuous mode operation is that, at the end of T1, the stored energy can force the voltage at the drains of the Q1, Q2, and Q3 devices to a high value, particularly if the stray inductance (L_c) is high. This could result, at worst, in avalanche mode failure of the devices.

The continuous mode of operation is obviously best for all new designs. Implementation of continuous current mode can be provided by making certain that only the top (Q1–Q3) output devices are switched by the PWM circuitry. The lower devices (Q4–Q6) are then permitted to switch in normal commutation fashion. Various schemes to accomplish this come to mind because it is possible to implement the

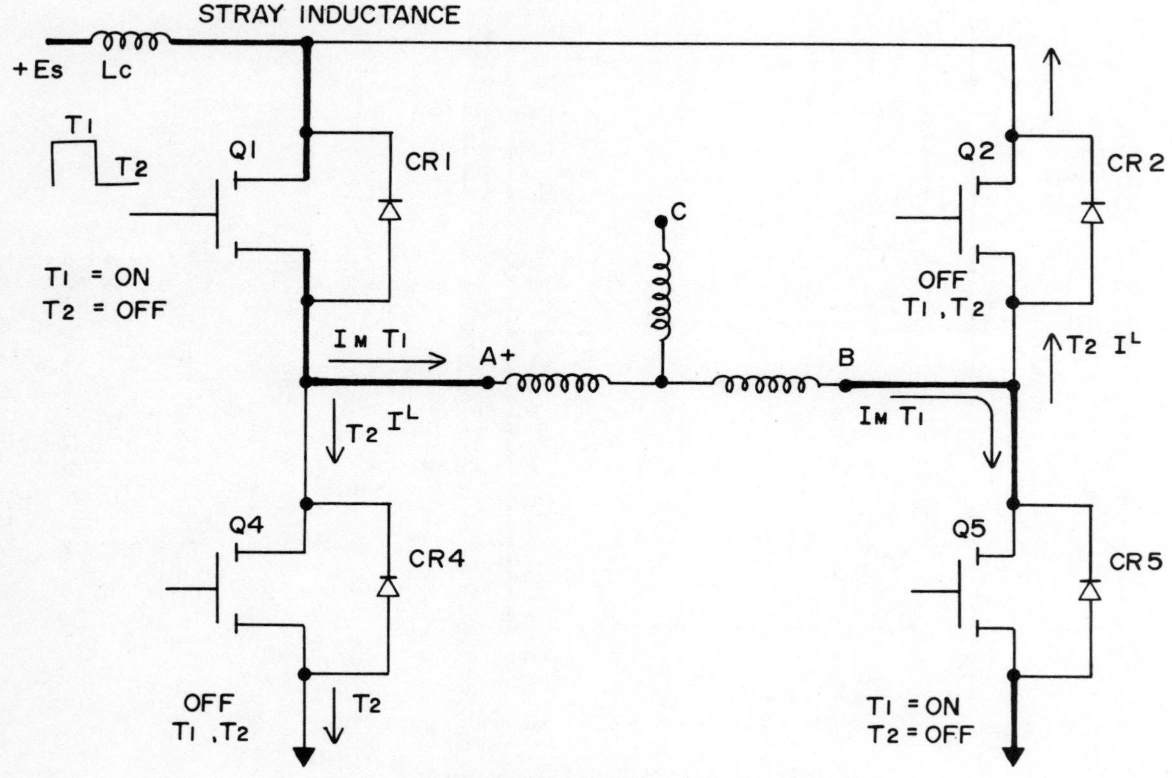

Fig. 6-24. Current flow in discontinuous current mode.

necessary logic states in the commutation logic thus saving ICs. When a ROM is used to decode the sensors, the logic truth table can be written to accomplish continuous mode quite easily.

The simplest speed control is that of Fig. 6-25. This method uses a *F-V* (frequency to voltage) convertor to generate a dc level as a function of speed. The F-V is usually the charge-pump type (LM2907). The component choices allow a small ripple voltage at the clock rate to ride on the dc level as shown in the figure. The comparator switches off the drive transistors when the ripple exceeds the control voltage by a few millivolts. In this manner, the output to the motor is pulse-width modulated. This system suffers problems at low to moderate speed because of the relatively low frequency of the PWM. At 1800 RPM, the output of the combining logic is 360 Hz [(1800 × 12)/60] if pulse combining is used as in the figure. This low PWM frequency produces a torque ripple effect that increases as the inverse of speed. The current pulses become large enough at low speeds to cause very erratic motion and considerable acoustic noise and vibration.

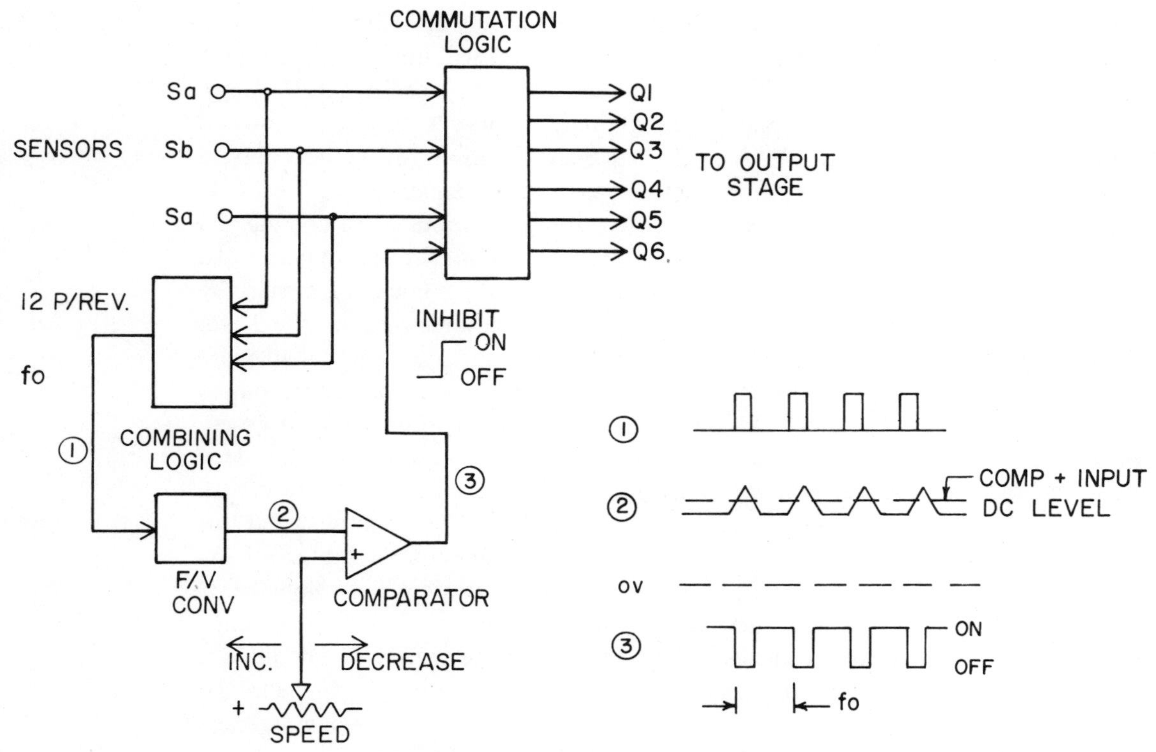

Fig. 6-25. Simple closed-loop speed regulator circuit.

pulses become large enough at low speeds to cause very erratic motion and considerable acoustic noise and vibration.

In spite of these drawbacks, the method does provide attractive cost savings, particularly at high speed where the frequency becomes more practical. In some instances, the sensor combiner can be replaced with a shaft encoder of approximately 250 lines. This arrangement will yield a clock of 7500 Hz at 1800 RPM. This higher frequency will improve performance to acceptable levels, although the control loop is still quite primitive.

A more advanced method which allows wide speed control is depicted in Fig. 6-26. This method is an adaptation of the PWM four-quadrant circuit described in chapter 4, Fig. 4-17. During clockwise motion input, d is fed with the variable width clock from comparator A. Comparator B functions for counterclockwise rotation. At rest, both comparators will output small pulses each half cycle of the clock f_o. These pulses cancel at the motor, resulting in no motion. The clock frequency f_o is chosen to suit the value of motor inductance and output transistor switching capabilities. Bipolar transistors can be operated to at least 15 kHz, and FETs can be utilized beyond 30 kHz. The motor inductance and desired current form factor will ultimately determine the frequency used.

Note that too low a switching frequency might result in poor low speed motion and acoustic noise. The minimum PWM clock frequency is chosen for the best current form factor for the particular motor in question. Generally frequencies below 7 kHz are to be avoided because of possible acoustic noise generation. Most commercial drives will use 15 kHz as a typical choice. In practice, the higher the frequency the better, within reason. In most PWM systems, the clock and commutation signals are not phase syncronous. This results in the PWM frequency *slipping* by the lower frequency commutation component. At the transistion boundaries, very small pulse widths can be encountered, which if not controlled could result in erratic output device turn on. This erratic turn on can lead to poor current form factor. As mentioned, the motor inductance is really the determining factor in the choice of clock frequency. In some systems, both the clock frequency and the duty cycle are varied. This operation can be very smooth at low speeds. If the frequency is higher at low speeds, there will be less torque ripple effect. The optimum control choice is governed by a great many variables, with system economics in the forefront. Note that in the example shown, both current and velocity feedback are used. This is common practice because the current feedback will serve to linearize the PWM circuits and thus improve the control-function transform. In many cases, the current feedback is the primary controlled parameter, such as in torque motor applications and certain traction systems.

In servo applications, the closed loop bandwidth is often large, 1 kHz or more. In such cases, careful attention must be paid to the design of the low-pass filter, or frequency roll-off networks must be used around the summing amplifiers. Servo drives often must respond to step function inputs and, along with wide band width, must be more or less critically damped. A judicious balance between the amount of feedback and summing amplifier frequency response is required to maintain stability over the operating range.

In most applications, the external system or the user will supply the input variable to control speed or torque. For bidirectional or four-quadrant systems, the usual analog input is ±10 V with +10 V corresponding to maximum useable speed in the clockwise direction. A negative 10 V will be the equivalent in the counterclockwise direction. The input interface can also be expressed in volts per RPM or in input volts versus output volts to the motor. In current-controlled drives, it is customary to express the input function in volts per ampere output. By using D/A convertors the input parameters might be digital in nature. This method is the obvious way to interface to the growing digital world. A separate microprocessor can be added to the basic analog PWM circuit to provide a quasi-intelligent motor drive. The various system points of interest can thus be monitored by the CPU, and a great deal of housekeeping can be attended to in this manner. Obviously the command inputs could be analog, then converted to digital, and processed and converted back to analog to feed the PWM. This is sometimes done to provide digitally adaptive filtering and control. However, in most CPU-based systems, the input to the controller is digital. In this case, the speed scale can be adjusted for *x* RPM per bit. This is analogous to the RPM per volts used in most closed-loop systems. It is a convenient way to express the no-load, closed-loop speed. The linearity, point to point, is often expressed as a percentage of the best straight line. The loaded speed for a conventional closed-loop system is a combination of factors and is sometimes difficult to predict. In some systems, the closed-loop speed-control factor is expressed as a function of loaded to unloaded speed. If the gain-stability margin is high, the speed-torque curve can be practically a straight line with speed regulation of 1 percent or better.

In position-control applications, the repeatability and settling error per degree is an important factor. The servo follower error, which is a measure of the ability of the system to follow an input, is often expressed in degrees electrical lag.

In general, system accuracy and linearity depend on careful attention to the analog circuit design and feedback circuits. It is usually necessary to use quality encoders/resolvers to minimize errors due to ripple introduced by run out, resonance, and other mechanical problems that become translated to error signals in the processing circuits.

In Fig. 6-26, the two operational amplifiers are shown with an integration function present. The need for low-pass filtering at the feedback nodes is a function of a great many system variables. It is usually necessary to tailor the feedback loop constants to suit the motor and load dynamics. Very careful attention must be paid to this aspect because without proper compensation, it will be impossible to run the loop with any value of usable gain. Most commercial drives make provision for bandwidth control by providing either potentiometer adjustments or by allowing for external components to be strapped in to accommodate the system response. The various parameters that must be adjusted for optimal performance also are usually provided with potentiometer adjustments. These are typically input gain, velocity feedback, current feedback, current limit, and system zero null.

In applications requiring very precise speed control, it is customary to use some form of PLL to lock the speed to an accurate reference frequency. There are many methods available to implement PLL operation. The industry standard 4046 *CMOS* (complementary metal-oxide-semiconductor) chip can be used for frequency lock but usually will not provide stable performance over a wide frequency range and can exhibit lock-up problems. This stems from the fact that in order to operate satisfactorily, the 4046 implementation requires an integration network of fairly low frequency. When the 4046 circuit is viewed from the frequency domain, the loop gain is

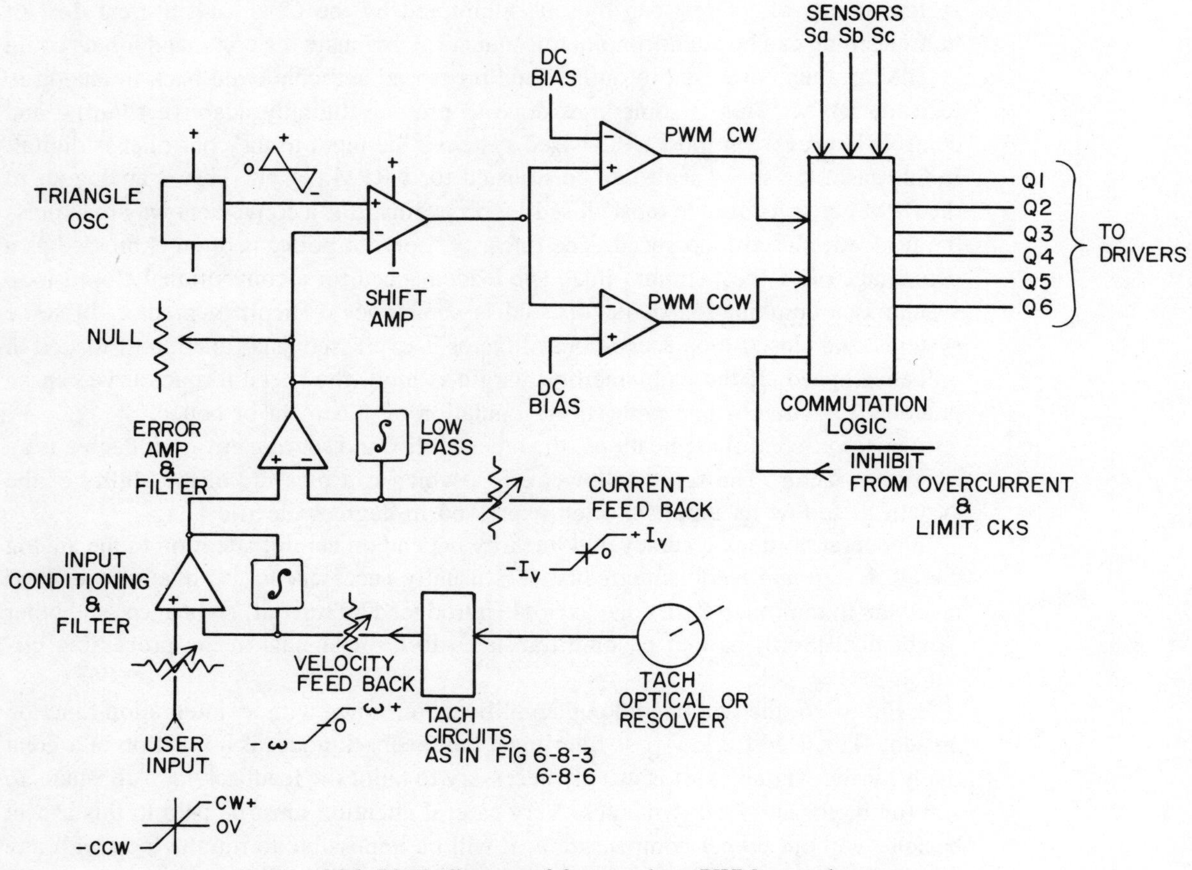

Fig. 6-26. Block diagram of four-quadrant PWM control system.

infinite. This places severe operating restrictions on the lockup and capture range of the 4046 in motor speed control applications. The circuit concept of Fig. 4-14 is, as mentioned, much more suitable for PLL operation. Figure 6-27 shows basic implementation of the PLL. The up-down counter, D/A convertor, and signal processing are as discussed in chapter 4 and of course in general literature. The remainder of the circuitry is the PWM of Fig. 6-26. Extremely good speed regulation is possible using this method, provided the following basic design criteria are met:

- The system response be adapted to provide linear frequency and phase response over the design operating range.

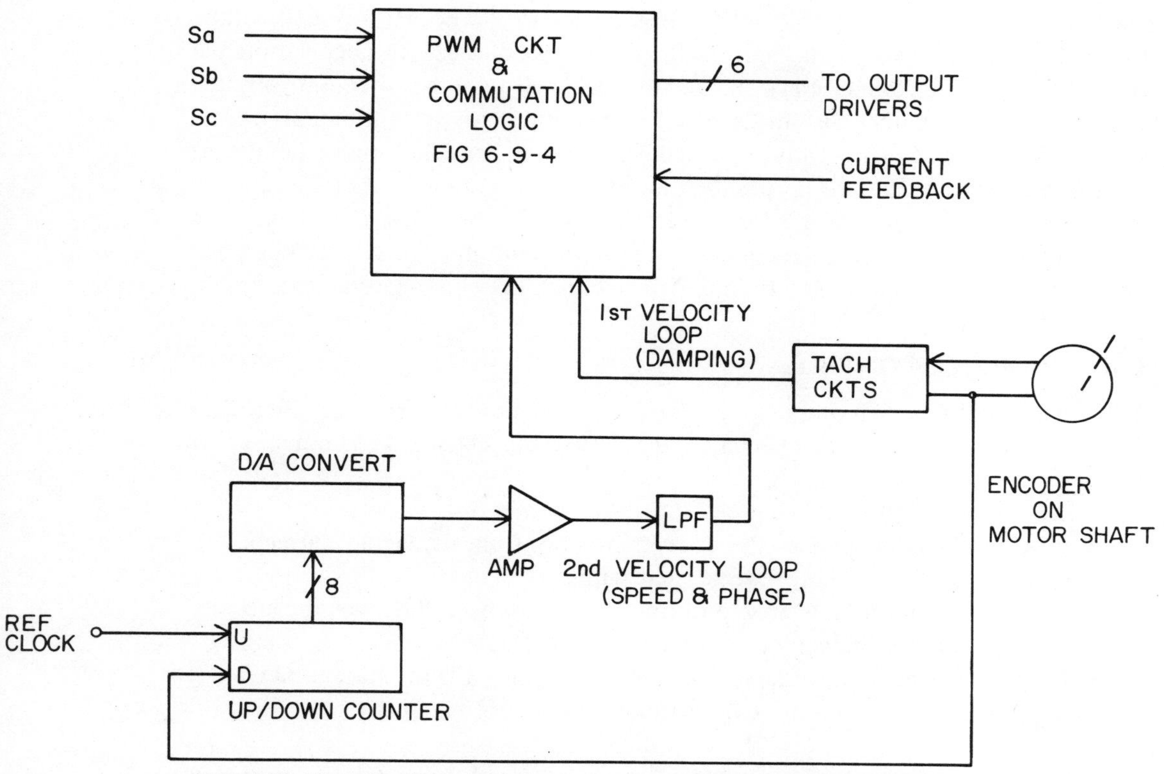

Fig. 6-27. Phase-Lock-Loop block diagram for constant speed or positioning.

- The first-velocity loop constants be selected such that the phase error due to the load is kept low. This is the basic system-damping source.
- The current limit point is set high enough to allow fast load acceleration to the lockup point. This is often a source of poor initial lockup stability.
- The PLL velocity data must be from a quality encoder or resolver, free of once around defects, jitter, or other frequency domain perterbations that would serve to cause a dimunition of usable headroom.

With circuit modifications, the circuit of Fig. 6-27 can be made into a digital positioning servo. A CPU could also be used for positioning. There is considerable data in general literature which can provide insight in this area.

Because of the flexibility with which the characteristics of a BLDC system can be modified, a great many dc and ac motor operating profiles can be simulated. There are many commercial packages available from which to choose. However, it will be found that there probably is no universal drive system that can be obtained off the shelf. Most high-performance systems of reasonable cost are usually *OEM* (original equipment manufacturer) custom designed from basic drive system modules. This follows the fact that there really is no industry-defined brushless motor family, as there is in the case of definite purpose ac motors. This fact often makes it difficult for the person whose job it is to specify a BLDC system. The best advice is to talk to as many motor and drive manufactures as possible to gain insight. The BLDC motor and drive is a maturing product and, in time, will no doubt undergo some standardization.

6.10. CURRENT CONTROL

The system of Fig. 6-1 would not be complete without some means of controlling the motor current. The need to monitor the system current can be summed up as follows:

- It is necessary to protect the drive transistors from damaging currents, particularly during start, reverse, and faults.
- Some means must be available to limit peak currents, which could cause damage motor windings or demagnetize rotor magnets.
- Because torque is the direct result of motor current, it is the current that is sometimes the more important parameter to control externally.

There are some very interesting problems associated with current measurement in BLDC motors. Unlike the conventional brush dc motor, the phase currents in a BLDC motor are, for a full-wave design, basically of an ac nature. The wave shape is usually a form of square wave, sometimes with PWM ripple added in. In half-wave designs, the current is unidirectional, often having a large crest factor. For most drive designs, particularly full-wave, the phases operate above system ground, thus complicating the measuring process. The purpose to which the current measurement will be put very often determines the method used to take the sample. For the first two items in the above list, the peak current value is of importance, followed by the steady-state or average current. This priority results from the fact that the drive transistors will be rated for a maximum safe peak current, beyond which failure is certain. The motor, of course, has a finite peak current limit beyond which the magnets may be demagnitized. For the last item in the above list, the current sample is usually the average value and because it is part of a closed loop, it must be a linear function and free of spurious noise.

In Fig. 6-28, the various current monitor points in a three-phase drive are shown.

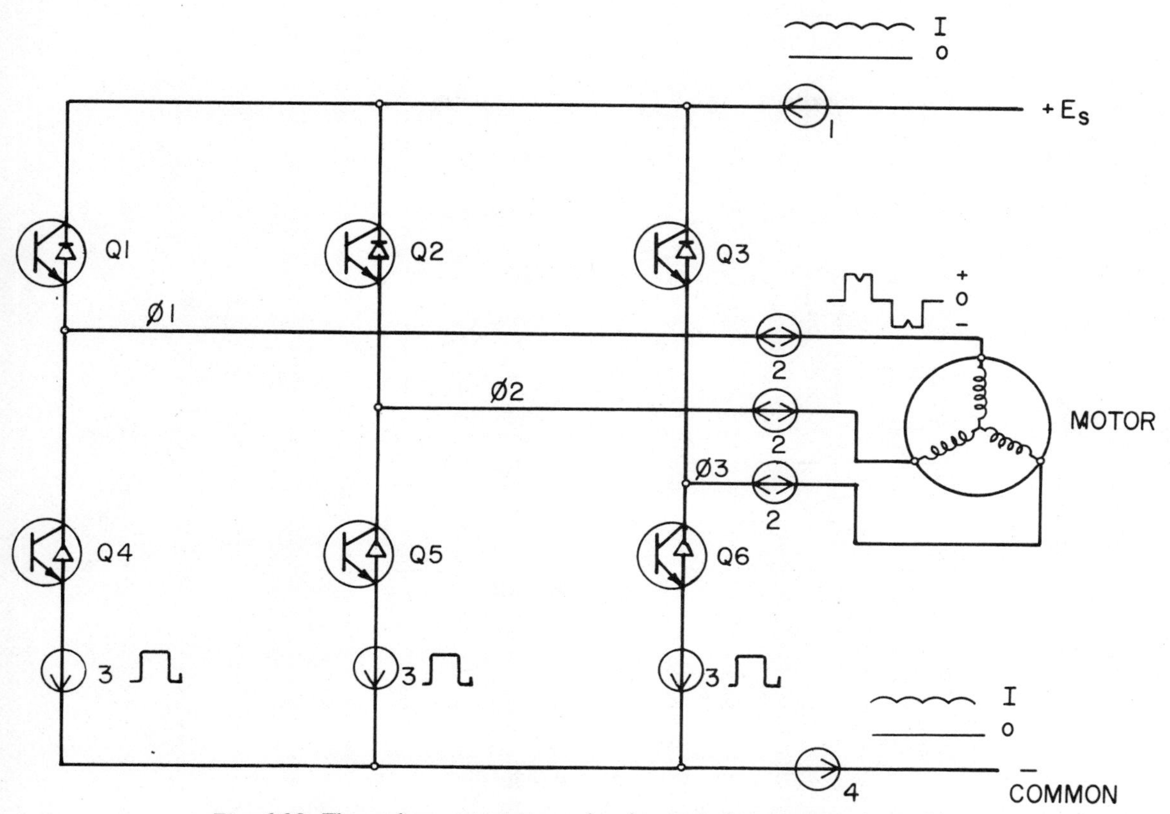

Fig. 6-28. Three-phase output stage showing typical current monitor points.

Points 1 and 4 are the gross current and are essentially dc. Point 2 is the phase current and is a form of ac current. The currents at 3 are dc pulses. Each of the points shown have advantages in current monitoring depending upon how the sample is to be used within the system. All points shown are at a potential that makes monitoring difficult except in the smallest of drives. It is the somewhat inaccessible feature of these currents that leads to many novel, and sometimes proprietary, measuring techniques. In a single-direction drive operating into a fairly constant load, the current can be monitored conveniently in the return leg (point 4). This monitoring can be done by using a sample resistor of low value or by magnetic means. Recently, several FET manufacturers have introduced devices with a built in current-monitoring feature. This current-sense feature is accomplished by isolating a few cells within the FET structure and bringing out the derived Kelvin voltage through a separate pin. The current-scale ratio ranges from 1000 to 1600 for most commonly used devices. This

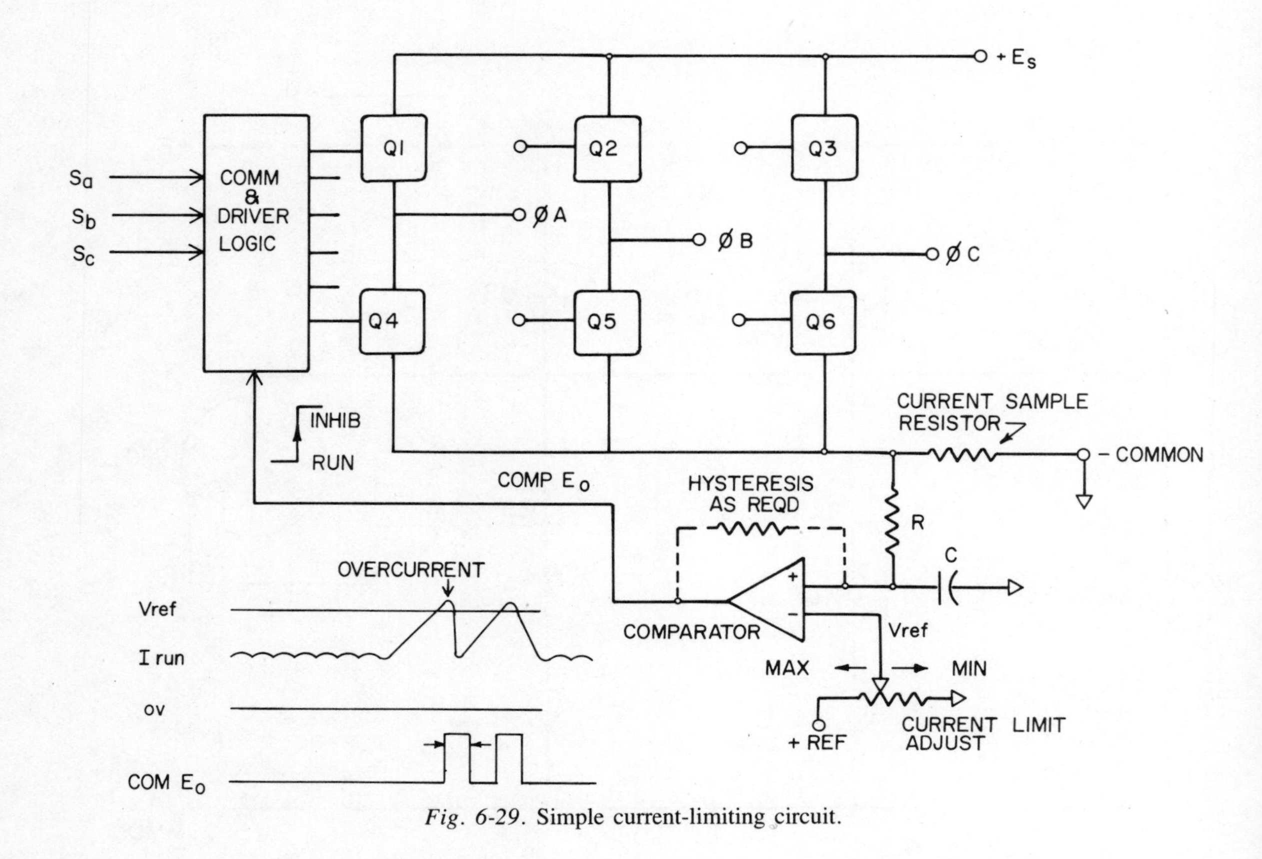

Fig. 6-29. Simple current-limiting circuit.

translates to about 1 mV per ampere. Obviously, this is a feature that eliminates the need for external sample resistors and their voltage-drop burden. An amplifier, usually differential, is required to raise this small sample voltage to a useable value. If the control system low-level circuits are referenced to the motor supply common; a sample resistor approach is the simplest. If there is a potential difference between the control circuits and the supply common, as is usually the case, there will be need of some form of electrical isolation to prevent catastrophic short circuits. This is definitely the case in line operated systems operating without isolation transformers. In the first condition above, the drive return is assumed to be the system common. The circuit arrangement of Fig. 6-29 will provide peak current limiting adequate for most noncritical applications. In operation, the current sample voltage is compared with a dc reference voltage. If the current sample voltage exceeds the reference, the comparator output will change state and inhibit the output transistor drivers. Thus the motor current will switch off. The *RC* (resistance-capacitance) network is used to eliminate noise spikes due to circuit capacitance and winding leakage inductance. Because the

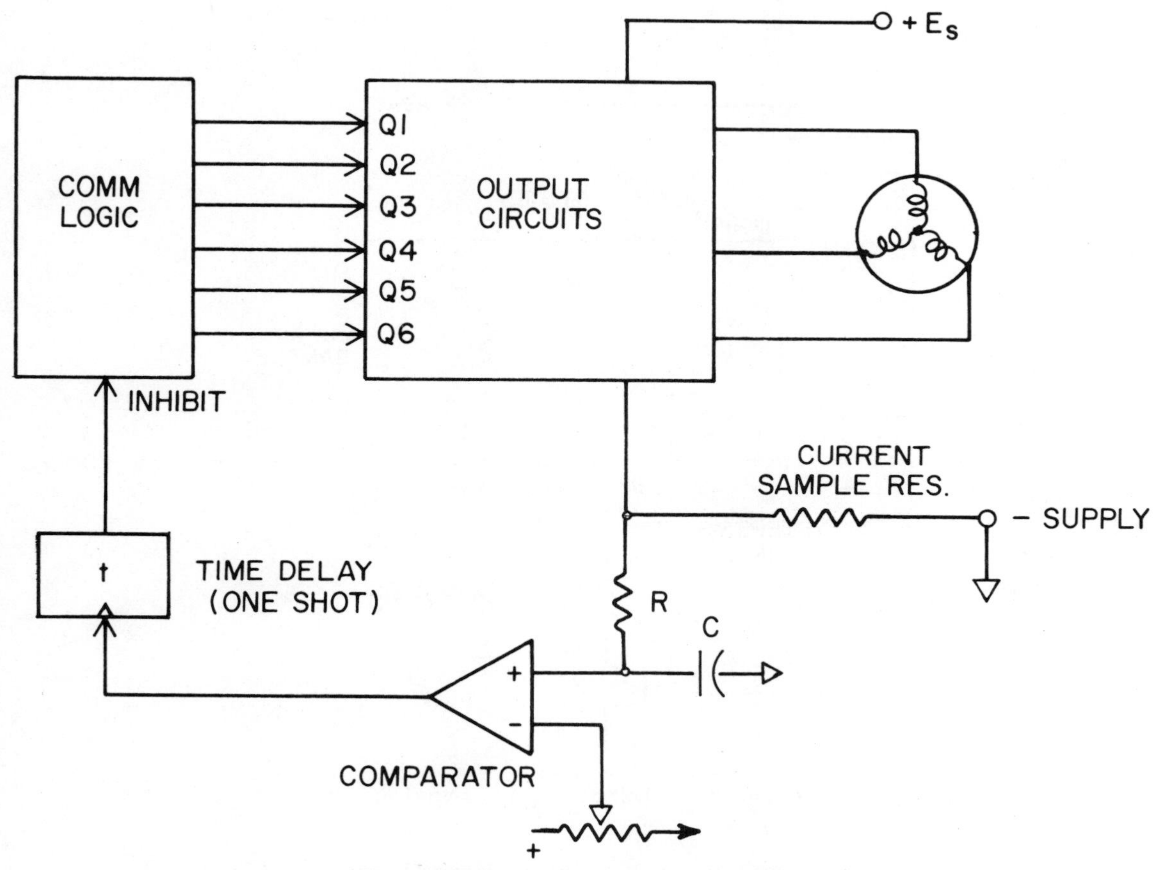

Fig. 6-30. Current limiting using time delay.

current through the windings will rise as a function of inductance, the actual cutoff point in time will be determined by the circuit values of inductance, logic delay and the RC constants. The operation of this form of current limiter is shown graphically in Fig. 6-29. Note that for conditions of sustained overload, the output of the comparator will be a series of pulses. The duty cycle is dependent on the circuit constants as mentioned above. In some cases, such as during starting, the average current through the windings might assume too low an average value to start the motor properly. This problem results from the uncontrolled mode of oscillation as determined by the circuit constants. Adding hysteresis around the comparator as shown in dotted lines will permit some control over the on-off time of the current. An alternate approach is to use a timing circuit such as in Fig. 6-30. The one-shot will establish the off time and permits the circuit to have a specified response time.

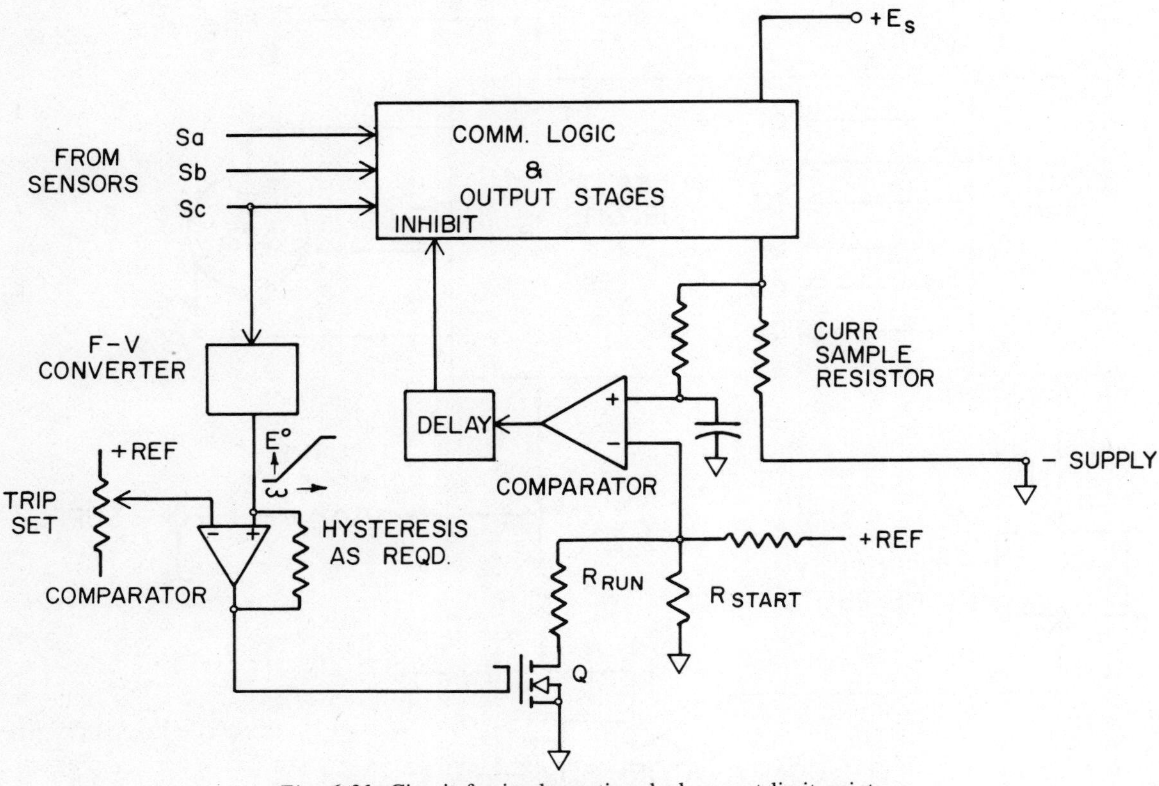

Fig. 6-31. Circuit for implementing dual current limit points.

A dual reference can be used as in Fig. 6-31. This permits a higher current limit during start, after a critical crossover speed has been reached, the current limit value is reduced for the run mode. In the example shown, the divider, formed by R and R_{start}, establishes the starting current limit. As the rotor gains speed, the circuit at A outputs a logic level that places *Q* in conduction, thus lowering the limit reference, hence the lower current limit point. Obviously, the speed at which the points are shifted must be carefully chosen because it is possible to get into an oscillatory condition, which could be detrimental to proper performance. An alternate method could use timers, which after a specific time, would drop the current limit to a low, safe value. There are a great many possible variations that are only limited by the designers ingenuity. It would be possible to use a pulse-by-pulse limit scheme by monitoring the current at point 3 in Fig. 6-28 and shutting down the output devices as a function of each branch current peak. This method is useful in PWM controls because the peak current monitored in this manner also will be the same as seen during reversing cycles and can be processed to permit very smooth current control.

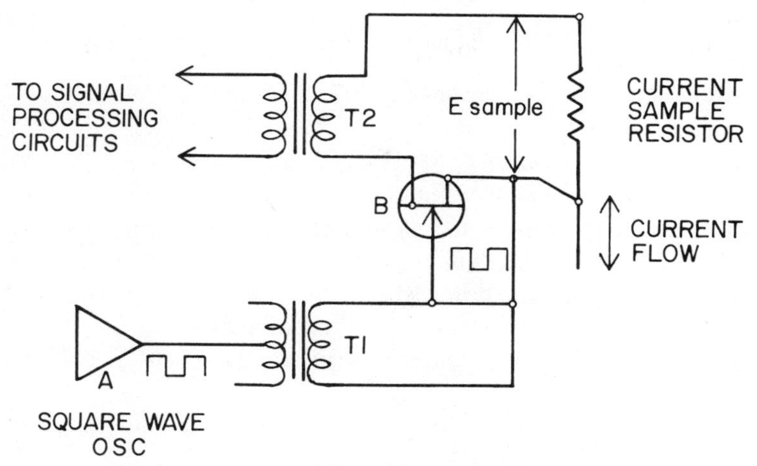

Fig. 6-32. Transformer-coupled method for monitoring current.

When the motor supply return must be isolated from the control logic as in line-operated drives, the monitoring and signal processing become more of a problem. Means must be provided for some form of electrical isolation between the two voltage levels of the subsystems involved. Magnetic methods such as linear Hall devices can be used to sense the current without direct electrical contact. In some cases, a current transformer can be used to monitor the current and provide the needed isolation. The Hall approach can be expensive and might require fabrication of the Hall element and the magnetic core into a single usable component. The current transformer, of course, can only be used where the current component is pulse or ac in nature. Both methods have merit and can be used where space and cost permit their use.

Various methods using optocouplers can be used to access measured quantities at greatly differing voltages. These methods usually require linear operation of the optocouplers and, if the necessary circuit precautions are taken, can be made to perform quite well. Another method using small ferrite cores is shown in Fig. 6-32. Here a square-wave oscillator at A is used to generate a 100 kHz or higher signal, which is transformer coupled to the gate of B. Component B is a small signal JFET (junction field-effect transistor), which functions as a bidirectional switch. The derived voltage (E sample) is thus chopped into a variable amplitude square wave and passed to the signal processing circuits via T2. Components T1 and T2 provide the dielectric isolation and can be made with as high a breakdown voltage as is needed. This circuit will operate bidirectionaly and can be used at any point in the circuit of Fig. 6-28, including point 2 in the phase legs. Of course, three switch circuits must be used at point 2, but T1 can be on a common core. Obviously, there are many other methods that can be used to isolate the sample point from the low-level circuitry. The major requirements are that the circuit used have good dielectric integrity and provide accurate signal process with fast slew rate. Slew rate is important because the sampled current is often used to limit fast-rise current pulses, which if not controlled could lead to system damage.

Protecting a BLDC drive from external malfunctions involves a few problems not considered in the discussion above. Figure 6-33 (a) shows the fault-current path for an output phase short circuited to ground. A similar condition would exist for a phase-to-phase short or an internal motor winding short to frame. In the fault path shown, the current can be large and the rise time fast because of the low circuit resistance and the usually low value of circuit inductance, L_c. For the steady-state fault current, assuming the supply voltage is 150 Vdc, the network would be:

$$\frac{150}{R_s + R_c} = \text{I fault } (I_f)$$

where R_s = Sample resistance
R_c = Equivalent circuit resistance

For the values shown:

$$I_f = \frac{150}{0.05 + 0.4} = 333 \text{ A.}$$

This current is far in excess of any normal transistor rating, and the current must not reach this value under any condition. If the value of L_c, the circuit inductance, were 5 μH, the fault current in 5 microseconds would reach 150 A, neglecting circuit resistance. This in simple terms is given by:

$$\frac{E \times T}{L} = I_f$$

In the example given, the 5 μH circuit inductance value (L_c) was used because this approximates the stray wiring inductance value often found in practice. The 5 microsecond period was used because, in a great many circuit configurations, this is a reasonable time to sense the current and turn off the output transistors. Faster current sense circuits will improve matters by turning off sooner at a lower current. The current in the example given is far too high for most output driver devices in bldc drives rated less than 5 hp. The circuit modification of 6-33 (b) has an additional inductance added (L_s) in the form of a surge inductor to limit the maximum current over a reasonable time. The choice of inductor value is based upon the maximum peak current that the transistor can safely handle during the maximum time that the

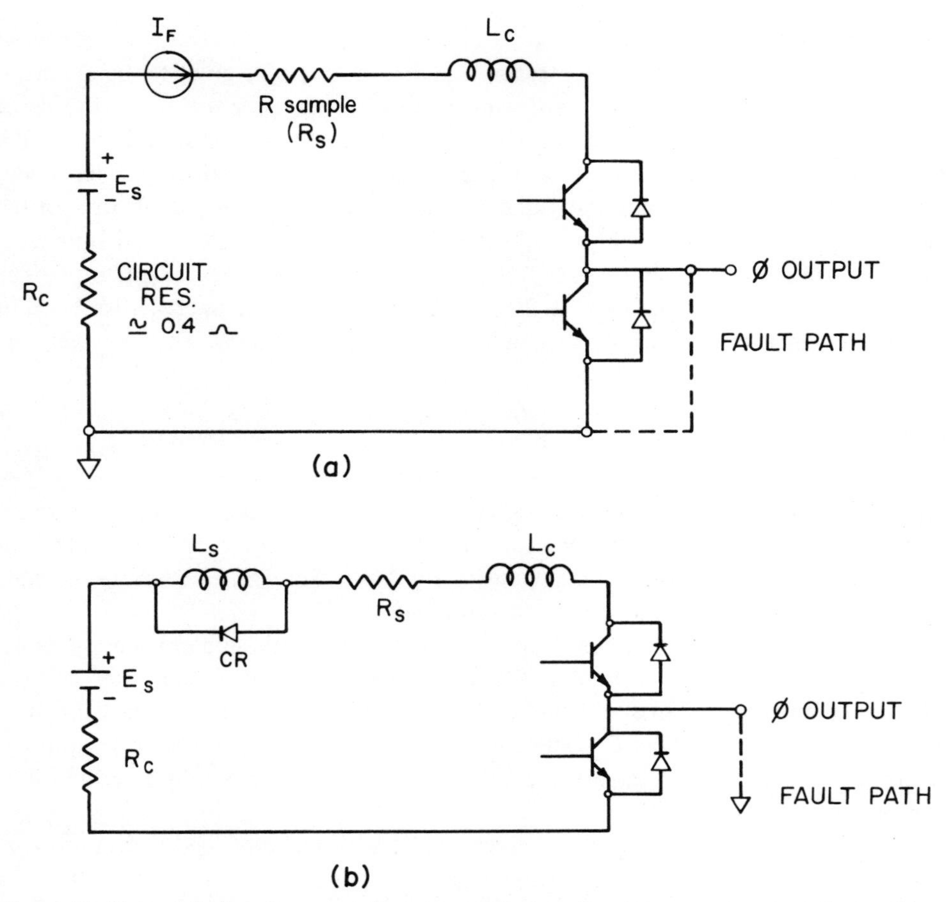

Fig. 6-33. Typical fault-path current flow (a) and fault path using current surge inductor (b).

shut-down circuit requires to turn off the transistor. If, for instance, the transistors could safely handle 25 A over 5 microseconds, the inductor Ls in Fig. 6-33 (b) would be roughly 150 μH. This value is from the following approximation:

$$\frac{E \times \Delta T}{I} = L_s\ (\mu\text{H})$$

where E = Voltage
ΔT = Time in seconds
I = Current at end ΔT

The diode, CR, across L_s is used to clamp the inductive voltage which would otherwise appear across L_s at turn off. Some attention should be given to the effects of stray circuit inductance when considering fast device turn-off under conditions of high current. In the above situation it was assumed that the current would reach 25 A in 5 microseconds from turn on. It would be necessary to turn off the transistor before the 25 A value is reached in approximately 3 microseconds. The turn-off time of the transistor plus and device delays could then bring this time to perhaps 4 microseconds, assuming a 0.5 microsecond delay and a 0.5 microsecond turn-off time. The current at turn off would be close to 20 A, and the voltage developed across 5 μH of stray inductance under the above conditions would be 200 V. This is given by:

$$V_p = L_c \frac{\mathrm{di}}{\mathrm{dt}}$$

This, voltage added to the 150 V supply voltage would be 350 V peak. This voltage can lead to excessive stress on the transistor, and steps should be taken to prevent such transients. It is possible to increase turn-off time, reduce circuit stays and possibly add a load-line snubber to limit transistor voltage. Sometimes all three methods are used to ensure a safe transistor operating point.

Sampling the current at point 1 in Fig. 6-28 can permit implementation of an electronic circuit breaker which, if the above precautions are taken, can be very effective in preventing damage to the motor and transistors. Because point 1 monitoring involves operation at the E_s voltage level, either transformer or optical coupling is required. Needless to say, the associated circuitry must be fast acting if good protection is to be assured.

The implementation of current monitoring for the purpose of feedback control, as in Fig. 6-26, requires that the derived signal be free of noise and represent either the average or RMS value of the motor current. The measuring point can be either that of 2 or 3, namely in the phase legs or the output device return. Summing the three values and either integrating or processing via a true-RMS circuit of high-crest capability is probably the most commonly used method. It is possible to use a combination of both or use an averaging circuit if the average value is of importance. The polarity of the sampled current is unidirectional except at point 2. The sample at point 2 could be synchronously rectified into a dc component having low ripple and a fast slew rate. The polarity of the derived signal can be switched by direction sense circuits as in Fig. 6-17 to yield a bidirectional current analog as in Fig. 6-18. This analog, if low in noise and ripple, can be fed to the appropriate node of the signal processing circuit for tight current control.

6.11. CONCLUSION

The system description given in this chapter should serve the novice in gaining insight into the basic parts of a brushless drive system. Many other methods are available to drive a BLDC motor. For instance, current-driven systems were not covered because in practice there is much in common between a current-driven unit and the voltage-fed system as described. There is a wealth of information on this subject in general literature. In similar concepts, the section on power devices can be enlarged by reference to the manufacturers' hand books, such as offered by Motorola, International Rectifier, RCA, GE, and Siliconix, to name a few. The handbooks often offer insights into the operation of devices that lie beyond the scope of this book. It is hoped that the discussion of the drive portion of a BLDC system will spur more novel thought into this interesting area of electronics. The semiconductor industry is constantly offering new devices in both power and logic which, coupled with imagination, can be used to advance the state of the art.

7

Applications and Uses of BLDC Motors

7.1. INTRODUCTION

This chapter deals with some of the practical applications of BLDC motors. This chapter is not intended to cover all possible applications, because such an endeavor would be a book in itself. Rather, some of the prosaic and more esoteric uses will be discussed to aid the designer in realizing some of the potentials of the BLDC motor.

7.2. SERVO APPLICATIONS

Almost all robotic and machine-tool positioning applications require servo-motor functions. Simply stated, a *servo system* consists of motor driver and feedback elements combined in a manner that gives accurate stable control over speed and position. The two key parameters, accuracy and stability, are the first considerations given in designing for a servo application. Accuracy is achieved through the use of quality mechanical and electrical components. Stability is similarly achieved through the use of quality components but with the added need for consideration of rotor inertia, loop gain, damping, and integrity of mechanical couplings. Invariably, servo applications will imply a four-quadrant drive and a motor designed for low torque ripple, good linearity, and a true bidirectional operation. A consideration of the ratio of rotor inertia to load inertia is required to ensure that the peak torque requirements of the overall system can be met. Because servos are called upon to slew or rapidly move a load through a specific number of degrees or revolutions, the damping and settling time of the system become important parameters. This need for rapid slew can result in very high instantaneous current and the designer needs to make prospective drive and motor vendors aware of this class of operation.

The trend in servos is towards six- and eight-pole motors using skewed stators and specially shaped rotor magnets. This is done to get the lowest torque ripple and thus improve motion at low speeds. Resolver commutation and position methods are used, but Hall-effect commutation with optical shaft encoders can be used to lower cost when some performance trade offs can be tolerated. For example, a 500-line optach can provide good motion control down to less than two RPM in a properly designed system. Of course, the environmental limits (temperature and vibration) of the Hall-optach must be taken into account as being a potential factor.

Linear positioning systems such as valve or gate operators can use less costly feedback devices when a gear head motor is used, if the temperature range is not severe. Remote position indicators are in the same category and the low maintenance of the BLDC motor makes it attractive for use in unattended locations or hard-to-reach places. For low power, very precise servo applications, the low-inertia, brush-type PM motor having a large number of commutator bars can outperform the BLDC at low speeds. This results from the relatively large number of commutation cycles per rpm of the PM servo. However, as the BLDC technology matures, the gap will slowly close.

7.3. CONSTANT-SPEED SYNCHRONOUS

As mentioned in previous chapters, the electronic nature of the BLDC motor and drive permits synthesis of a great many basic motor types. One of the most obvious and widespread applications is to replace the ac synchronous motor. In fact, a BLDC system can provide synchronous motor operation over a very wide speed range and exhibit less cogging and hunting than a conventional synchronous type. In a great many instances the cost trade off is small and often at par with the older technology.

For most higher-speed applications (> 1000 RPM) a four-pole motor is adequate. Where very low torque ripple is required, the toothless stator has some merit. Of course the quality of the feedback device plays an important role in the overall system performance. In many cases, the Hall-commutation devices can provide adequate feedback thus allowing a lower overall cost.

Most constant-speed brushless systems employ a crystal-controlled clock source, thus making a very accurate speed source. The system can also be slaved off a user-supplied clock, which offers great versatility in some critical applications.

The use for synchronous speed devices are myriad; some common uses are as capston drives, disc drives, timing applications, laser scanners, and precision optical grinders. The key parameter of a synchronous drive is, of course, the shaft speed.

However, in some applications the *TDE* (time displacement error) is a very important specification. TDE can be simply stated as the time error, in microseconds, of the arrival of the rotating shaft past a fixed point per revolution. In a practical system, the shaft will complete a partial or full revolution in some period of time, plus or minus a small increment.

The primary contributors to the TDE are: velocity sensor, commutation sensor, rotor uniformity, winding uniformity, bearing accuracy, clock jitter, and speed control stability. All of the above or in combination can directly affect the quality of motion and the cost of a given system will increase as the inverse of the TDE value. A reasonably priced system properly optimised can yield a TDE of <50 microseconds at 1800 RPM. This is equivalent to a dynamic speed stability of better than 0.01 percent. Naturally, such factors as the load type will also affect performance. A varying load will place stringent demands on the speed correction circuitry and, if the load variations are severe, will cause speed instability. Thus the torque rating of the motor comes into play. A load exhibiting large variations will require a stiff mechanical output from the motor, and this translates as torque. The load inertia can be an asset in some cases and a hindrance in others. This follows from the fact that the load is seen as being inside the feedback loop as it is viewed by the motor and drive. For many high-inertia loads, the motor-control parameters must be trimmed to permit proper loop phase and gain to be met. It is always a wise bet to discuss the nature of the load with the motor and drive vendor when considering driving anything but the basic rotor inertia in tight, accurate speed applications.

7.4. CENTRIFUGE AND FAN APPLICATIONS

Centrifuges play an important role in industry, science, and medicine as the most cost effective way to separate, by weight, components in liquids. Traditionally, the prime mover in the area of centrifuges was the series-wound universal motor and the polyphase ac induction motor.

The BLDC motor is making important inroads into the centrifuge market. BLDC systems can provide direct control of acceleration times, deceleration times, and speed. They can do so in a quieter fashion than the conventional technology. In a great many cases, the cost trade offs are attractive given the relative ease with which a BLDC motor system can be controlled.

Essentially a centrifugal load contains an inertial component during acceleration and deceleration along with a windage component, which is maximum at steady-state speed. Because most centrifuges operate in only one direction, bidirectionality is not a requirement, and many BLDC designs become practical. Small units can benefit from two- and four-phase, half-wave circuits driving four-pole motors. Large types would require three-phase, full-wave drives because of the improved efficiency of this configuration. Half-wave drives are available and are practical for outputs not exceeding 0.3 hp, and full-wave drives are used up to and beyond 10 hp.

Because centrifuges are, by nature, high-speed devices ranging in speed from 5000 to over 100,000 RPM, some special motor construction considerations must be observed.

The rotor must be designed to withstand the extreme centrifugal forces that act upon it. It is not unusual to find sleeved rotors in use. Sleeving the rotor with a stainless steel or other high-strength tube prevents the rotor magnets from being torn away. Needless to say, the motor bearings must be chosen with care if long life is to be obtained. Heat rise of the motor and the shaft is often a prime concern in some medical applications.

In most low-speed applications, iron core stators can be used, but at speeds over 10,000 RPM iron losses can sometimes be a problem, and toothless rotors can offer greater efficiency. This is certainly the case above 40,000 RPM. For very high speeds, two-pole motor designs can offer very attractive performance, especially with high-inertia loads, which help smooth out the motion at lower speed during the acceleration and deceleration periods.

As mentioned, many centrifuge applications can be met with single-quadrant drives. Larger three-phase applications might require two-quadrant, quasi-regenerative drives to aid in deceleration of the work load in the proper time-speed envelope. This can place very stringent peak current demands on the motor and drive because of the often large moment of inertia and high stored energy content of the load. Very often, resistance can be switched across phases during deceleration to aid in controlling the curve and reducing the load on the drive. The BLDC system offers fascinating alternatives to conventional motors for use in centrifuge applications providing you are willing to learn and appreciate the electronic nature of this new technology.

Fan and blower applications also are areas in which BLDC technology can offer interesting possibilities. Quiet operation and long life are the two major advantages. Ease of speed control is an important, often overlooked, plus in fan applications. Constant-mass blowers as used in aircraft, clean room, electronic cooling, and environmental-box applications can readily benefit from the variable speed feature of the BLDC motor and drive. The load line of large blowers and fans is both windage and inertial with the greater part being windage. Small fans and blowers are mostly windage in nature. Both usually are constant load, and motor-drive combinations can be tailored to suit the specific application. As BLDC technology matures, it is expected that brushless motors will be seen in automotive and home air conditioner blower and fan systems. This is a good field for the designer to work on because the high production volumes involved with consumer applications can be a driving force in lowering cost and forcing automated production methods into the BLDC industry just as was the case with the ac induction motor.

7.5. PUMPS

BLDC-driven pumps ranging in size from subfractional to horsepower ratings are becoming a reality as BLDC technology progresses. This increased use is a result of the ease of speed control and low maintenance features of the BLDC motor. Sizing a motor and drive can be a difficult problem because of the high average-to-peak torque requirements in some piston-pump designs. Most pump applications also require starting under load unless pressure bypass or clutch disconnect methods are used. Thus, high starting torque is needed, and the motor and drive must be rated for this class of service. Usually multilevel current-limiting circuits are used in the drive package to protect motor and electronics in the event of lockup or high-pressure starting. The variable speed feature of the closed-loop BLDC is a distinct advantage in controlling flow rates, but the design of the speed loop must be stable with the pulsating load found in many pump applications. Even a centrifugal pump can present load transients to the drive motor under certain system conditions, such as valve porting, fluid viscosity changes, etc. The speed-control loop must be tailored to accept rapid changes in torque or reflected load without going unstable. Clearly, the designer must work closely with the motor and drive supplier to ensure a properly sized and stable system. Pump drives are a new and exciting field for the maturing BLDC concept.

7.6. INDUSTRIAL PROCESSES

There are many conveyors, bins, hoppers, and other mechanical elements throughout industry that can benefit from advanced BLDC technology. As the horsepower rating of practical systems spirals upwards, the cost per horsepower trade offs will no doubt make the BLDC a serious contender for variable-frequency induction and SCR PM drives. These applications include high-speed spindle drives, which, like some centrifuge applications, were once the sole province of the polyphase induction motor. It would seem that in very high-speed spindle applications, the BLDC system offers a quieter alternative because of the higher commutation frequency. Many induction drives operate at frequencies in the several hundred to few kilohertz range and can emit considerable acoustic noise. Another advantage the BLDC has is very high starting torque, which is a decided asset in a great variety of industrial applications. The industrial market will no doubt see a steady increase in the use of BLDC technology.

7.7 TRACTION AND TORQUING

As new high-energy product magnetic materials become an economic reality, it will be possible to obtain greater horsepower per unit volume and a considerable reduction in weight. This along with advanced FET technology will permit the BLDC motor to be used in traction and propulsion applications that were unheard of only a few years ago. Robotic mail handlers, parts stockers, and similar industrial applications, will no doubt benefit from this new technology. Individual wheel drives are now in use, and it is expected that efficiency will improve and size will diminish. This area is an exciting one for the aspiring product designer to contemplate.

Industrial screw drivers and nut runners will be able to make use of BLDC technology, thus eliminating the brush maintenance problem that is so common. Nut runners, screw drivers, etc., are high peak torque applications, and they require special design considerations. The electronics must be designed for handling large stall torque currents and be capable of precise current limiting. Acceleration time must be short, and this implies high starting current. Dynamic braking is often required so that a modified version of a four-quadrant drive is often used.

In torque motor applications, such as magnetic tape, textile, and film transports, the BLDC has not made many gains due to rough motion at very low speeds. However, six-, eight-, and ten-pole designs will probably overcome some of these limitations. Ratings in this class of service often approach stall torque values and must be rated as such. Most drives for operating BLDC motors in torquing applications are of the current-fed or current-loop type, where the motor current is controlled. This feature is accomplished either by insertion of large inductance at the PWM power stage or, more preferably, by active current feedback.

Some torquing systems can benefit from resolver or shaft encoder velocity feedback to provide linearization of the overall speed-torque curve. Choice of motor and drive for torquing applications involves special considerations of current, heat rise, control type, and feedback method.

7.8. ESOTERIC APPLICATIONS

There is a wide range of applications in which the BLDC motor has seen considerable success even in its earliest days. One of the first practical applications of the BLDC motor was in modern high-fidelity turntables where low wow and flutter combined with low rumble made it a natural choice. Crystal-controlled, high-performance turntables are now the standard for audiophiles. These turntables use unique designs, usually of twelve or more poles and of flat construction. The primary design goals are high starting torque, smooth motion, and low power consumption. The need for a large number of poles results from the low speed (33 1/3 RPM) and the smooth, linear flux needed to afford smooth motion.

Similarly, low speed (<100 RPM) laser scanners are now becoming useful in material analysis, computer imaging, and industrial process control. An entirely new host of problems is incurred in designing direct-drive, low-speed BLDC systems. Aside from exact speed, the TDE is usually required to be kept to very low values. This requires a low-jitter design using a large number of poles. This, in turn, results in a high-impedance winding having high torque sensitivity but usually running at very low voltage. It is then difficult to get high torque. Low-speed designs require a very accurate commutation system and tachometer generator (magnetic or optical) if low TDE is to be realized. Bearings can present a problem because of smoothness limitations. Lubrication efficiency is low because of the lack of centrifugal force normally available to distribute the lubrication. Often sleeve bearings are used to provide greater life if side loading values allow sleeves.

In spite of the many design problems encountered, the BLDC motor is the only accurate drive currently on the horizon for low-speed laser scanning. The availability of neodynium-based magnetics will permit higher torques to be realized. New sintered bearing construction will solve the bearing problems. This is an emerging area for the modern BLDC system.

Brushless motors are used in floppy disk drives, VCR head drives, tape transports, and a host of other applications. One long-standing use has been high-speed laser scanners, familiar as the bar-code reader at your supermarket. In this application, the BLDC motor is a natural as the scanning speeds range from 1800 to 12,000 RPM, right in the BLDC superior speed range.

7.9. SPECIAL DRIVE SYSTEMS

As mentioned in this text, the most common configuration for BLDC drives is the voltage-fed type. Where size permits, the drive can be made inductively current fed or, alternatively, a tight current feedback loop can be used. The inductive method involves use of a significant amount of circuit inductance switched in such fashion as to provide a constant current source to the motor. Such inductors tend to be large and dissipative but result in low switching transient current being fed back into the power line. Current fed drives permit linear acceleration of inertial loads and very rapid starting of low inertial loads. When used in large (>1 hp) system, the current fed drive can be configured into a bang-bang control, which can lead to reduced cost. Size and bulk of the controller is increased. *Bang-bang* controllers feed current to the motor through a suitable circuit inductance up to a given current level; then they switch off and repeat for the next cycle. Stored inductive energy is either returned to the power supply or fed to the motor. Such drives are useful for single or limited-speed range applications. Low-speed performance can be severely limited by rough motion. If the motor inductance itself is high enough, an external inductor is not needed, although this is rarely the case.

Sinusoidal drive is possible but results in very high output device dissipation because of the need to operate the drive transistors in the linear mode. Usually restricted to two-phase, low-power applications, this method is capable of providing very smooth motion. The smoothness results from the almost continuous rotating flux generated by a sinusoidal sine-cosine field. Little commercial work is being done in this area. Perhaps this method will experience a revival for special applications.

Because electronics technology has been advancing at a rapid rate, entirely new power switching devices will no doubt appear that will result in simpler, more cost-effective drive systems. The obvious result will be seen in applications that are now limited due to cost or size. It would seem that the major breakthrough will be in self-contained, line-operated systems that can compete with conventional ac motors while offering speed and torque control. At present, practical integrated motor drives are available in the 1/50 hp range. Units will no doubt appear over the next few years with ratings in excess of 0.5 hp. At this point, the BLDC technology will be on its way to maturity.

8

Testing Methods and Evaluation of Motors and Controls

8.1. PURPOSE OF TESTING

Motors and controls are not the end product but necessary components of an end product. A motor and controller might be required to drive a drill at various speeds and torques, and the drill might have to be listed by Underwriters Laboratory. The motor and controller have to be reliable and safe; brushes and bearing life should be reasonable. In order to find out if a motor meets the performance standards set for it, a number of appropriate tests must be performed in order to evaluate the system properly.

In previous chapters, the inherent characteristics of motors and systems were described. Depending on the sophistication of the ultimate performance requirement of the system, the test might be a routine performance test such as simply driving a fixed load like a blower. The test would determine the watts input, current, and speed of the motor. This might be all that is required for incoming inspection.

The initial evaluation of a motor calls at least for torque-speed measurements, commonly called a brake test, a heat run, and life test. Depending on the application and type of motor, additional tests might have to be performed.

Information from a single unit cannot be fully relied upon as the unit might or might not represent the average performance of future motors due to manufacturing tolerances, possible damage done to the sample received during shipping, etc. As for electronic controls, not only are heat runs and life tests important, but also familiarity with wave shapes at different locations of the control circuit at predetermined performance points is invaluable.

The test methods described in this chapter are of a general nature. The chapter acquaints the reader with some of the most common test procedures. Where additional tests are required, consult specialized publications on this subject.

8.2. GENERAL MEASUREMENTS

8.2.1. Torque-Speed Measurements

A dynamometer is frequently used to measure torque at various speeds. There are different kinds of dynamometers, but all are equipped with a means of indicating torque. Some also indicate speed. Figure 8-1 shows such a setup. Speed can be measured with a tachometer such as a stroboscope. It is important that the motor and the dynamometer be lined up, and the dynamometer must be well calibrated. The stroboscope must also read correctly, and the calibration should be checked before running a test. Different metering will be required for different kinds of motors. If a dynamometer is not available, the string-and-pulley system can be used to measure torque. Figure 8-2 shows how it is done. A scale is required for the test. The torque is the product of the scale reading and the radius of the pulley. It is very important that

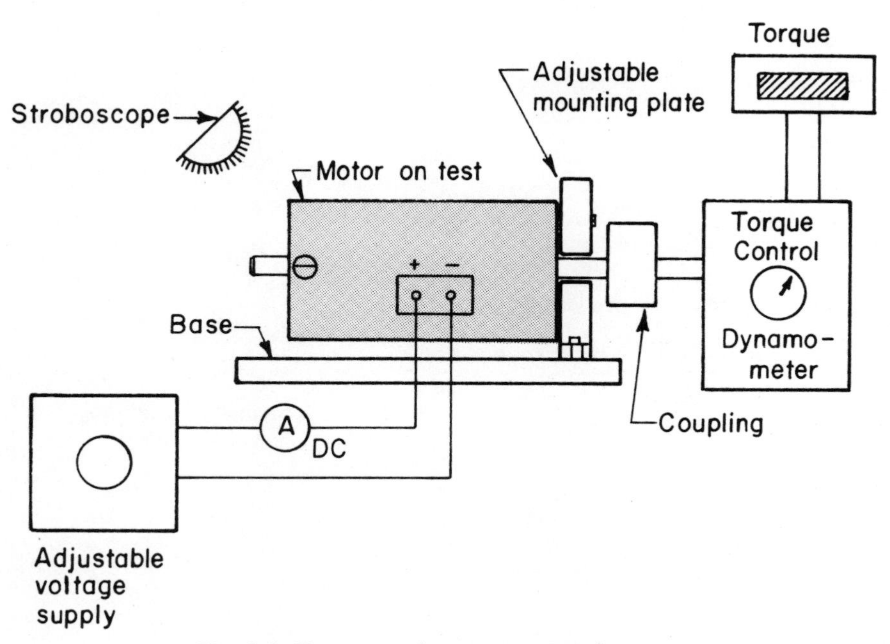

Fig. 8-1. Torque-speed measurements of a motor.

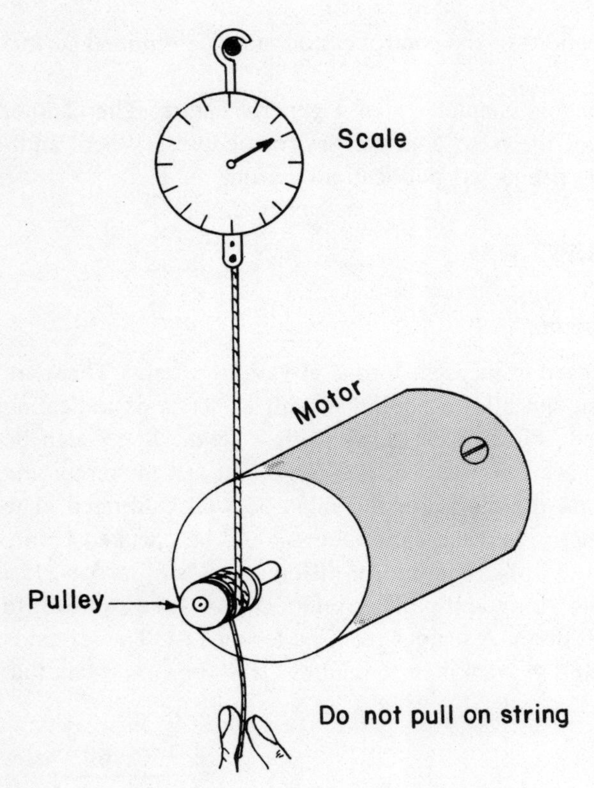

Fig. 8-2. String-and-pulley system to measure torque.

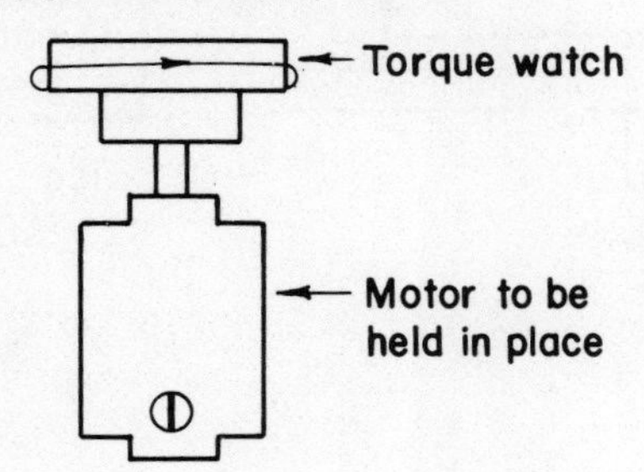

Fig. 8-3. Method of measuring friction torque with a torque watch.

the friction of the string and pulley represents the load and that no additional load is added by pulling on the string. The speed can be measured with a stroboscope.

The torque required to overcome static friction is called friction torque. One way to measure this torque is with a torque watch (Fig. 8-3). The torque watch is rotated slowly and the torque indicated will be friction torque. This procedure should be repeated for several shaft positions in both clockwise and counterclockwise rotation.

8.2.2. Resistance and Inductance Measurements

Resistance of a winding is often simply measured with a multimeter. These meters are frequently not accurate enough, particularly for measuring windings with lower resistances. In general, a Wheatstone bridge will give a more accurate reading. When very low resistances are involved, a Kelvin bridge might be required.

For measuring winding inductances, a number of inductance bridges are available. Accurate digital impedance meters can very much simplify these measurements. Inductance measurements are usually done at a frequency of 1000 Hz. This parameter corresponds to the inductance information generally quoted by motor manufacturers. At 60 Hz, the winding inductance is likely to be higher, and at higher frequencies it is likely to be lower. The inductance of a BLDC motor with a conventional stator core will vary proportionally more with frequency than the inductance of the toothless version. The above is simply because the permeability of steel varies with frequency. Figure 8-4 illustrates the inductance measurement of a PM dc motor winding. Contact with the commutator bars is made with probes. The inductance must be measured with the armature in place because the field flux will change the permeability of steel and therefore the inductance.

In a typical ferromagnetic circuit, the magnitude of the current in the winding will help to determine the permeability of steel and therefore the inductance. The impedance bridge only uses a low-amplitude signal to determine the inductance, and motor currents are considerably larger in magnitude, which also introduces an error.

To determine winding inductance at lower frequencies, you also can use a circuit like the one shown in Fig. 8-15. In a PM motor there is usually no harm done in passing a 60 or 120 Hz ac current through the motor as long as the peak current is less than the peak current permitted by the manufacturer for this motor. Knowing current, voltage, power, and frequency, you can calculate an inductance. Depending on the particular motor, this approach might or might not be practical.

Other methods are used to determine inductance, often based on observing the transient condition of a current with respect to an applied voltage or sudden short circuit in the winding.

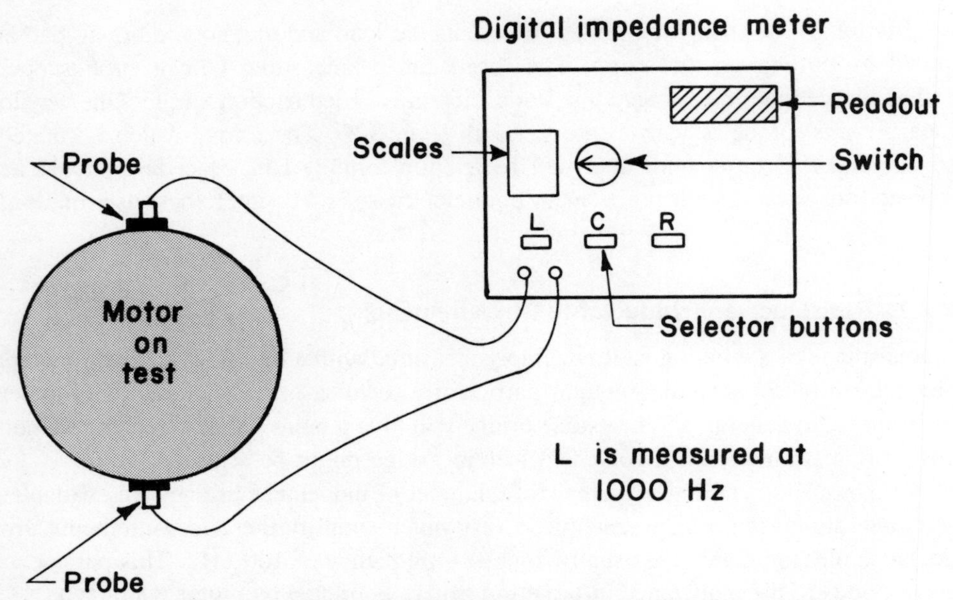

Fig. 8-4. Inductance measurements of a permanent-magnet dc motor.

8.2.3. Temperature Measurements

To evaluate a motor as to its suitability for a certain application, it is often important to determine the temperature the motor reaches at a certain location to make sure that it keeps within its rating. There are a variety of ways to measure this. Thermometers are of course well known. It is possible to attach a thermometer to the exterior of the motor, but it is more of a problem to attach it to a winding, and even if one manages to do so, it becomes difficult to monitor. One way to measure temperature rise in motor windings is to measure the rise by resistance. The following equation applies when copper wire is used:

$$\frac{R_2}{R_1} = \frac{234.5 + t_2}{234.5 + t_1} \tag{8-1}$$

where R_1 = Resistance of winding at ambient temperature before heat run

t_1 = Ambient temperature before heat run

R_2 = Final resistance of winding after heat run

t_2 = Temperature of winding after heat run

Temperature rise would be $t_2 - t_1$ if the ambient temperature has not changed during the heat run. If ambient has changed, the calculated rise has to be corrected by the amount of change in ambient.

Another way of measuring temperature is with thermocouples as shown in Fig. 8-5. A thermocouple is basically a pair of conductors of dissimilar materials which are generally joined together at one end. They generate an EMF as a function of temperature. The other end of the conductors are free to be connected to a potentiometer, bridge, or recording instrument that measures the EMF. It is important to use the same thermocouple materials for which the meter has been calibrated. Typical materials are iron and constantan or copper and constantan. Thermocouples can be located at several spots on the winding and other parts of the motor that are to be monitored for temperature rise.

To determine the temperature rise of an armature winding as in dc motors is somewhat more complicated. Rise by resistance measurements are possible, but this has to be taken fast with probes and it should be taken across the same commutator bars. Brushes should be removed during resistance measurements. One way of being sure that readings across the same bars are used is to take hot readings first. Then wait for the motor to cool down without moving the armature and repeat the reading.

There are different color markers with which you can mark an armature. These markers change color at a certain temperature. This way you can determine if a certain temperature has been exceeded.

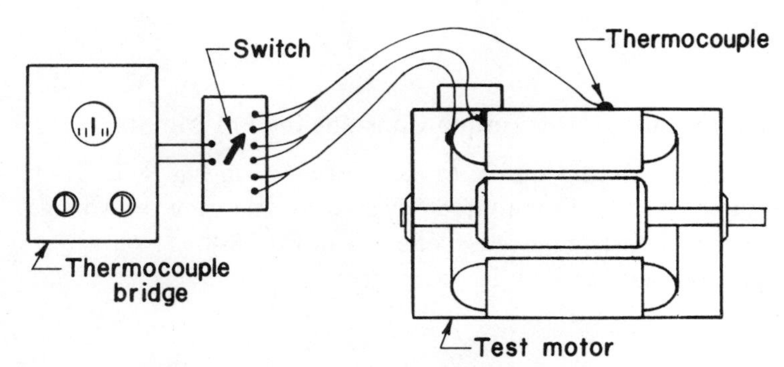

Fig. 8-5. Measuring temperature with thermocouples.

8.3. DC MOTOR TESTS

8.3.1. Determination of Voltage Constant for PM Motors

Drive the motor to be tested as a generator as in Fig. 8-4 and measure the voltage generated by the motor and the speed at which it is running.

$$K_E = \frac{\text{voltmeter reading}}{\text{drive motor RPM} \times 1000} \text{ [V/K RPM]}$$

To convert to SI units: 1000 RPM $= 9.549 \times 10^3$ V/rad s^{-1}. Brushes must be well run in to perform this test. The voltmeter must also be accurate. It is sometimes convenient to use a synchronous motor with accurately known speed (Fig. 8-6) as a drive motor. Make sure, however, that the motor is running at synchronous speed.

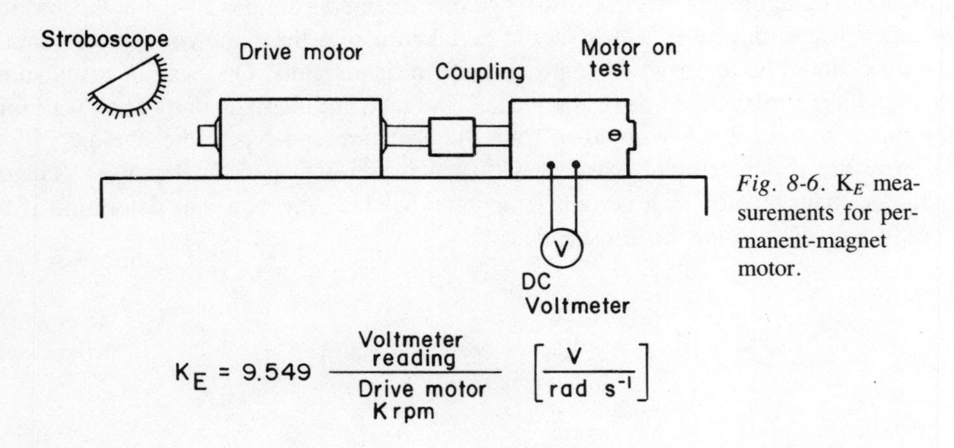

Fig. 8-6. K_E measurements for permanent-magnet motor.

8.3.2. Determination of the Torque Constant for PM Motors

This test requires a setup similar to the one shown in Fig. 8-7. But this time the speed is kept constant and the torque is varied by adjusting the voltage.

Current versus torque points are plotted as in Fig. 8-8.

The torque constant can now be calculated:

$$K_T = \frac{T_2 - T_1}{I_2 - I_1}$$

In SI units, T is in newton · meters and I is in amperes. In customary U.S. units, T is in ounce-inches and I is in amperes.

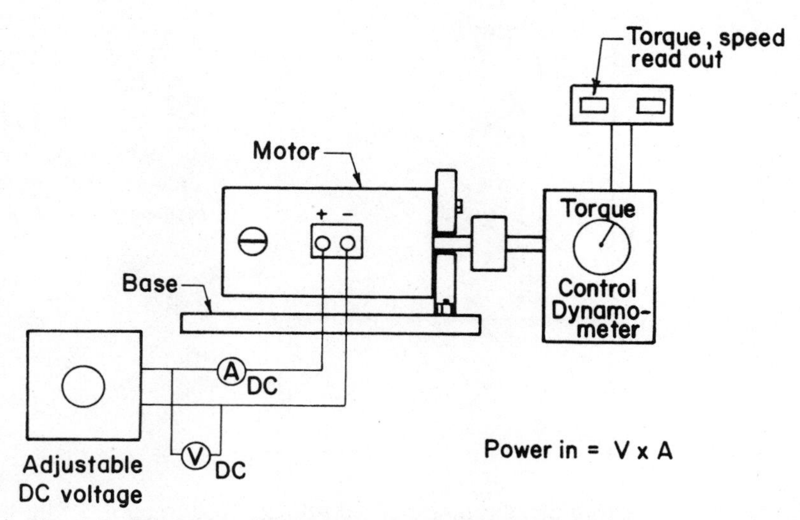

Fig. 8-7. Torque-speed-current measurements of a permanent-magnet motor.

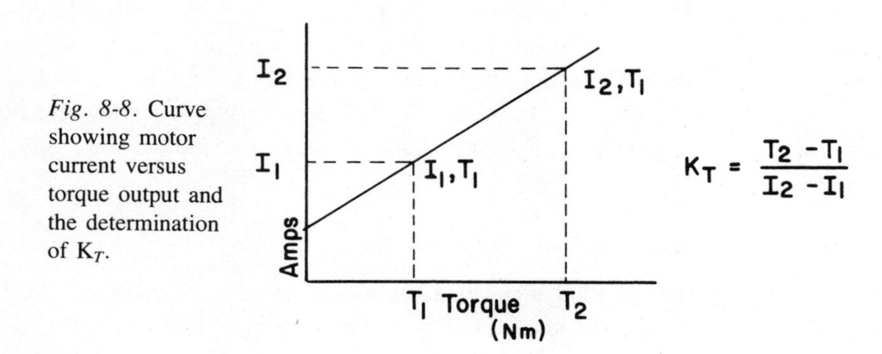

Fig. 8-8. Curve showing motor current versus torque output and the determination of K_T.

8.3.3. PM DC Motor Performance

The test setup shown in Fig. 8-7 is used to determine the torque-speed curve for this motor. The voltage is kept constant. The torque is increased in constant increments, and current, speed, and torque are recorded for every point. A typical torque-speed curve is shown in Fig. 8-9. The motor should be maintained at about a constant

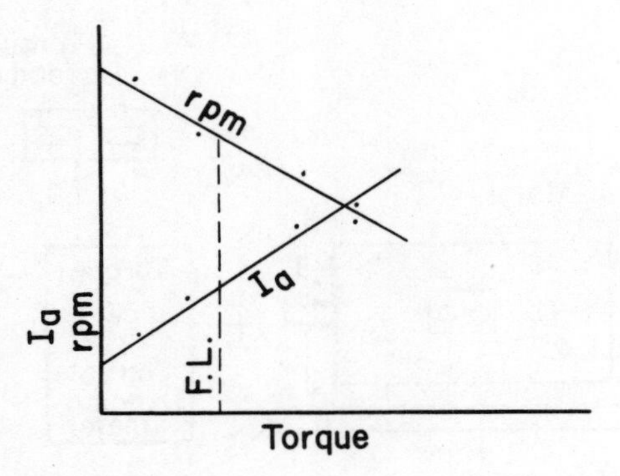

Fig. 8-9. Torque-speed and torque-current curves for a permanent-magnet dc motor.

temperature. Upon heating up, the motor should be allowed to cool before proceeding. Care must be taken that the current does not exceed the maximum current rating of the motor. Exceeding this current might demagnetize the magnets.

When applying rectified currents, a small known resistance, such as a known meter shunt, can be added in series to the line as shown in Fig. 8-10. An oscilloscope across that resistance will measure its voltage drop. Knowing the value of the resistance, the peak current can be determined by applying Ohm's law. This peak current should not exceed the maximum current permitted for this motor. In any case, it might be worthwhile at the end of the test to check the K_E as explained in section 8.3.1, and make sure that no demagnetization has occurred. It must be stressed that when checking K_E, the motor temperature should be the same as when the motor was originally tested.

8.3.4. Generated Voltage of a dc Shunt Motor

This test is commonly called a no-load saturation test. In a permanent-magnet motor, the generated voltage is determined by the flux produced by the magnet. In the shunt motor, the field is determined by the number of turns in the field and the current that passes through the winding. The shunt current is often called the excitation current. Figure 8-11 shows how to set up for a test. For this test, the speed of the motor must remain constant. Power is connected to the shunt field. Current is first gradually increased by changing the setting of the rheostat and the generated voltage recorded for each current setting. Then current is gradually decreased and the generated voltage also recorded. The two curves will generally not be exactly alike and are plotted as in Fig. 8-12. If the motor has run before, there might be a voltage reading with zero current reading; this is called a residual voltage.

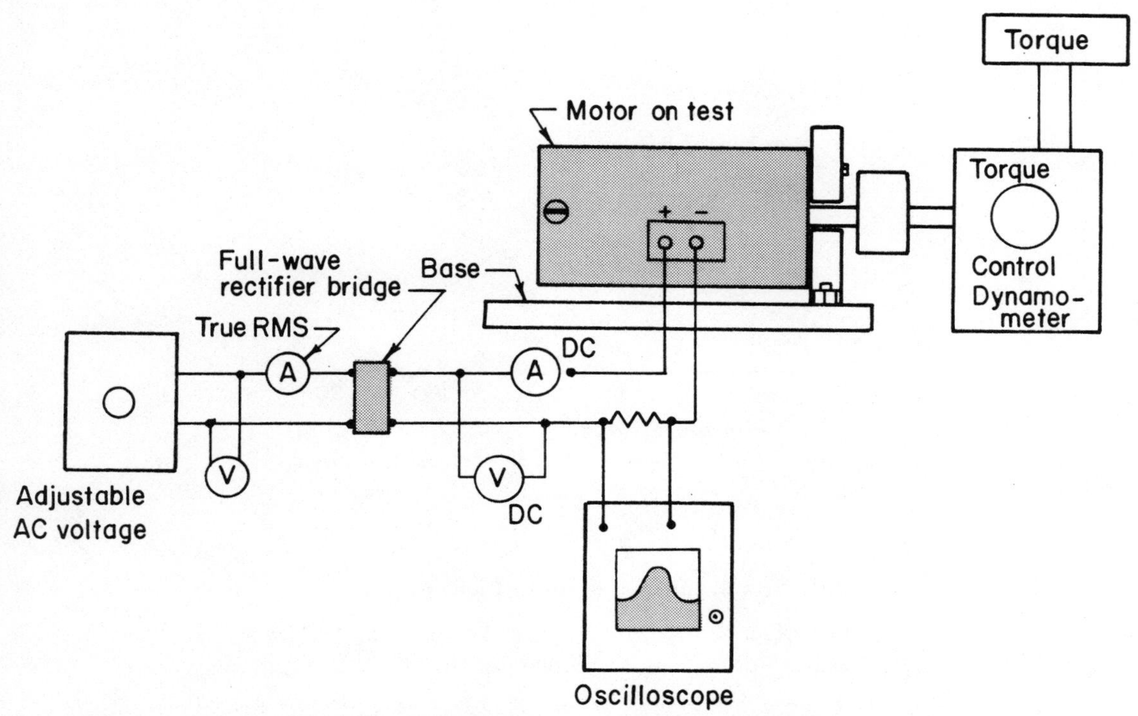

Fig. 8-10. Torque-speed and current measurements with unfiltered full-wave rectified power supply.

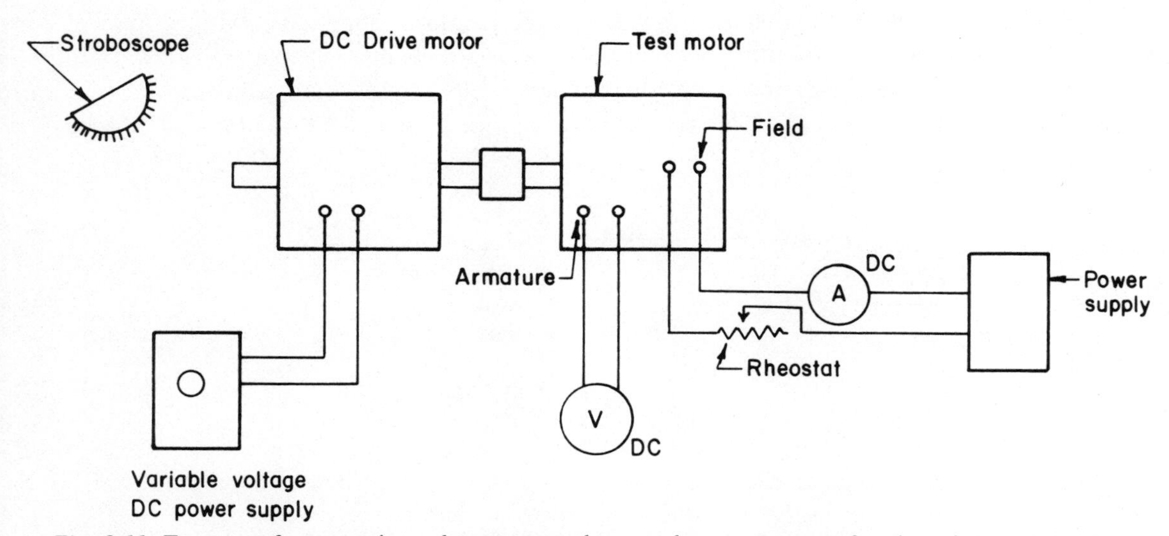

Fig. 8-11. Test setup for measuring voltage generated across the armature as a function of shunt field current.

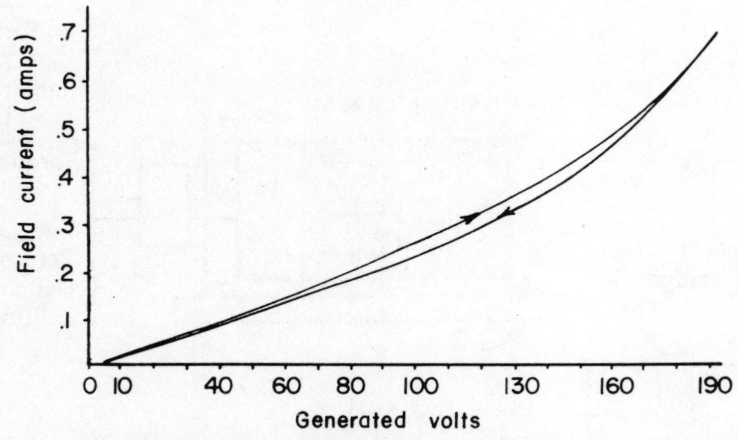

Fig. 8-12. Curve showing generated voltage as function of shunt field current.

8.3.5. Brake Test for Shunt, Series, and Compound-Field Motors

A brake test of a shunt motor can be performed much like the brake test for a PM motor in section 8.3.3. Various curves can be plotted for different field currents. These can be set by varying a rheostat setting as indicated in Fig. 8-10. For a load saturation curve, use a setup similar to Fig. 8-7, but connect the shunt field to a separate power supply. For a connection diagram, see Fig. 8-13. Set the shunt field current and vary the load on the motor. Maintain a constant speed on the motor by varying the input voltage to the armature. Figure 8-14 shows a load saturation curve and the resulting nonlinearity resulting at higher armature currents due to armature reaction. Alternatively, armature generated voltage can be calculated by subtracting the I_aR_a drop from the input voltage. This generated voltage can be compared with the

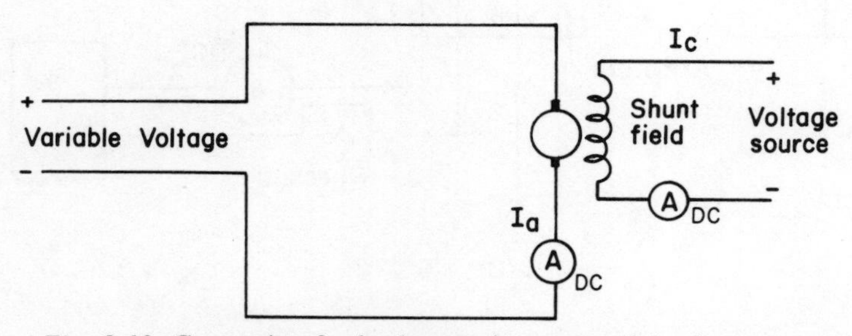

Fig. 8-13. Connection for load saturation curve of dc shunt motor.

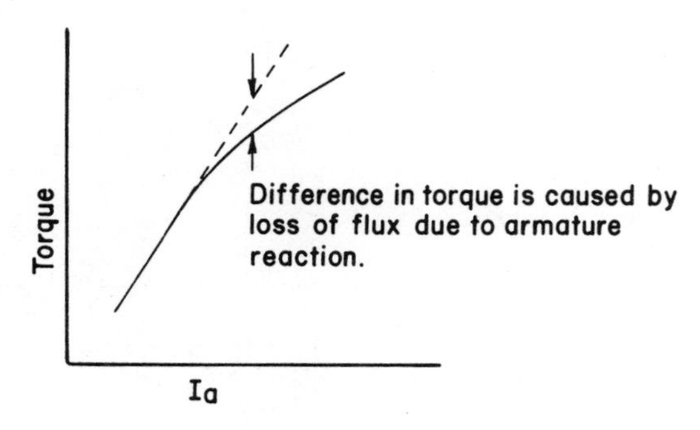

Fig. 8-14. Load saturation curve for a shunt motor; shunt field current constant, speed constant.

data obtained from the no-load saturation curve. After compensating the generated voltages for any differential in speed, any really noticeable differences in that data are due to armature reaction.

The series and compound-wound motors would also follow procedures similar to those laid out for the shunt motor. The shunt field current in the compound field motor can be equally varied by changing the rheostat setting as is done for the shunt motor. In the series motor, the series field can be separately excited, and no-load saturation curves as well as load saturation curves can be obtained.

8.4. AC MOTOR TESTS

8.4.1. Single-Phase AC Motor

Torque-speed measurements and no-load data test procedures for many single-phase ac motors follow much the same way as is the case with the dc motor, differing from the latter in that ac instruments must be used. Figure 8-15 shows the hook-up for a single-phase ac motor. A wattmeter must be used when measuring ac, in addition to a voltmeter and ammeter. Unless the wattmeter is specially designed for reading on low power factors, check the meter specifications if the power factor is less than 0.5. With single-phase motors, which use a capacitor in auxiliary winding to start and run the motor, the voltage across the capacitor should be checked with a voltmeter.

For a synchronous motor with a wound field, the torque-speed curves can be taken at various values of magnetizing currents. As the field is excited with a dc current, the current can be monitored with a dc ammeter much like in the dc shunt motor.

For additional performance analysis of single-phase motors, many analytical tools have been developed and ample literature is available on this subject.

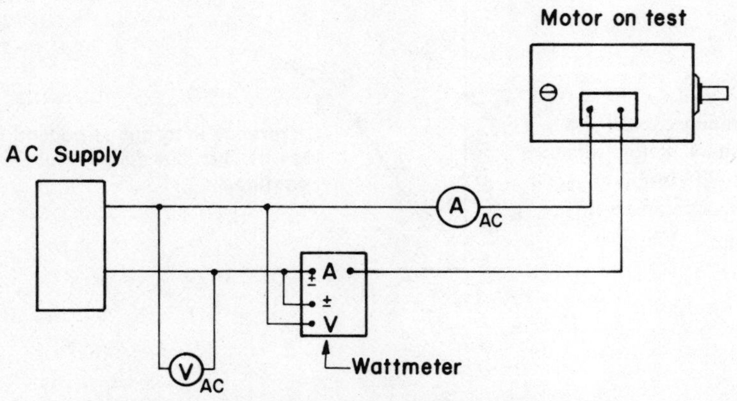

Fig. 8-15. Instrumentation for single-phase ac motor.

8.4.2. Polyphase Motors

Typical instrumentation for testing a three-phase motor is shown in Fig. 8-16. Only one ammeter and voltmeter are shown. Ammeters and voltmeters can be added to measure the current and voltage across the other phases. Alternatively, meters can be switched around as shown in Fig. 8-17. Any number of switching arrangements can be made. It is important that current not be interrupted while switching meters and

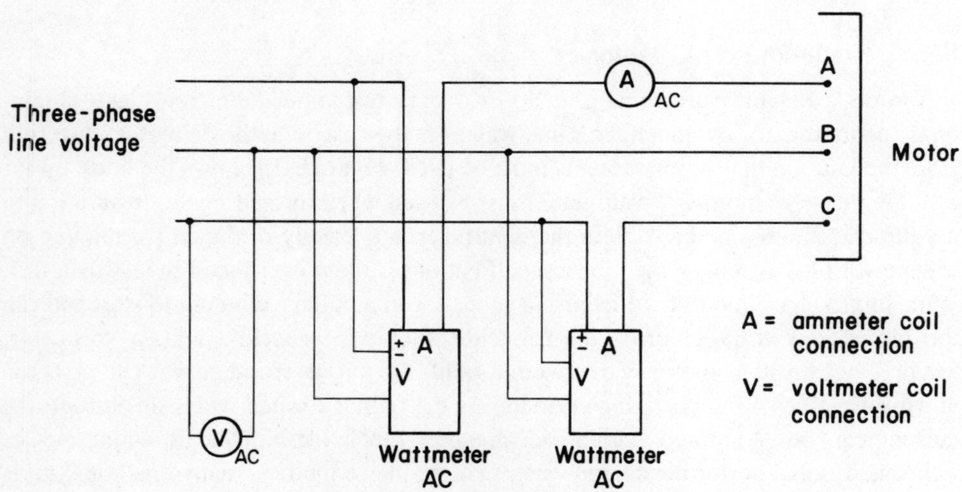

Fig. 8-16. Test setup for three-phase motors.

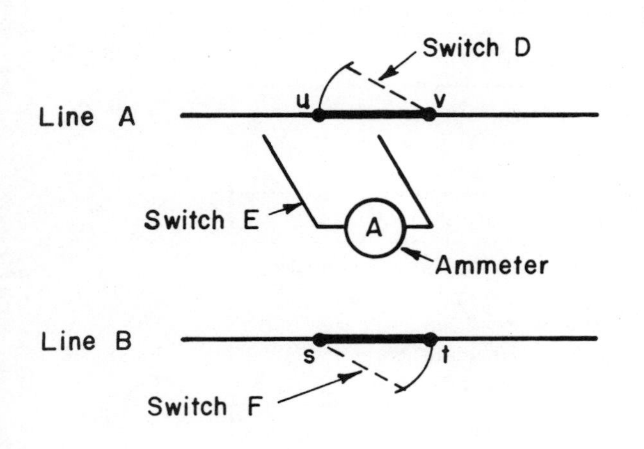

Initially, switch D is across u-v
switch F is across s-t

To connect ammeter and read currents:

Step 1 – switch E across u-v
2 – open switch D
3 – read amps in power line A
4 – close switch D
5 – open switch E
6 – switch E across s-t
7 – open switch F
8 – read amps in power line B
9 – close switch F
10 – open switch E

Important: Following above or similar procedure, currents in the motor are not interrupted while switching ammeter in or out of line.

Fig. 8-17. One way of switching ammeter without line current interruption.

that no harm is done to the meter itself. The total power in Fig. 8-16 is the algebraic sum of the readings of the two watt meters. If one meter reads negative, reverse the voltage leads, and this means that the readings should be subtracted. Polarities are usually marked on the watt meters. Always start out connecting the same polarity of the potential coils of the meters to the common line (power line B in Fig. 8-16).

8.5. TESTING BRUSHLESS DC MOTORS

8.5.1. General Considerations

Testing BLDC motors presents a real challenge. It is not the lack of knowledge of what needs to be done and frequently not even how to do it, but the challenge consists in finding meters and instruments that provide reasonably accurate readings. The nature of the voltage and current waves seen in BLDC motors are such that you must be very careful that the meters you use are actually capable of giving an accurate reading. Table 8-1 lists some of the most common meter movements and how they might respond to true readings. There is simply no easy rule to predict which meter will be best suited under all conditions. Even meters that in theory should give good RMS readings might not respond to certain frequencies, peak currents etc. Many

Table 8-1. Common Analog Meter Movements and RMS Measurements.

Instrument Type	Comments
Dynamometer	Very commonly used for ac and dc measurements. Might or might not respond to a particular wave shape found in BLDC motors. Frequency limited.
Moving Iron	Unpredictable with nonsinusoidal wave shapes.
Electronic Voltmeters	Modern instruments can provide very accurate measurements of nonsinusoidal wave shapes having high crest factor. Frequency response can be excellent. Instruments are available with programmable conversion factors. The instrument performance is in direct proportion to cost.
Electrothermic	Slow to respond and prone to accidents. These meters also have frequency limitations. Recommended for use in current and voltage measurements.
Permanent Magnet moving Coil Instrument	Converts ac to dc and responds to average value. This movement is not suitable for measuring nonsinusoidal wave shapes.
Electrostatic Instrument	Can read true values. However, it might have frequency limitation. Comes only as a voltmeter.

RMS meters respond to ac only. It is often worthwhile to discuss a particular problem with the technical departments of instrument manufacturers.

Digital meters also have their limitations, but these are usually very poorly spelled out. You must study how an individual meter is programmed to arrive at a certain reading before you can pass judgement on the quality of its RMS readings.

As a general rule, however, the published crest factor specification is a good indication of the ability of a meter to provide valid RMS readings on complex wave forms. High-grade laboratory digital meters will usually have a crest factor of 4:1 or greater. Avoid less expensive instruments having crest factors of 2:1 or less. It is best to use a meter using a true-RMS converter circuit rather than an instrument that is of the averaging type and RMS calibrated. The frequency response of the meter is also an important consideration because there are often high-frequency components in the measured quantity, and these must be included in the final data. For most BLDC motor/drive combinations, a usable bandwidth of 100 kHz is adequate, although lower bandwidth instruments can sometimes be used.

In recent years, the combination of oscilloscope and computer have made it possible to compute average and RMS voltage and current value almost instantaneously. However, these systems are very costly.

There are several good software packages now available made to run on the usual personal computer. Properly used, these programs can perform excellent wave-form analysis. By means of *FFT* (fast fourier transform) methods, the complex current and voltage wave forms often seen in brushless systems can be analyzed in detail. These FFT data analysis systems are also useful in analyzing servo-system transient performance. Cost of the software and interface is approximately $1,000.00, but the price will probably come down because of market pressure. Of course, you must have a suitable PC to use the system.

The permanent-magnet, moving-coil instruments frequently are acceptable for reading average dc values. But for these measurements too, it pays to look at the wave forms. If very steep, short pulses occurring unevenly are to be measured, or if a part of the instantaneous current values exceed the scale of the meter, the instrument might not respond properly, and reservations as to the accuracy of the readings are justified. Average values of currents or voltages can be estimated or calculated from the traces on the screen of oscilloscope. RMS values can also be calculated, but this can be rather tedious. One way of checking on the ammeter is to compare the value of K_T calculated from K_E (obtained in section 8.5.2) and the K_T obtained from the brake test in section 8-5-3. If these two do not coincide, chances are that the ammeter reads incorrectly.

It is sometimes useful to determine current values by using the heat rise in a calibrated resistor placed in series with the load. Devices containing a resistor/thermocouple combination in an evacuated glass envelope are commercially available.

Used in current or voltage mode through the use of suitable shunts or voltage dividers, these devices can yield very accurate data on the average power of a system. It is usually necessary to rig up such test devices for specific tests and their use in production testing is limited.

8.5.2. Determination of Voltage Constant for BLDC Motors

The BLDC motor under test is driven at a certain constant speed. An oscilloscope is connected across the line terminals of the motor. The K_E will be a function of the actual magnitude and wave shape of the generated voltage. For test setup, see Figs. 8-18 and 8-19. For a sine-wave generated voltage of a three-phase, full-wave motor:

$$K_E = 9.549 \times 0.95 \times \frac{\text{Peak volts}}{\text{K RPM}} \left[\frac{\text{V}}{\text{rad s}^{-1}}\right]$$

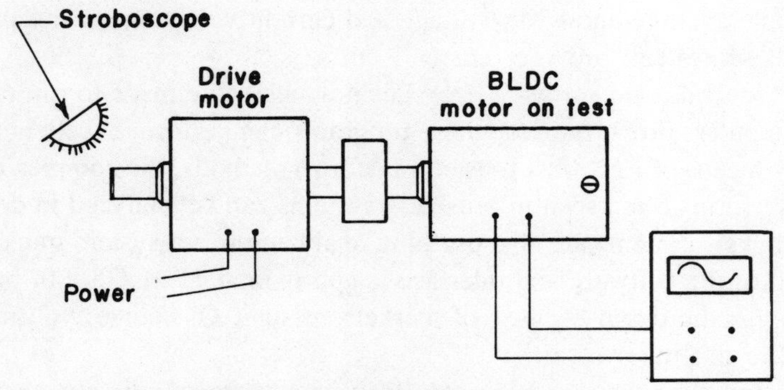

Fig. 8-18. Test setup for determining K_E for BLDC motor.

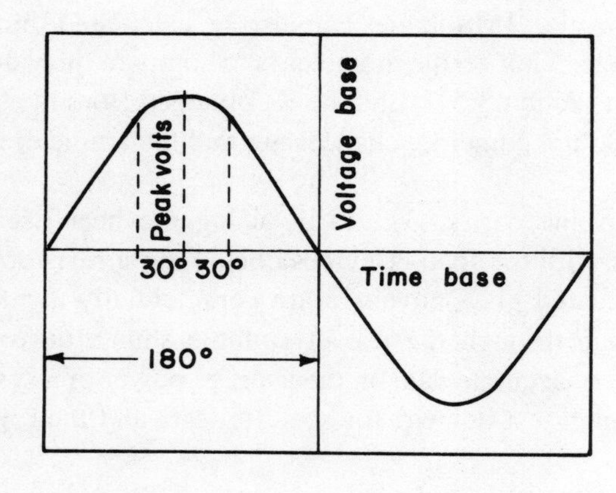

Fig. 8-19. Sine wave voltage generated by a BLDC motor.

For a trapezoidal wave form:

$$K_E = 9.549 \times 1 \times \frac{\text{Peak volts}}{\text{K rpm}} \left[\frac{\text{V}}{\text{rad s}^{-1}} \right]$$

Multiplying constants for additional modes of BLDC motor operations are listed in Table 5-3. An ac voltmeter can be used in case of the sinusoidal generated voltage. In this case:

$$\text{Peak voltage} = \sqrt{2}\ V_{RMS}$$

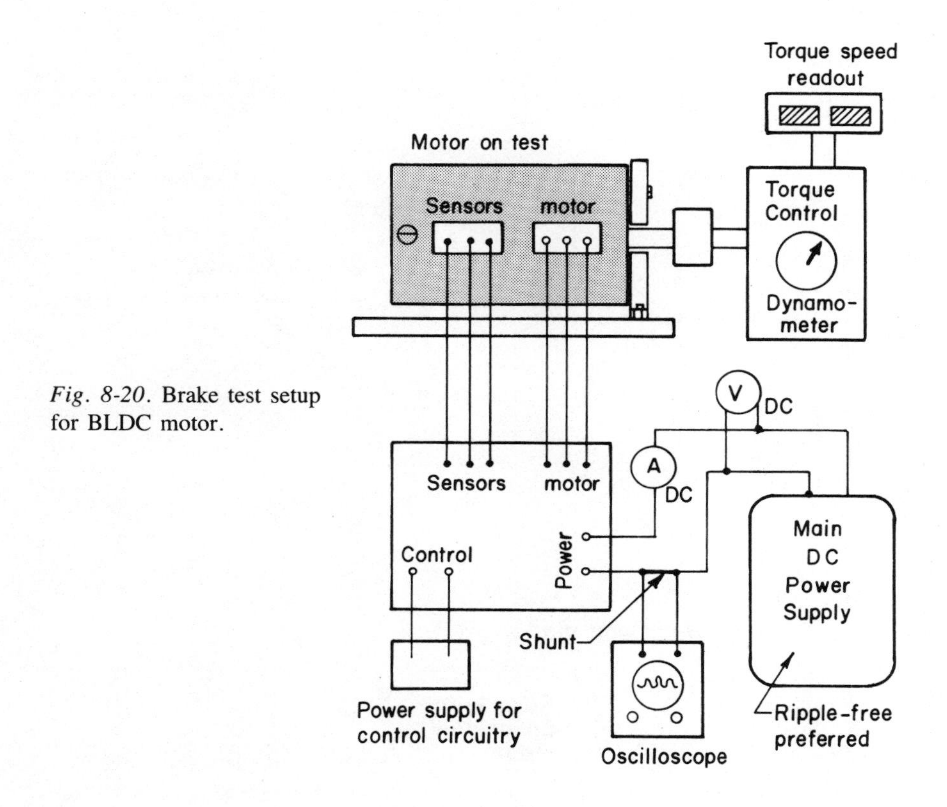

Fig. 8-20. Brake test setup for BLDC motor.

8.5.3. Brake Test

A typical test setup is shown in Fig. 8-20. Always check which operating mode the controller is set for, open or closed loop. It is recommended that a first brake test always be performed in the open-loop mode.

In this particular setup, it is assumed that the power supply is a ripple-free supply. A dc voltmeter is connected across the power supply to monitor the output of the power supply voltage, and a dc ammeter is connected to monitor the dc or average current in the line. A shunt or very small resistor is connected in one of the lines that serves as a voltage drop monitored by an oscilloscope. The resistance of the shunt must be sufficiently small to not affect the performance of the system. If the voltage drop across the shunt can not be neglected, the voltmeter can be located at the input terminals of the control rather than the output of the power supply. The voltage appearing on the oscilloscope screen will be proportional to current $I = V/R$. Practically all controllers for BLDC motors have current limiters and you can observe, on the oscilloscope when the current limiter goes into effect. It is generally a good idea

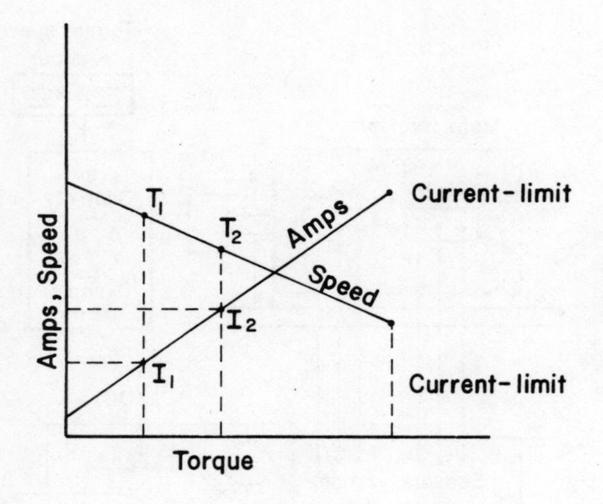

Fig. 8-21. Performance characteristics of a BLDC motor open-loop test.

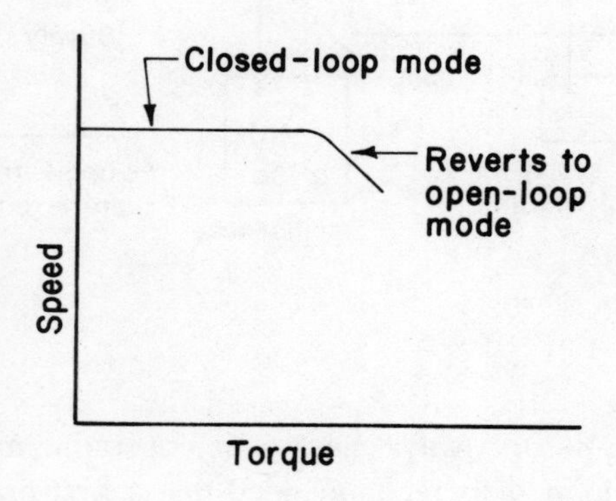

Fig. 8-22. Torque-speed curve for closed-loop setting.

to become familiar with the current shapes, and you can often estimate the average current on the oscilloscope and compare it with the ammeter reading. Do not carry on a brake test beyond the point at which the current limiter becomes effective. A typical torque-speed curve is shown in Fig. 8-21. The torque constant can be determined by calculating:

$$\frac{T_2 - T_1}{I_2 - I_1}$$

If the K_T is in the SI system, it should be identical to the K_E determined in section 8-5-2.

Figure 8-22 shows a typical torque-speed curve for a closed-loop setting. The system stays in closed-loop mode until the torque required exceeds the torque that the motor can produce at that speed. At this point the motor reverts to open-loop performance.

8.5.4. Power Relationships

In section 8-5-1, it was pointed out how important it was to use appropriate meters for measuring different wave shapes of voltages and currents. However, it is not sufficient to just read meters, but it is also important to relate the different readings to each other. Figure 8-23 (a to f) illustrates a typical problem. Figure 8-23 (a) shows a simple dc circuit with a resistive load. Figure 8-23 (c) shows the same circuit, but the current is chopped, resulting in a square wave current with on-time equal off-time. The result would be the following ammeter readings:

Ammeter Readings	I_{dc}	I_{RMS}
Circuit (a)	I_a	I_a
Circuit (c)	$0.5\ I_a$	$0.707\ I_a$

Power relationships are as follows:

	Power in	Power across the load
Circuit (a)	$E_{dc}\ I_a$	$I_a^2\ R$
Circuit (c)	$E_{dc}\ \frac{I_a}{2}$	$(0.707\ I_a)^2 \times R$

See also Figure 8-23 (e) and (f).

It is well to remember that power can only be generated by a voltage and current of the same frequency. In this case, a ripple-free dc source was assumed, and power into the circuit will be the product of dc current and dc voltage. However, the power loss across the resistor will be the product of the square of the RMS current times the resistance no matter what frequencies this current is made up of.

In BLDC motors, the wave shapes are generally not so easy to analyze, so it becomes more difficult to establish the relationships. It becomes particularly difficult where the dc supply is not ripple free. If a ripple-free power source is assumed as in Fig. 8-20, the power into the motor system would be $I_{dc} \times E_{dc}$.

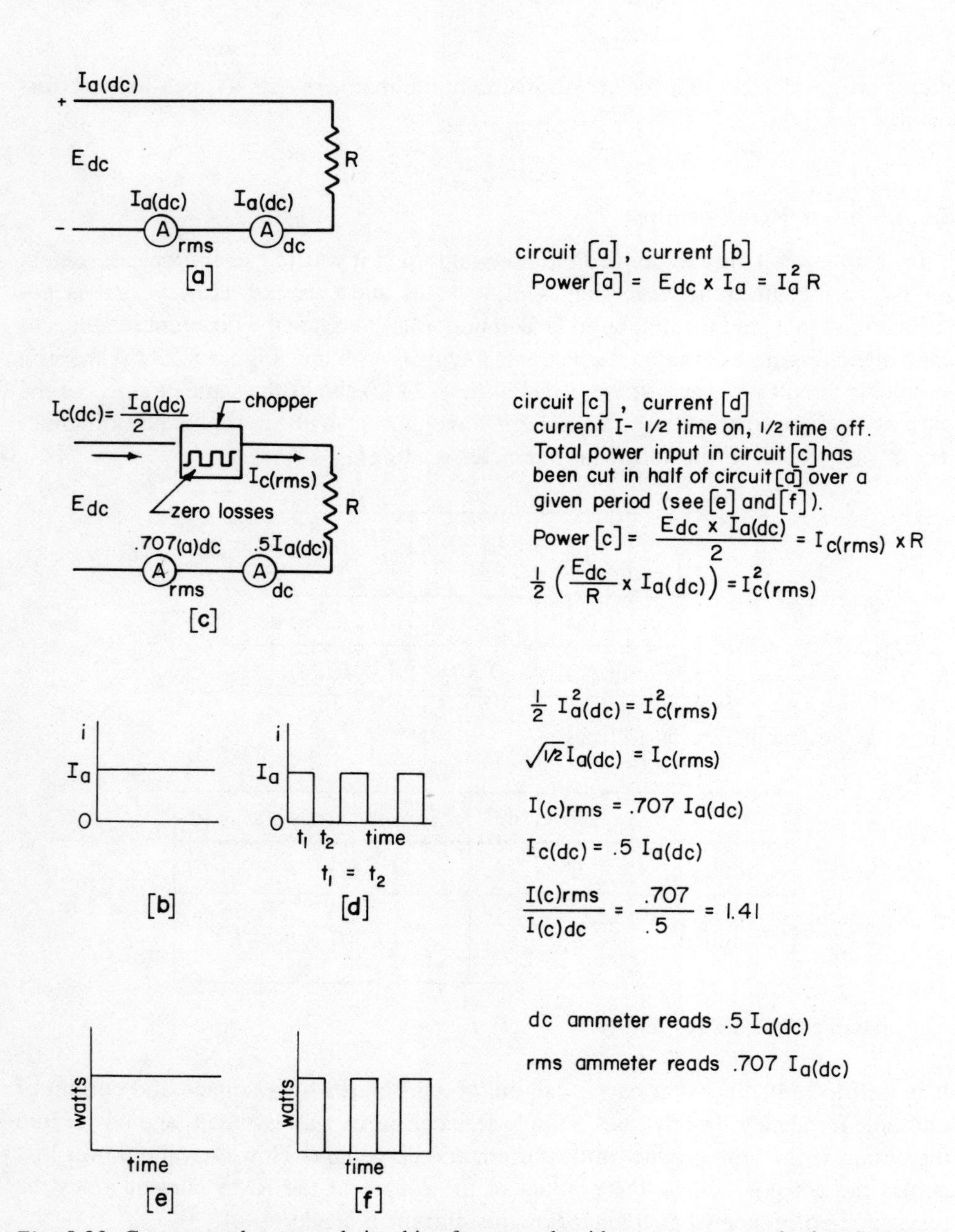

Fig. 8-23. Currents and power relationships for network with square-wave, pulsating dc current supply.

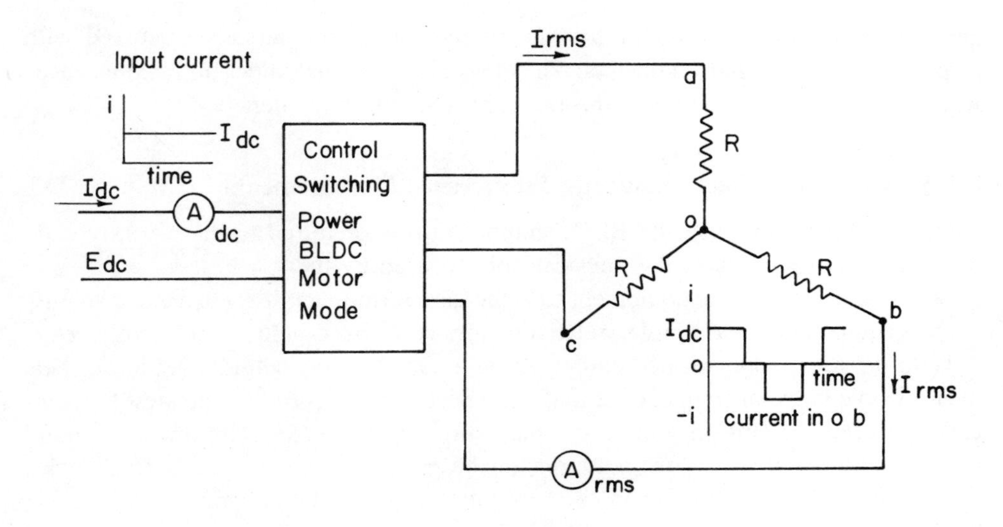

$I_{rms/phase} = .817\ I_{dc}$

Total power to resistors
(No losses in controller)

Power supply		Load	
$E_{dc}\ I_{dc}$	=	$3 \times (.817 I_{dc})^2\ R$	(3 phases)
$E_{dc}\ I_{dc}$	=	$2\ I_{dc}^2 R$	

Fig. 8-24. Current and power relationships for three-phase BLDC motor switching with resistive network.

If the motor windings in a BLDC motor system are replaced by a resistance network, while still maintaining commutation as shown in Figure 8-24, the following relationships apply:

$$I_{RMS/phase} = 0.817\ I_{dc(line)}$$

and

$$E_{dc}\ I_{dc} = 3 \times I^2_{RMS/phase} \times R_{phase} = 3 \times (0.817\ I_{dc})^2 R_{phase}$$

or

$$E_{dc}\ I_{dc} = 2\ I^2_{dc} \times R_{phase}.$$

One of the obvious solutions to reading power would be the use of wattmeters. However, wattmeters are often unsuitable because of their generally severe frequency and phase limitations, in addition to instrument limitations already discussed with respect to ammeters and voltmeters. This does not mean that under no circumstances wattmeters should be used, but the limitations should be understood.

8.5.5. Sound and Electromagnetic Interference Measurements

One of the reasons that the BLDC motor is often preferred to the brush-type dc motor is that it eliminates the physical noise caused by the brushes.

Sound-level measuring equipment runs the gamut from very expensive and sophisticated equipment to a simple, relatively low-cost, hand-held sound level meter.

With the more sophisticated equipment you can chart the sound level in decibels over a whole range of frequencies, making it possible to identify the noisiest frequencies and often helping in identifying the source of the noise. The low-cost sound meter generally only gives one noise reading based on a weighted scale of frequencies deemed most irritating to human ears. In most cases, the latter approach to judging the noise of a motor is quite satisfactory. To measure noise, a quiet room is required to reduce as much as possible any ambient noise. Also, noise-absorbing walls are preferred to avoid echoes. In mounting the motor, take care to not amplify the noise. Related readings should always be taken under identical circumstances. Place the microphone at the same distance and the same position with respect to the motor. Noise levels are likely to vary depending how long the motor has been running and what temperature is reached. The meter might not even read the same from one day to the next. If a maximum noise level is specified for a motor, the manufacturer and customer should agree on the testing procedure and both should follow the same procedure with the same model sound meter. If this procedure is not followed, there is likely to be no end to the arguments over which motor is or is not acceptable.

Ambient noise levels should always be at least 10 decibels below the measured motor noise level. There are usually compensating curves for noise levels with differences of fewer decibels, but this compensation is generally undesirable.

For measuring electromagnetic interference, a special shielded room is required. The equipment necessary for such testing is often specified by regulatory agencies that also prescribe the procedures which must be followed for such measurements. There are basically two kinds of interferences, conducted and radiated. The former consists of the motor and/or control feeding interference into the power line or wiring. The latter is caused by the motor and/or controller acting like a transmitter radiating noise at all kinds of frequencies, which are picked up by surrounding antennas etc.

Most methods for measuring line-conducted noise, such as *FCC* (Federal Communications Commission), *CSA* (Canadian Standards Association) and *VDE* (Verband Deutscher Electrotechniker), require a *LISN* (line stabilizing network) be inserted in the system (motor) supply leads. A spectrum analyzer or calibrated receiver is then capacitively coupled to one or the other supply line on the load side of the LISN. The portion of the spectrum as called out in the test specification is then swept and amplitudes logged or recorded by a plotter. The equipment used in these tests is somewhat expensive, and most work of this type is best farmed out to specialized test laboratories. Radiated EMI is measured at a prescribed distance from the test sample, using similar equipment connected to antennas cut for the frequencies of interest. Methods vary, and these tests do not come cheap.

8.5.6. Drive System Tests and Setup

When a controller/motor combination is purchased from a single source, the best rule is to ask that the system be tested as a system; that is, it be set up prior to shipping. This request will result in minimum problems when it is received. Always be sure to indicate to the vendor what type of load is to be seen by the motor: frictional, inertial, etc. It is often desirable to supply a sample load to the vendor if this is practical. This will permit testing of the drive/motor combination by the vendor and checking out all pertinent parameters.

When purchasing a motor and drive from separate sources, you become the system integrator. The success of a system integration depends heavily upon understanding what the limitations of the drive and motor are and how to properly set up the drive. Failure to educate yourself and appreciate the vagaries of system integration can lead to disappointing results, smoke, frantic phone calls, and a general feeling of failure (usually the drive).

Because of the many variations of drives now available, it is very difficult to set down specific instructions on how to set up a system for the first time. However, the following list might serve as a guide to the uninitiated. The professionals can skip this section.

1. Always read, in detail, the drive manufacturers' operating and hookup manual. Do not take short cuts. Most manuals do not say "READ IN EVENT OF SMOKE" on their covers.
2. Always observe proper power supply polarity. Many a warranty repair has resulted from not observing dc polarity (ac also, if marked).
3. Make certain that the motor phases are connected to the drive in the proper sequence. This rule also applies to the commutation sensors, resolvers, and shaft encoders that might be connected to the drive. It is often a good idea to send the motor to the drive manufacturer and let him check it out. Some will charge for this little help, others will not. The rule is: if in doubt, let someone else who knows do it. Always tell the drive manufacturer what make and type

motor you plan on using with his drive. This can avoid warranty arguments later and enable the drive manufacturer to guide in test and hookup.

4. If the drive uses an external dc source for motor run voltage, it is often wise to bring this voltage up slowly using a variable voltage supply. Do this only if you check with the drive manufacturer first. Some drives do not like this. Bringing up the voltage allows you to check that commutation is in the right sequence etc.

   Never bring up the ac voltage slowly on self-contained, integrated drives. This will cause the logic and analog circuits to get confused. At the very best, this procedure will provide no meaningful results.

5. It is wise to check voltage between control inputs and ground of line-operated units before connecting them to expensive, external signal-processing equipment such as computers etc. This simple test can prevent damage to the equipment and operator.

6. Always fasten or otherwise restrain the motor with a suitable mechanical means when powering up for the first time. It is also best not to connect the mechanical load at this time. This is so that a sudden application of power to the motor will not allow it to jump off the bench or worse, harm you and the load. A wild, one-horsepower motor out of control and running around your work bench is an awesome thing to behold. Also, analog control inputs must be at zero volts and digital inputs must be at the lowest speed/bit value when power is first applied. If all is well, the motor shaft will turn slowly or be stopped. The input stimulus can now be carefully applied. The shaft should now turn in accordance with the input. This is usually the first sign of success.

   In closed-velocity loop systems, the phase (sense) of the velocity signal should be such as to provide negative feedback. In systems using shaft encoders, it is easy to reverse the two quadrature outputs, thus making the loop positive. This will result in sudden runaway of the motor, often only when the input control voltage is raised (in the case of built-in dead band) up a few hundred millivolts. Exercise extreme caution in these cases. Some resolver-based feedback loops can also effect positive feedback if the resolver phases get reversed. This reinforces the need to physically restrain the motor during setup.

7. Observe good grounding at all times so as to eliminate shock hazard. It is wise to ground the motor to the drive chassis and then to a safe, low-impedance ground. Follow the drive manufacturers recommendations here.

   When making control connections to peripheral controls, make certain that signal grounds and returns are intact and that no ground loops develop, especially with analog inputs. Hum and noise on control inputs can be very perplexing and can even damage drive and motor.

8. Tests to check system damping, slew rate, and general transient response should use a suitable function generator or computer generated pattern as stimulus. An oscilloscope connected to the velocity feedback signal can permit adjustment of damping (amount of velocity feedback). An oscilloscope can also be connected to current monitor outputs (if provided) to check on peak current limit settings. It is not advised to go into a drive and twiddle pots unless you know what you are doing. Read the manual or call the manufacturer if in doubt. There are many more do's and don'ts that could be stated but those above give you the general idea. Caution and common sense along with good engineering principles can go a long way in making a system setup a productive, successful experience.

8.5.7. Sensor Setup

Motors are usually received from their sources with the sensor or commutating system set for proper function. However, it might sometimes be necessary to adjust the sensor system, such as when the motor is disassembled for bearing replacement, maintenance, etc. It is best to return the motor to the manufacturer for this work to be done. It is not recommended that adjustments of the commutator sensor system be made without proper equipment and knowledge. However, if it is to be attempted, then an open loop drive capable of being fed a variable drive voltage is needed. The drive must be capable of operating with a low-voltage input and be rated for sufficient current capability as determined by motor rating.

It is usual practice to use a dc supply of one tenth to one twentieth the nominal supply voltage when making sensor adjustments. Basically the motor is run at greatly reduced voltage (say 5–10 V for a 90 V stator), and the dc input current is monitored while adjusting the sensor. Correct sensor setting usually occurs at the lowest current. The shaft direction should be observed because in some cases, the direction of rotation can be reversed by improper sensor setting. Once the current null has been found, the direction can be reversed by issuing a reverse command to the controller. Current in a properly setup motor will be equal or nearly equal in both directions if the motor is designed for bidirectional operation. The voltage can now be raised, and the no load speed current checked against the known test data. As mentioned, this is a tricky procedure and will sometimes require a good deal of tweaking to get things right. Do not attempt this procedure with a closed-loop drive or at full rated voltage. Always lock down the sensor magnet or sensor adjustment screws when adjustment is complete to ensure nothing moves out of alignment.

9

Additional Application Notes and Summary

9.1. INTRODUCTION

Inherent motor characteristics as well as motor and control systems characteristics are covered in previous chapters, and a variety of applications that are suitable for a particular motor or system are mentioned. It is also fairly obvious that there is hardly ever a single solution to a drive system need, but there are generally a variety of options available. It must be understood too, that yesterday's best option might not look very smart today, and today's option might look downright silly in the future.

9.2. DIRECT DRIVE, BELT DRIVE, AND GEAR DRIVE

Much thought should be given to the mechanical connection of a motor to a machine. If the speed of the motor can be the same as that of the machine to which it is to be connected, the motor shaft can be directly coupled to the machine shaft. If the speed of the motor is different from the speed of the machine it is to drive, a connection must be made to give the proper speed ratio between the two. This is usually accomplished with belt drives, chain drives, or gear drives. Which drive to use depends largely on physical considerations, such as the space available for mounting the motor, the speed at which the machine operates, and the practicality of operating a motor at that speed.

A grinder for instance might run at 3600 or 1800 RPM, and the grinding wheel can be mounted directly on an induction-motor shaft. A lathe might be running at only a few hundred RPM, and a speed reducer would be required. For very low speeds, gear motors are used. These are electric motors where gear boxes are attached to the endframe of the motor. The speed of the output shaft of the gear may be only a few RPM and can be directly coupled to a machine.

The mechanical connection of the motor to the machine is really an integral part of the drive system, and how well and how smooth the transfer of power occurs from the motor to the load can be pivotal in the overall performance of the system.

When the machine or load is directly coupled to the motor, or simply mounted on the shaft of the motor as is the case of a fan or a grinding wheel, there is no loss in the transmission of power. Any vibration caused by the motor, however, is also directly translated to the machine or load and vice versa. Transmitted vibrations might have undesirable side effects. Frequently a flexible coupling is used that would have a tendency to absorb the vibrations and also make the alignment of the motor and machine less critical. A flexible coupling would be particularly desirable where motor speed control is accomplished by means of an SCR or triac circuit. However, in applications where the relative position of the shaft of the machine and that of the motor must remain fixed, a rigid coupling is required.

Belt drives have the advantage of being able to absorb vibration, and alignment might not be as critical. Short of having complicated pulley arrangements and possibly rather large pulleys, the maximum speed ratio is limited. For motors of the size considered here, a ratio of 5 to 6 is practical even though ratios of 8 to 10 are not out of range. Multiple speeds can be accomplished by changing pulley diameters.

A belt drive with V-belts or flat belts will cause some slip losses. Timing belts are frequently used where the relationship between motor and load speed must be maintained accurately.

Belt drives are usually very good where motor speed control is not smooth. This kind of mechanical connection is ideal for drives with motors with low cost SCR or triac speed control as it reduces the transmission of vibration and torque pulsations. As a consequence it also reduces acoustical noise. Of course, belts wear and if they start slipping beyond a certain point, they produce a noise of their own.

A gear drive is usually the most direct and compact way of obtaining a speed ratio. Gear motors are available with speeds of under 10 RPM or even a fraction of a revolution per minute, depending on the number of stages in the gear box. These gear drives also can cause a considerable amount of acoustical noise. Gear drives can be very efficient drives, but they are not necessarily so, particularly for a multistage gear train.

For some very low speed applications such as certain laser drives where timing is of highest importance, even a gear drive might not be acceptable because of possible backlash. Very low-speed, direct-drive motors of the brushless type have been developed for this purpose. In general, it is not very practical to build an electric motor with very high torque and only a few rpm output.

Occasionally it is desired to run a machine faster than the motor. This of course also can be accomplished with a belt or gear drive. This drive would permit the use of a standard induction motor and avoid the use of a higher frequency power supply.

9.3. APPLICATION CONSIDERATIONS FOR BLDC MOTORS

The versatility of a BLDC motor system is shown in chapter 5 and 6. In practice there must be few applications for which the BLDC motor has at least not been considered, yet relatively few are presently in high production. Cost is certainly a major consideration, but the performance is frequently not what it ought to be. The responsibility for poor performance usually lies with both the manufacturer and the user. Frequently, because the system is still in the development stage and must be considered state of the art, motors and controls often are not as well suited to each other as might be hoped for. Users are often not fully aware what is required of a drive until they test the system and find out the motor either does not accelerate fast enough, or the drive is not smooth enough, or the speed range not wide enough. Occasionally the drive might even be too quiet and not cover up some other noises. Because the BLDC motor system is so adaptable, close cooperation between the motor and control people, as well as with the user, is essential to develop a successful product.

9.3.1. Constant-Speed Performance

Constant-speed performance must always be fully defined. It makes a big difference if the speed is permitted to vary by either 0.1 or 1.5 percent from a specified speed over a given range of torque outputs, voltages, and temperatures. If the motor is to operate over a certain voltage input range such as 100 to 130 V line voltage, it should be so specified. In general, the BLDC motor with its control in closed-loop mode will maintain a far better speed regulation over a given torque range or a constant torque over temperature and voltage range than in induction motor. The regulation for an open-loop BLDC motor can be compared to that of a PM dc motor.

9.3.2. Synchronous-Speed Performance

The BLDC motor will perform as a synchronous motor if the system is specially designed to do so. The amount of flutter permitted under this mode of operation is important, and so is the nature of the load.

The BLDC motor performs much more efficiently than will either the hysteresis- or the reluctance-type synchronous motors. Some types of BLDC motors and drives can be better adapted than others to very stringent specifications. It pays to shop around.

9.3.3. Variable-Speed Performance

Most BLDC motor systems can be operated over a wide speed range. This variable speed feature has created a lot of interest in the industry and also has caused many disappointments. The sensing system consisting of three Hall devices in a typical three-phase, full-wave BLDC motor simply has an insufficient number of sensing positions to permit a smooth motor operation at low speeds of several hundred RPM. To alleviate this situation, an encoder is often added to the motor. If the whole speed range from 0 RPM to full-load speed is required, the sensing system might consist of a resolver. In practice, for economy reasons the motor frequently has been called upon to perform under conditions for which it was not designed.

The trend in the motor industry is to increase the number of poles in BLDC motors. Six and eight-pole motors are becoming common, which will help in smoother, lower-speed motor operations.

9.3.4 Torque Motor Performance

Torque motors is one application that has been looked at repeatedly by the machine tool industry, and initially many drawbacks were discovered. The locked-rotor torque varies with rotor position, and it was difficult to position the rotor accurately and hold it. Largely by increasing the number of poles of the motor, an accurate sensing system and the help of microprocessors, this drawback has been overcome.

9.3.5. Cost

The future success or failure of the BLDC motor will depend increasingly on its cost effectiveness. Some disk drives operated from low-voltage dc supplies are using BLDC motors very cost effectively, primarily because of the low cost electronic system.

In applications where ac motors and inverters are presently used, as in many spindle motor applications, disk drives, and high-speed centrifuge applications, the BLDC motor is becoming competitive—in most cases it outperforms either a synchronous or induction motor system. Even in many present dc motor applications where the drive requires a sophisticated electronic system, as in servosystems and robotics, a BLDC motor is likely to be, or shortly become, cost effective. Where presently no electronic package is used, and particularly in higher voltage applications, the BLDC motor will demand a premium for its quiet operation, long life, no arcing, versatility, and high efficiency. The cost of the electronics has been falling rapidly, so that present cost premiums will continue to be reduced. There is little doubt that in specialty applications the BLDC motors will continue to make inroads on the use of conventional motors. Frequently a belt drive can be replaced by a direct drive, which may be more desirable or more economical. The cost of manufacturing BLDC motors is likely to remain higher than that of squirrel-cage induction motors, even after the investments have been made to mass produce BLDC motors.

9.4 CONCLUSION

The number of options to the machine or systems designer as to the kind of drive suitable for an application have mushroomed tremendously in recent years. Motors that used to perform a single function, with the help of electronic systems are now much more versatile so that the simple classifications of motors as to their particular functions have all but disappeared. If this is bewildering to the user, it is just as bewildering to the manufacturers of motors and control systems. The industry is in a state of flux and is likely to remain so for many years to come.

In this book, traditional motors and systems are discussed and typical applications mentioned. The present state of the art of the BLDC motor system has been extensively covered. It is felt that some basic understanding of motors and controls as well as the knowledge of *inherent* plusses and minusses of each motor and control system are necessary to arrive at an intelligent solution. Most manufacturers of motors and controls can be consulted for certain applications. However, they are liable to be most helpful in finding solutions recommending motors and controls which they manufacture, not necessarily the best solution to the problem.

Appendix A

List of Symbols

α	brush shift
a	acceleration; number of parallel path in armature
AC, ac	alternating current
A/D	analog to digital
B	flux density
BLDC	brushless direct current
CSA	Canadian Standards Association
CW	clockwise rotation
CCW	counterclockwise rotation
D/A	digital to analog
DC, dc	direct current
E	voltage
e	instantaneous voltage
E°	voltage, output function
E_a	armature voltage
E_b	back EMF
E_d	voltage drop in circuit
E_{dc}	supply voltage
e_{fb}	feedback voltage
e_{in}	input voltage, control function
E_L	line voltage
EMI	electromagnetic interference
E_s	supply voltage
ESR	equivalent series resistance
f	frequency (line)
FB	feedback
fc	frequency of current in rotor conductor
FCC	Federal Communications Commission
FET	field effect transistor
f_{in}	input frequency
f_o	output frequency or clock frequency
f_{out}	clock output
f_{vel}	velocity, frequency function
G	gauss
H	magnet field strength
h_{FE}	dc current gain
hp	horsepower
I	current
i	instantaneous current
I_a	armature current
I_b	base current
I_c	collector current
I_{dc}	dc or average current

I_f fault current, field current (dc motor)
I_L line current
I_m motor current
I_{RMS} root mean square current
I_s supply current

j rotor moment of inertia

K_E voltage constant
K_T torque constant

L inductance
L_c circuit inductance
LED light-emitting diode
lg length of airgap
LISN line stabilizing network
L_L leakage inductance
L_s self-inductance
LSB least significant bit
LVDT linear variable displacement transformer

M mutual inductance
m number of phases
Mx maxwell
μ absolute permeability
μ_γ relative permeability

NEMA National Electrical Manufacturers Association
N · m newton meter
Φ flux

Oe oersted

P power
p instantaneous power
p number of poles
$P_{G\text{-}out}$ gross power output
PLL phase locked loop
PM permanent magnet
P_w power dissipation
PWM pulse width modulation

R resistance
r_2 rotor resistance
R_a armature terminal resistance
R_b base resistance
R_c equivalent circuit resistance
R_{ds} drain to source resistance
R_f field resistance (dc motor)
R_H Hall coefficients
R_m speed regulation constant
R_s sample resistance
R_t armature terminal resistance

S speed
s percent slip
$S_{a,b,c}$ sensor phases
SCR silicon controlled rectifier
SOA safe operating area

Θ power factor
T torque
t time
TDE time displacement error
τ_e electrical time constant
τ_m mechanical time constant
Γ_m permeability in vacuum or magnetic constant

UL Underwriters Laboratories

V volume of rotor cylinder
V_a armature voltage
V_{bc} base to emitter voltage
V_{ce} collector to emitter volts voltage
VDE Verband Deutscher Electrotechniker
V_H Hall voltage
V_m motor voltage
V_p peak voltage
V_s voltage supply

ω pole of motion
Wb weber

ωc	phase comparator	Z	impedance
W_h	area of hysteresis loop	Z_a	number of armature conductors
X	reactance		

Appendix B

Conversion Table

	SI or derivative	CGS	ENGLISH
Area	1 m^2	10^4 cm^2	1550 in^2
Flux	1 Wb	10^8 Mx	10^8 lines
Flux density	1 T	10^4 G	6.45×10^4 lines/in^2
Force	1 N	101.97 g*	3.597 oz
Length	1 m	100 cm	39.37 in
Magnetic field Intensity	1 A/m	1.257×10^{-2} Oe	2.54×10^{-2} A-turn/in
Mass	1 Kg	1000 g	35.27 oz**
Moment of Inertia	1 Kg m^2	10^7 g cm^2	141.61 oz-in-sec^2
Torque	1 Nm	1.02×10^4 g*-cm	141.61 oz-in
Volume	1 m^3	10^6 cm^3	61×10^3 in^3

*units of force-p
**avoirdupois

Index